© David Hughes | Dreamstime.com

C000258568

Welcome to the 2009 edi~~tion~~ ...~~of~~ ...Small Hotels, Inns & Restaurants ~~of Great Britai~~n and Ireland.

Each year we are able to bring you a more diverse and comprehensive portfolio of places to stay thanks to the concerted effort of our experienced inspection team. We pride ourselves on understanding the expectations of our discerning readership and in anticipating those needs, not only for high standards, a welcoming atmosphere, relaxation and a good night's sleep but also for discovering new and special corners of Great Britain and Ireland.

Whether you are looking for a delightful old coaching inn, all the charm of a classic country house, a chic city base, a small intimate hideaway or a special restaurant, we have found plenty to inspire you for the year ahead.

Few guides offer such rich diversity and accommodation experience which makes your search for that extra special stay easier and more rewarding.

You may be in need of inspiration or simply want to search a specific location, either way our guide is designed to help you make the right choice. Now also interactive on www.johansens.com you can 'check availability' and communicate directly with the Recommendation of your choice. Each hotel's entry page invites you to 'Tell us about your stay' so we look forward to your comments when you return.

Our portfolio comprises 6 published Guides, featuring more than 1,100 annually inspected and recommended hotels, resorts, inns, spas and venues across more than 60 countries. See them all at www.johansens.com.

Wishing you safe and rewarding travels in 2009.

Andrew Warren

Andrew Warren
Managing Director

1

L'INSTANT
TAITTINGER

Vitalie Taittinger, who works for the family Champagne house

The Mill At Gordleton, Lymington, hampshire, p74

About this Guide

Introduction 1
County Maps 4, 5
Key to Symbols 6
Awards for Excellence..11

Recommendations and regional maps:
Channel Islands 14
England 20
Ireland 166
Scotland..170
Wales 190

Mini Listings:
Hotels & Spas – Great Britain & Ireland 2009...................................204
Historic Houses, Castles & Gardens 2009 206
Hotels & Spas – Europe & The Mediterranean 2009 209
Hotels, Inns, Resorts & Spas –
The Americas, Atlantic, Caribbean & Pacific 2009 213

Indexes...235
Guest Survey Report..240

To find a hotel by location:

- Use the **county maps** at the front of the Guide to obtain a page number for the area of the country you wish to search.
- Turn to the **indexes** at the back of the book, which start on page 235.
- Alternatively, use the **maps** at the front of each colour coded country section where each hotel is marked.

If you cannot find a suitable hotel you may decide to choose one of the properties within the *Condé Nast Johansens Hotels & Spas Guide*. These establishments are listed on pages 204–205.

Once you have made your choice please contact the hotel directly. Rates are per room, including VAT and breakfast (unless stated otherwise) and are correct at the time of going to press but you should always check with the hotel before you make your reservation. **When making a booking please mention that Condé Nast Johansens is your source of reference.**

Readers should be aware that by making a reservation with a hotel, either by telephone, e-mail or in writing, they are entering into a legal contract. A hotelier under certain circumstances is entitled to make a charge for accommodation when guests fail to arrive, even if notice of the cancellation is given.

Recommendations can be found plotted on more detailed maps at the front of each colour coded country section

Channel Islands 14
England 20
Ireland 166
Scotland 170
Wales 190

Moray p185

Higland p176

Aberdeenshire p172

SCOTLAND

Edinburgh p175

Scottish Borders p186

South Ayrshire p188

Dumfries & Galloway p173

N. IRELAND

IRELAND

Kerry p169

ENGLAND

WALES

SCOTLAND

N. IRELAND

IRELAND

Northumberland p106

Cumbria p47

North Yorkshire p156

Lancashire p95

East Riding of Yorkshire p155

West Yorkshire p162

Merseyside p99

Conwy p193

Denbighshire p194

Gwynedd p195

Derbyshire p54

Lincolnshire p98

Nottinghamshire p109

ENGLAND

WALES

Satffordshire p134

Shropshire p122

Rutland p119

Norfolk p100

Worcestershire p151

Warwickshire p143

Northamptonshire p105

Cambridgeshire p39

Pembrokeshire p200

Carmarthenshire p192

Herefordshire p78

Suffolk p136

Bedfordshire p31

Monmouthshire p198

Gloucestershire p67

Buckinghamshire p37

Hertfordshire p83

Essex p66

Vale of Glamorgan p202

Oxfordshire p112

Bath & NE Somerset p30

Berkshire p32

Wiltshire p145

Surrey p140

Somerset p125

Hampshire p74

Kent p90

Devon p59

West Sussex p142

Dorset p64

Cornwall p41

Isle of Wight p86

Channel Islands

Guernsey p16

Jersey p19

Key to Symbols

23   Total number of bedrooms

Owner managed

CC   Credit cards not accepted

Quiet location

Wheelchair Access. We recommend that you contact the hotel to determine the level of accessibility for wheelchair users.

Chef-patron

M 23   Meeting/conference facilities with maximum number of delegates

8   Children welcome, with minimum age where applicable

Dogs welcome in rooms or kennels

At least 1 bedroom has a four-poster bed

Cable/satellite TV in all bedrooms

CD player in bedrooms

DVD player in bedrooms

ISDN/modem point in all bedrooms

WiFi   Wireless Internet connection available in part or all rooms

Non-smoking bedrooms available

Lift available for guests' use

Air conditioning in all bedrooms

Gym/fitness facilities on-site

SPA   A dedicated spa offering extensive health, beauty and fitness treatments together with water treatments

Indoor swimming pool

Outdoor swimming pool

Tennis court on-site

Walking – details of local walking routes and packed lunches can be provided and an overnight drying room for clothes is available.

Fishing on-site

Fishing can be arranged

Golf course on-site

Golf course nearby, which has an arrangement with the property allowing guests to play

Shooting on-site

Shooting can be arranged

Horse riding can be arranged

Property has a helicopter landing pad

Licensed for wedding ceremonies

Ard Na Sidhe, Killarney, Kerry, Ireland, p169

Sans Pareil - Without Equal

www.cafedumonde.co.uk tel:01322 284804

SERVICE
EN
CHAMBRE

photo: M. Marcato – Verona, Italy

Beautiful Furniture for
Hotels and Homes.

SELVA

40 Years of Timeless Beauty

photo: © Moreno Magg
Hotel St. George, Roma

Selva SpA   Via Luigi Negrelli 4   39100 Bolzano (Italia)   Tel. +39 0471 240 111   Fax +39 0471 240 112   selva@selva.com   www.selva.com

Hey Green Country House Hotel, Marsden, West Yorkshire, p163

Condé Nast Johansens

Condé Nast Johansens Ltd, 6-8 Old Bond Street, London W1S 4PH
Tel: +44 (0)20 7499 9080 Fax: +44 (0)20 7152 3565
E-mail: info@johansens.com
www.johansens.com

Publishing Director:	Patricia Greenwood
PA to Publishing Director:	Clare Freeman
Hotel Inspectors:	Jean Branham
	Peter Bridgham
	Geraldine Bromley
	Robert Bromley
	Charlie Bronks
	Tim Fay
	Audrey Fenton
	Maureen Flynn
	Edward Gallier
	David Innes-Edwards
	Marie Iversen
	Pauline Mason
	John Morison
	Mary O'Neill
	Fiona Patrick
	Liza Reeves
	Leonora Sandwell
	Nevill Swanson
Production Manager:	Kevin Bradbrook
Production Editor:	Laura Kerry
Senior Designer:	Michael Tompsett
Copywriters:	Norman Flack
	Debra O'Sullivan
	Rozanne Paragon
	Leonora Sandwell
Client Services Director:	Fiona Patrick
Venue Advisory Service:	Lesley Ulrick
Managing Director:	Andrew Warren

Copyright © 2008 Condé Nast Johansens Ltd.
Condé Nast Johansens Ltd. is part of The Condé Nast Publications Ltd.
ISBN 978-1-903665-40-4
Printed in England by St Ives plc
Distributed in the UK and Europe by Portfolio, Brentford (bookstores).
In North America by Casemate Publishing, Pennsylvania (bookstores).
Front cover picture: Hipping Hall, Cumbria, p51

Discover KOHLER. A world of innovative and inspiring bathroom design awaits.

KOHLER: As I See It, #5 in a series

ARTIST: Mark Holthusen

BATHROOM: Stillness® Collection, including basins, furniture, toilet, bidet and taps

Inspired by Mother Nature, without all of her storms and bluster.

+44 (0) 1242 221221
kohler.co.uk

THE BOLD LOOK
OF KOHLER.

Awards for Excellence

The Condé Nast Johansens 2008 Awards for Excellence were presented at our Awards Dinner held at Jumeirah Carlton Tower, London, on 12th November, 2007. Awards were received by properties from all over Europe that represented the finest standards and best value for money in luxury independent travel.

An important source of information for these awards was the feedback provided by guests who completed Condé Nast Johansens Guest Survey Reports. Forms can be found on page 240.

You can also nominate a hotel via its entry page on the website www.johansens.com, under 'Tell Us About Your Stay'.

2008 Winners appearing in this Guide:

Most Excellent Value
- PORTH TOCYN COUNTRY HOUSE HOTEL
  – Abersoch, Gwynedd, p195

Most Excellent Waterside Hotel
- BALCARY BAY HOTEL
  – Auchencairn, Dumfries & Galloway, p173

Most Excellent Inn
- THE PHEASANT
  – Bassenthwaite Lake, Cumbria, p47

Condé Nast Johansens Readers' Award
- EAST LODGE COUNTRY HOUSE HOTEL
  – Bakewell, Derbyshire, p55

Champagne Taittinger Most Excellent Wine List Award
- THE CORMORANT HOTEL AND RESTAURANT
  – Fowey, Cornwall, p41

Sleepeezee

the perfect end to every day.

Makers of world-class, quality pocket sprung beds for over 80 years, Sleepeezee has become one of the leading and most respected bed manufacturers in the UK.

Recognised and highly regarded for craftsmanship, design and innovation, we have remained dedicated to the creation of luxurious beds and mattresses which provide supreme comfort and support, night after night.

CONDÉ NAST JOHANSENS · PREFERRED PARTNER · J

Preferred bed supplier to Condé Nast Johansens.

Sleepeezee Contract Beds enquiries:
Tel: +44 (0) 1384 455515   •   email: contractservices@sleepeezee.co.uk   •   online: www.sleepeezee.co.uk

The Perfect Combination...

Condé Nast Johansens Gift Vouchers

Condé Nast Johansens Gift Vouchers make a unique and much valued present for birthdays, weddings, anniversaries, special occasions and as a corporate incentive.

Vouchers are available in denominations of £100, £50, €140, €70, $150, $75 and may be used as payment or part payment for your stay or a meal at any Condé Nast Johansens 2009 recommended property.

To order Gift Vouchers call +44 (0)207 152 3558 or purchase direct at www.johansens.com

Condé Nast Johansens Guides

  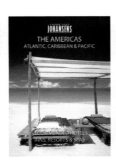  

As well as this Guide, Condé Nast Johansens also publish the following titles:

- Recommended Hotels & Spas, Great Britain & Ireland 2009
- Recommended Hotels & Spas, Europe & The Mediterranean 2009
- Recommended Hotels, Inns, Resorts & Spas, The Americas, Atlantic, Caribbean & Pacific 2009
- Luxury Spas Worldwide 2009
- Recommended International Venues for Meetings & Special Events 2009

To purchase Guides please call +44 (0)208 955 7067 or visit our Bookshop at www.johansens.com

Channel Islands

GUERNSEY

La Fontenelle

St Sampson

Saint Peter Port

Richmond

18

La Planque

16

HERM ISLAND

17

SARK

Saint John

Saint Peter

Saint Mary

Trinity

19

Quennevais

Gorey

Saint Helier

JERSEY

Channel Islands

For further information on the Channel Islands, please contact:

Visit Guernsey
North Esplanade, St Peter Port, Guernsey GY1 2LQ
Tel: +44 (0)1481 723552
Internet: www.visitguernsey.com

Jersey Tourism
Liberation Place, St Helier, Jersey JE1 1BB
Tel: +44 (0)1534 448800
E-mail: info@jersey.com
Internet: www.jersey.com

Sark Tourism
The Visitors Centre, The Avenue, Sark, GY9 0SA
Tel: +44 (0)1481 832345
E-mail: office@sark.info
Internet: www.sark.info

Herm Tourist Office
Administration Office, Herm Island, Guernsey GY1 3HR
Tel: +44 (0)1481 722377
E-mail: admin@herm-island.com
Internet: www.herm-island.com

or see **pages 206-208** for details of local historic houses, castles and gardens to visit during your stay.

For additional places to stay in the Channel Islands, turn to **pages 204-205** where a listing of our Recommended Hotels & Spas Guide can be found.

The White House

HERM ISLAND, GUERNSEY, CHANNEL ISLANDS GY1 3HR
Tel: 0845 365 2735 **International:** +44 (0)1481 722159 **Fax:** 01481 710066
Web: www.johansens.com/whitehouseherm **E-mail:** hotel@herm-island.com

Our inspector loved: This quiet retreat with sandy beaches and sensational sea food - an invigorating walk right round the island is as much as you like to do!

Price Guide: (including dinner)
single £85–£130
double/twin £170–£234
crows nest £260

Awards/Recognition: 1 AA Rosette 2007-2008

Location: Via St Peter Port, Guernsey, 20-min ferry

Attractions: Swimming; Walks; Fantastic Beaches; Bird watching

Herm Island's magic will start working on you as soon as you arrive at the harbour. There are no cars so a tractor full of luggage chugs up from the jetty to the gleaming White House. Adrian and Pennie Heyworth are marvelous hosts and will be able to help even the most stressed arrival to relax. You will love exploring the island and will hardly notice the absence of TV's. You can picnic in sandy coves, walk the cliff tops, go in search of wildlife or just snooze by the pool. Most of the bedrooms have sea views, the remainder over the gardens. Plenty of flexibility for families including several charming cottages. Menus make the most of the daily catch - Guernsey lobster, scallops and crab.

LA SABLONNERIE

LITTLE SARK, SARK, GUERNSEY GY9 0SD
Tel: 0845 365 1972 **International:** +44 (0)1481 832061 **Fax:** 01481 832408
Web: www.johansens.com/lasablonnerie **E-mail:** lasablonnerie@cwgsy.net

Our inspector loved: *The total feeling of escapism from the real world - it is just such a wonderful place to recharge the batteries.*

Price Guide: (including dinner)
single from £78
double/twin £156–£198

Location: Via St Peter Port, Guernsey, 45-min ferry

Attractions: George's boat trip around the island; Cycling, walking, swimming and bird watching; Champagne and lobsters; La Seigneurie Gardens

Owner and manager Elizabeth Perrée considers La Sablonnerie an oasis of good living and courtesy rather than a luxury hotel. It is an hotel of rare quality situated in a time warp of simplicity on a tiny, idyllic island where no motor cars are allowed and life ambles along at a peaceful unhurried pace. A vintage horse-drawn carriage collects guests from Sark's tiny harbour. Tranquil cosiness, friendliness and sophistication characterise this hotel with its low ceilings and 400-year-old oak beams. Elizabeth has extended and discreetly modernised the hotel with bedrooms which are charmingly individual in style. The hotel has a reputation for superb cuisine. Many of the dishes are prepared from produce grown on its own farm and in its gardens, and enhanced by locally caught lobster and oysters.

THE FARMHOUSE

ROUTE DES BAS COURTILS, ST SAVIOURS, GUERNSEY GY7 9YF
Tel: 0845 365 4023 **International:** +44 (0)1481 264 181 **Fax:** 01481 266 272
Web: www.johansens.com/thefarmhouse **E-mail:** enquiries@the farmhouse.gg

Our inspector loved: The sophisticated, stylish and contemporary presentation.

Price Guide:
boutique/superior £120-£190
suite £190-£250

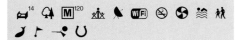

Location: Guernsey Airport, 1.5 miles; St. Peter Port, 4 miles

Attractions: The Little Chapel and Guernsey Clockmakers; War Museums; Telephone and Folk Museum; VAT Free Shopping

Created from an ancient farmhouse, this smart yet informal hideaway is set in the heart of rural Guernsey in the parish of St Saviour a short walk from one of the prettiest bays on the island, Petit Bot. Dating back to the 15th century the Farmhouse has undergone an impressive transformation focusing on today's discerning visitor and their needs. The emphasis is clearly on warm hospitality and fine service against a contemporary backdrop. Bedrooms are comfortably sophisticated in soothing muted tones. A destination itself for dining on the island, the Chef presents an adventurous menu where unexpected flavours abound together with traditional favourites. It's up to you to choose your setting from 5 distinctive dining areas; inside, pool-side, quiet, informal or with live music. In summertime, guests can enjoy lying idly by the pool while in winter, log fires add to the inviting ambience.

CHÂTEAU LA CHAIRE

ROZEL BAY, JERSEY JE3 6AJ
Tel: 0845 365 2863 **International:** +44 (0)1534 863354 **Fax:** 01534 865137
Web: www.johansens.com/chateaulachaire **E-mail:** res@chateau-la-chaire.co.uk

Our inspector loved: The intricate plaster-work and handsome woodcarving which are original features of this outstanding building.

Price Guide: (inclusive of morning paper and afternoon tea)
classic double from £120
superior double from £170
suite from £220

Awards/Recognition: 2 AA Rosettes 2008-2009

Location: A6, 1.5 miles; St Helier, 7 miles; Jersey Airport, 11 miles

Attractions: The Durrell Wildlife Conservation Trust; Jersey Pottery; Occupation Museum; Stunning Coastal Scenery

You can see that care and great attention to detail are important at this charming hotel. Built in 1843 as a rather grand elegant home today's owners have kept many original antiques and classical paintings to enhance the period charm. Nestled in a romantic spot high in a wooded valley close to the sea this is a great location from which to explore the island. The garden, currently awaiting restoration, will delight botanists. An excellent reputation follows the oak-panelled restaurant with a menu full of both Gallic and English influences whilst the sunny terrace seems a popular place for locals to catch up on news and chat during the islands many warm months.

North West England

SCOTLAND

Berwick-Upon-Tweed

Northumberland
National Park

Carlisle

Lake District
National Park

Windermere

Kendal

Yorkshire Dales
National Park

Isle
of
Man

Douglas

Barrow-in-
Furness

Skipton

Fleetwood

Blackpool

Preston

Southport

Bolton

Wigan

Manchester

Liverpool

WALES

© Lovell Johns Limited, Oxford

Berwick-Upon-Tweed

A698
A1
A697
106
A1
108
A697
A1068
A1
A696
Newcastle
A69
Newcastle
A68
A692
A693
A691
A690
A19
A167
A688
A1(M)
A689
A68
A66
Durham
Teeside
A172
Middlesbrough
159
A171
A19
North York Moors
National Park
A170
Dales
157
Park
Thirsk
A19
161
A64
158
A6108
A1(M)
A168
155
Skipton
A59
A166
A59
A165
Harrogate
A59
160
York
A1079
A163
A65
A658
A64
A1079
A61
A1035
Leeds
Bradford
A64
A19
164
A1
A63
A63
A614
A63
A164
Hull
Halifax
162
A63
A1041
A646
M62
A19
M62
Wakefield
34
A15
163
M62
Huddersfield
M18
A628
A638
A1
A19
M18
A180
M180
A628
Doncaster
A46
A616
M1
M18
A1(M)
A15
Sheffield
A631
A631
A46
58
A57
A15
A57
A623
A16
A158

Eastern England

23

© Lovell Johns Limited, Oxford

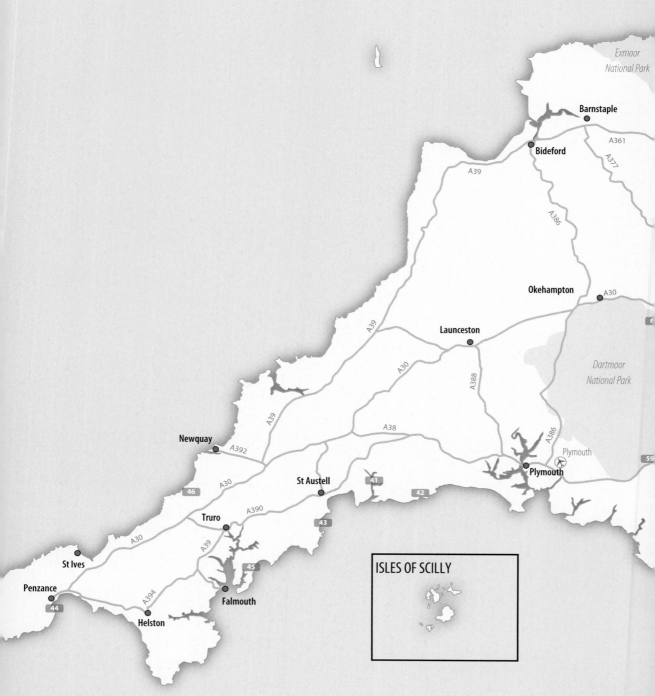

South West England

WALES

Exmoor
National Park

Barnstaple
A361
Bideford
A377
A39
A386
Okehampton
A30
Launceston
Dartmoor
National Park
A30
A388
A38
Plymouth
A386
Plymouth
Newquay
A392
St Austell
46
A30
41
42
Truro
A390
43
A39
St Ives
45
Penzance
A30
Falmouth
44
A394
Helston

ISLES OF SCILLY

WALES

South West England

Bristol

Bristol

Bath

Warminster

Exmoor
National Park

Taunton

Yeovil

**Blandford
Forum**

Bridport

Exeter

Exeter

Dorchester

Bourne

Bourner

Weymouth

Torquay

Kingsbridge

Southern England

Stow-on-the-Wold

Brackley

Milton Keynes

Cheltenham

Aylesbury

Cirencester

Oxford

Luton

Swindon

Windsor

Reading

Heathrow

Marlborough

Newbury

Basingstoke

Guildford

Salisbury

Winchester

Southampton

Chichester

Southampton

Portsmouth

Bognor Regis

New Forest

Bournemouth

Cowes

Bournemouth

Isle of Wight

South East England

Individuality Matters to our Partnership

We take pride in watching our clients' businesses grow and assisting them in that process wherever we can.

Goodman Derrick, founded over 50 years ago, have developed an acknowledged expertise in the areas of corporate and commercial law, litigation, property, employment and franchising law. We also have a leading reputation as legal advisors in the media, hotel and historic and collectors cars sectors. For personal matters, we also have a dedicated Private Client Group which provides a comprehensive and complementary range of services to the individual and their families.

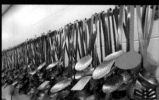

© Richard Thomas | Dreamstime.com

England

For further information on England, please contact:

Cumbria Tourist Board
Tel: +44 (0)1539 822222
E-mail: info@cumbriatourism.org
Web: www.golakes.co.uk

East of England Tourist Board
Tel: +44 (0)1284 727470
E-mail: info@eet.org.uk
Web: www.visiteastofengland.com

Heart of England Tourism
Web: www.visitheartofengland.com

Visit London
Tel: 0870 156 6366
Web: www.visitlondon.com

North East England Tourism Team
Web: www.visitnortheastengland.com

North West Tourist Board
Web: www.visitnorthwest.com

Tourism South East
Tel: +44 (0)23 8062 5400
Web: www.visitsoutheastengland.com

South West Tourism
Tel: 0870 442 0880
E-mail: info@westcountryholidays.com
Web: www.visitsouthwest.co.uk

Yorkshire Tourism Network
Tel: +44 (0)1904 707961
Web: www.ytb.org.uk

English Heritage
Tel: +44 (0) 870 333 1181
Web: www.english-heritage.org.uk

Historic Houses Association
Tel: +44 (0)20 7259 5688
E-mail: info@hha.org.uk
Web: www.hha.org.uk

The National Trust
Tel: 0844 800 1895
Web: www.nationaltrust.org.uk

or see **pages 206-208** for details of local historic houses, castles and gardens to visit during your stay.

For additional places to stay in England, turn to **pages 204-205** where a listing of our Recommended Hotels & Spas Guide can be found.

Saco House, Bath

ST JAMES' PARADE, BATH BA1 1UH
Tel: 0845 365 3782 **International:** +44 (0)1225 486540 **Fax:** 01225 480025
Web: www.johansens.com/saco **E-mail:** bath@sacoapartments.co.uk

Our inspector loved: The contemporary, fresh and clean finish and fantastic location for exploring Bath.

Price Guide:
studio apartment from £104
1-bedroom apartment from £126
2-bedroom apartment from £208

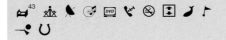

Saco House stands in the very centre of Bath, the most complete and best preserved Georgian city in Britain, famous since Roman times for its warm mineral springs. This is an ideal location for visitors seeking to immerse themselves in local history, marvel at the splendour of beautiful and majestic stone-fronted buildings and enjoy shopping in and around the bustling streets. An entire Georgian terrace that has been sympathetically converted into stylish 4-star apartments with everything required by the discerning guest, the style of each accommodation is contemporary, fresh and clean with excellently proportioned rooms. The apartments' home-from-home comforts include sumptuous bathrooms, flat-screen TVs and fully-equipped kitchens, which give you the flexibility to dine in or out. Reception is manned 24 hours a day and rooms are serviced twice a week.

Location: City Centre/A4, 0.5 miles; M4 jct 18, 10 miles; Bath Spa Train Station, 3-min walk

Attractions: Thermae Bath Spa; Roman Baths; Bath Abbey; Bath Theatre Royal

CORNFIELDS RESTAURANT & HOTEL

WILDEN ROAD, COLMWORTH, BEDFORDSHIRE MK44 2NJ
Tel: 0845 365 3246 **International:** +44 (0)1234 378990 **Fax:** 01234 376370
Web: www.johansens.com/cornfields **E-mail:** reservations@cornfieldsrestaurant.co.uk

Our inspector loved: *The new furnishings in the bar make relaxing by the fire even more tempting.*

Price Guide:
single £80–£90
double £120–£150
four poster £150

Location: A1, 3 miles; M1, 9 miles, A421, 3 miles Bedford, 5 miles Cambridge, 30 mins; London Luton Airport, 40 mins

Attractions: Cambridge; Cecil Higgins Gallery in Bedford; Woburn; Grafham Water

Nestling in the undulating Bedfordshire countryside Cornfields Restaurant & Hotel is a haven for those in search of a peaceful retreat to unwind and indulge. The inn dates back to the 17th century and features original beams and an inglenook fireplace. King-size beds invite guests to retire in the spacious, individually appointed bedrooms.However, the property's true appeal lies in its cuisine and its owners' vision to create freshly cooked dishes using locally sourced produce. Starters such as stilton, walnut and bacon fritters with a redcurrant and port sauce are delicious and main courses available include British classics such as pork with mild grain mustard and caramelised apples. The smaller of the 2 dining rooms can be hired for private use and is ideal for exclusive dining or business meetings.

THE CHRISTOPHER HOTEL BAR & GRILL

110 HIGH STREET, ETON, WINDSOR, BERKSHIRE SL4 6AN
Tel: 0845 365 2418 **International:** +44 (0)1753 852359 **Fax:** 01753 830914
Web: www.johansens.com/thechristopher **E-mail:** reservations@thechristopher.co.uk

Our inspector loved: The cosmoplitan bar, comfortable bedrooms and superb location.

Price Guide:
single £90-£115
double £120-£160
junior suite £160-£210

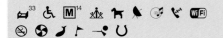

Location: A332, 2 miles; M4 J6, 3 miles; Windsor, 0.4 miles; Heathrow Airport, 7 miles

Attractions: Windsor Castle; Eton College; Legoland; Ascot Racecourse

A recently modernised hotel in an enviable location, The Christopher stands within the heart of historic Eton, close to the River Thames, Windsor Castle and the famous racecourse, Ascot. All around are art galleries, antique shops, upmarket men's outfitters, where boys and masters of the famous school can often be seen, and superb town shopping. Little wonder this former 18th-century coaching inn is popular for those searching for a short break or a comfortable base for touring and visiting London. Bedrooms are well-sized, tastefully decorated and some surround the attractive courtyard leading to an al fresco dining area. The Bar & Grill is one of the best places in Eton to experience modern English and International cuisine with a twist of Moroccan. A small meeting room comes complete with private decked area.

THE OLDE BELL COACHING INN

HIGH STREET, HURLEY, NEAR MAIDENHEAD, BERKSHIRE SL6 5LX
Tel: 0845 365 4038 **International:** +44 (0)1628 825881 **Fax:** 01628 825939
Web: www.johansens.com/oldebellhurley **E-mail:** theoldebellreception@coachinginn.co.uk

Our inspector loved: *The contrasting mix of traditional England with modern style.*

Price Guide:
single £115-£225
double £125-£235
suite £300

Location: A4130, 0.5 miles; M4 Jct 8/9, 6 miles; Henley, 6 miles; London Heathrow Airport, 20 miles

Attractions: Henley; Marlow; Windsor; Panoramic Riverside and Country Walks

This is a property whose modern facelift has been so successful it can only be described as fabulous! The celebrated designer Ilse Crawford of Studio Ilse should feel proud for retaining the traditional heart of this 12th-century coaching inn whilst creating gorgeous spaces for locals and the discerning contemporary traveller. In places, walls have been stripped back to show the original architecture and open fires are surrounded by traditional armchairs covered in felt, and Ercol rocking chairs with fur throws. Refurbishing continues with the annexe across the way later next year. The contemporary restaurant has a mediaeval feel with tapestry coverings on the banquettes and serves hearty food including "puddings that make you feel happy." In summer there are barbecues on the terrace and the option to disappear into the countryside with a ready-made picnic.

THE INN ON THE GREEN, RESTAURANT WITH ROOMS

THE OLD CRICKET COMMON, COOKHAM DEAN, BERKSHIRE SL6 9NZ
Tel: 0845 365 2547 **International:** +44 (0)1628 482638 **Fax:** 01628 487474
Web: www.johansens.com/innonthegreen **E-mail:** reception@theinnonthegreen.com

Our inspector loved: *This tucked away inn in a lovely village.*

Price Guide:
standard £85-£115
superior £95-£130
four poster £110-£150

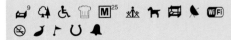

Awards/Recognition: 2 AA Rosettes 2008-2009

Location: A404, 4 miles; M40, 6 miles; Maidenhead, 6 miles; Heathrow Airport, 18 miles

Attractions: Windsor; Ascot; Henley; River Thames walks

Wind your way through the pituresque Thames Valley and you'll find this sophisticated 'restaurant with rooms' overlooking the village green. Ideal for romantic dinners, a group of friends or business colleagues, meetings, weddings and even exclusive use. Colours are warm, décor imaginative, and the nine bedrooms are thoughtfully furnished with antiques and modern facilities. Popular with locals for its atmosphere and modern European cooking, the chef sources locally and makes the best of the seasons. Downstairs is a rather cosy lounge bar. Local attractions include Windsor Castle, Legoland and the pretty riverside town of Marlow with its unique shops and restaurants. This boutique hotel is only 45 minutes from central London, making it a great escape for city dwellers.

STIRRUPS COUNTRY HOUSE HOTEL

MAIDENS GREEN, WINDSOR, BERKSHIRE RG42 6LD
Tel: 0845 365 2369 **International:** +44 (0)1344 882284 **Fax:** 01344 882300
Web: www.johansens.com/stirrups **E-mail:** reception@stirrupshotel.co.uk

Our inspector loved: *This friendly family run hotel with its comfortable rooms and lovely garden.*

Price Guide:
single from £120
double/twin from £130
suite from £150

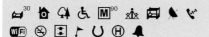

Location: A330, 250yds; M4 J8/9 M3 J3, 8 miles; Windsor, 6 miles; Heathrow, 18 miles

Attractions: Legoland; Windsor and Windsor Great Park; Thorpe Park; Ascot

Sitting in 10 acres of pretty grounds and in an enviable location close to the golf at Wentworth and the racing at Windsor and Ascot, you can see why this family owned country house is popular with those wishing for a few days break. At the heart of the hotel is Stirrups Bar and Restaurant which has recently undergone a modern redesign enhancing its older features of exposed brickwork, open fireplace and wooden beams. Passionate presentation of the imaginative menu is led by Head Chef, Aaron Stubbs. Bedrooms are well sized and have been subtlety decorated in natural woods and pastel colours. The hotel also proves popular for weddings, from a small gathering to a full blown party, business meetings, family breaks to Legoland and other attractions

CANTLEY HOUSE HOTEL

MILTON ROAD, WOKINGHAM, BERKSHIRE RG40 5QG
Tel: 0845 365 3223 **International:** +44 (0)118 978 9912 **Fax:** 0118 977 4294
Web: www.johansens.com/cantley **E-mail:** reservations@cantleyhotel.co.uk

Our inspector loved: This traditional country house hotel exudes staff friendliness, comfortable bedrooms, exceptional bathrooms and flexible dining and meeting facilities

Price Guide:
single £119–£135
double/twin £155–£185
suite £195–£205

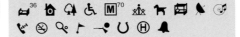

Location: A321, 0.20 miles; M4 jct 10, 5 miles; Wokingham, 0.75 miles; Heathrow, 25 miles

Attractions: Windsor; Legoland; Ascot Racecourse; Oxford

Cantley House Hotel is a spacious 36 bedroom Victorian Country House Hotel set in 50 acres of Berkshire parkland. Formerly the home of the Marquis of Ormonde, the mansion was built with wonderful Victorian proportions & detail. The building has been restored over the years and in 2001 the Clocktower Wing was added to allow for 15 executive rooms and suites, many with patios leading onto the glorious landscaped grounds featuring a sunken garden, lavender walk and peaceful ponds. Miltons Restaurant serving modern European cuisine is to be found in its own secluded 17th century courtyard and a generous touch is that their excellent wine list only has a standard per-bottle mark up – so a great bottle needn't cost the earth. Non-smoking throughout the hotel.

FOX COUNTRY INN

MAIN ROAD, IBSTONE, NEAR HIGH WYCOMBE, BUCKINGHAMSHIRE HP14 3XT
Tel: 0845 365 4039 **International:** +44 (0)1491 639333 **Fax:** 01491 639444
Web: www.johansens.com/foxcountryinn **E-mail:** info@foxcountryinn.co.uk

Our inspector loved: The informal and relaxed atmosphere, the pretty flower beds and glorious views.

Price Guide: (room only)
single from £97
double from £117
family room from £137

Location: A40, 2 miles; M40 J5, 2 miles; High Wycombe, 11 miles; Heathrow Airport, 29 miles

Attractions: Oxford; Chiltern Villages and Lovely Walks; Marlow and Henley; High Wycombe - Eden Shopping Centre

Whilst completely redesigned in a contemporary style, The Fox Country Inn retains many original features that will be appreciated by all who delight in a peaceful rural experience. Old Chimney breasts, alcoves, Windsor chairs and window seats all bring warmth to this inn. There is an excellent balance between the comfortable and the stylish. Bedrooms have been designed to be a space in which to relax unwind and offer gorgeous views across the Chilterns. The kitchen team are passionate about sourcing local produce and deliver appetising restaurant menus as well as excellent traditional pub dishes for the bar. An impressive range of local and international beer should satisfy most palates. The location is brimming with wildlife and there are miles of countryside to explore on foot, bike or horseback. The Fox country Inn is an ideal location for your business meetings, the peaceful and secluded surroundings, ensure maximum benefits for those important conferences.

THE CROWN

THE HIGH STREET, AMERSHAM, BUCKINGHAMSHIRE HP7 0DH
Tel: 0845 365 3270 **International:** +44 (0)1494 721541 **Fax:** 01494 431283
Web: www.johansens.com/crownamersham **E-mail:** crownreception@coachinginn.co.uk

Our inspector loved: This attractive and contemporary coaching inn with its flexible space in which to eat, drink and socialize.

Price Guide:
single £115-£225
double £125-£235
suite £300

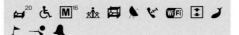

Location: A404, 0.5 miles; M25 /M40, 5 miles; Heathrow Airport, 19 miles

Attractions: Chiltern Open Air Museum; Woburn Abbey; Model Village Beaconsfiled (Oct - March); St Albans

The owners of this remarkably pretty property have succeeded in celebrating Old World charm alongside superb modern design. A gorgeous Elizabethan coaching inn and romantic hideaway in an award-winning village, has been beautifully renovated in the main building and the contemporary innovative interior design is delightful. The staff are friendly and put you at ease from the moment you arrive. Its not surprising that this inn is very much a central part of the Amersham community and you will often find people popping in to read a newspaper over a steaming cup of coffee by a fire or enjoying a delicious cream tea in the flower filled courtyard. The intimate restaurant serves dishes that clearly focus on the wealth of local seasonal produce. Johansens guests should ask for refurbished bedrooms in the main building although we hear they will be updating the courtyard rooms later in the year.

THE ANCHOR INN AT SUTTON GAULT

BURY LANE, SUTTON GAULT, SUTTON, NEAR ELY, CAMBRIDGESHIRE CB6 2BD
Tel: 0845 365 4029 **International:** +44 (0)1353 778537 **Fax:** 01353 776180
Web: www.johansens.com/anchorinn **E-mail:** anchorinn@popmail.bta.com

Our inspector loved: *The enthusiastic young owners of this traditonal hostelry.*

Price Guide:
single from £59.50
double £79.50-£155

Awards/Recognition: 1 AA Rosette 2007-2008

Location: B1381, 1½ miles; A17, 8 miles; A10, 10 miles; A14/M11, 18 miles

Attractions: Ely; Cambridge; Bury St Edmunds; Horse Racing at Newmarket and Huntingdon

In tranquil surroundings alongside the Bedford River, this is an ideal base from which to tour the triangle between the university city of Cambridge, the cathedral city of Ely and historic Huntingdon, birthplace of Oliver Cromwell. Built in the 1630s and host to Cromwell prisoners working on the drainage of the fens, the updated Anchor retains many charming features including gently undulating floors, open fires, scrubbed pine tables and walls adorned with a range of amusing pictures. Chef proprietor Adam Pickup and his partner, Carlene Bunten, have worked ceaselessly to make their inn a friendly, relaxing, comfortable haven whilst amassing handfuls of cuisine awards and guide recognitions. An intimate place, there are just 4 rooms available, each superb and well furnished; two having sitting rooms with sofa beds that are ideal for that extra guest.

THE TICKELL ARMS, RESTAURANT

1 NORTH ROAD, WHITTLESFORD, CAMBRIDGESHIRE CB2 4NZ
Tel: 0845 365 2710 **International:** +44 (0)1223 833128 **Fax:** 01223 835907
Web: www.johansens.com/tickellarms **E-mail:** dine@thetickellarms.co.uk

Our inspector loved: *The delightful peacocks and the elegant black swans on the small ornamental lake*

Price Guide:
starters from £5.50
mains from £10.50

 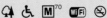

Location: A505, 1.5 mile; M11 jct 10, 2 miles

Attractions: The Imperial War Museum at Duxford; Cambridge; Newmarket Racecourse

Stylish, and just a little different, the Georgian Grade II listed Tickell Arms has quirky touches and many unusual antique furnishings. The main dining area is traditionally decorated with dark polished tables and candlesticks, while the conservatory boasts stunning Bougainvillea in the summer. Further tables are set in the award-winning garden, filled with oriental ducks and peacocks. Michelin trained chef Michael Henry Burgoyne brings forth some great dishes using the very best of East Anglian produce. Fantastic combinations include 28 day aged roe venison with lavender jus and ramson crushed ratt potatoes. Another delight is the Tickell walnut frangipane tart with Devon blue cheese ice cream. The menu evolves over every service, taking into account both seasonality and the producer's ability to impress with their fresh and local ingredients, but all have the same aim, to lift the bar in this stunningly unique restaurant.

THE CORMORANT HOTEL AND RESTAURANT

GOLANT BY FOWEY, CORNWALL PL23 1LL
Tel: 0845 365 2875 **International:** +44 (0)1726 833426 **Fax:** 01726 833219
Web: www.johansens.com/cormorant **E-mail:** relax@cormoranthotel.co.uk

Our inspector loved: The superb refurbishment accomplished during the last 12 months.

Price Guide:
single £75-£160
double £105-£195
cormorant £165-£235

Awards/Recognition: Condé Nast Johansens Taittinger Wine List Award, Small Hotels, Inns & Restaurants Category 2008

Location: B3269, 1.5 miles; A30, 11 miles; Exeter, 72 miles

Attractions: Eden Project; Lost Gardens of Heligan; Fowey Estuary; Lanhydrock House

Few hotels can match this magical location of sitting perched above the upper reaches of the Fowey Estuary. A total refurbishment of this delightful small hotel under the new ownership and creative eye of Mary Tozer has worked wonders. Many of the crisp bedrooms have full-length windows leading on to balconies where you can sit and enjoy the changing tide and life on the river. The restaurant like the drawing room has big windows and delightful views and the menu has been composed using seasonal and local ingredients. On warm days you can enjoy a leisurely meal on the terrace or when things get cooler a wood burning stove transforms the restaurant. The refurbished swimming pool and hot tub, are housed in their own building, with a wonderful sun terrace for simply stretching out and unwinding.

TALLAND BAY HOTEL

PORTHALLOW, CORNWALL PL13 2JB
Tel: 0845 365 2386 **International:** +44 (0)1503 272667 **Fax:** 01503 272940
Web: www.johansens.com/tallandbayhotel **E-mail:** info@tallandbayhotel.co.uk

Our inspector loved: After a day walking the cliff tops taking drinks on the terrace before an exceptional dinner in the panelled restaurant

Price Guide:
single £75–£105
double/twin £95–£225

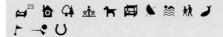

Awards/Recognition: 2 AA Rosettes 2008-2009

Location: A387, 1 mile; A38, 9.5 miles; Looe, 3.2 miles

Attractions: St Ives; National Maritime Museum, Falmouth; Eden Project; Lost Gardens of Heligan

A place to unwind and recharge, Talland Bay tucked away in a wild and romantic location on the Cornish coastline with cliff tops, estuaries and abundant wildlife is wonderfully appealing in a classic yet unpretentious way. Charming bedrooms with some leading out onto their own patio, a cosy light filled drawing room and delicious food that has the benefit of locally sourced ingredients all make this an ideal hideaway. Winter can be as impressive along this coast as the summer months and there are some great value breaks to take advantage of. Incredibly well positioned to explore both Cornwall and the south coast of Devon there is a tremendous amount to see and do from art galleries and coastal walks to the Eden Project and Heritage gardens. The staff are wonderfully keen to help you plan your exploration of the area and welcome well-behaved dogs.

TREVALSA COURT COUNTRY HOUSE HOTEL

SCHOOL HILL, MEVAGISSEY, ST AUSTELL, CORNWALL PL26 6TH
Tel: 0845 365 2765 **International:** +44 (0)1726 842468 **Fax:** 01726 844482
Web: www.johansens.com/trevalsa **E-mail:** stay@trevalsa-hotel.co.uk

Our inspector loved: The informal ambiance of a country house and the breathtaking location.

Price Guide:
single £70–£106
double/twin £130–£168
suite from £172

Location: B3273, 0.5 miles; A390, 4.7 miles; A30, 15.5 miles; Newquay Airport, 20 miles

Attractions: Lost Gardens of Helligan; Eden Project; Lanhydrock Manor House; Tate Gallery in St Ives

With such a glorious location on this dramatic coast line this classic 1930s house has no doubt been a place of entertaining house-parties over the decades and so today the hospitality continues under the warm and welcoming eye of Sue and John Gladwin. Beams, mullioned windows and painstakingly waxed wooden floors are all enhanced by the antiques, personal curious and warm rich colours that so much care has been taken over. The food, influenced by the morning haul from the fishing boats at close by Mevagissey and the seasonal produce from the farms around, is superb. The elegant yet informal atmosphere of the panelled dinning room makes a truly romantic setting. Whether you enjoy walking the coastal paths, lazing in the garden or listening to the waves crashing on the beach on wilder winter nights Trevalsa offers a place to simply relax and feel at home.

The Old Coastguard Hotel

MOUSEHOLE, PENZANCE, CORNWALL TR19 6PR

Tel: 0845 365 2610 **International:** +44 (0)1736 731222 **Fax:** 01736 731720
Web: www.johansens.com/oldcoastguard **E-mail:** bookings@oldcoastguardhotel.co.uk

Our inspector loved: Watching the boats and yachts from this delightful coastal location.

Price Guide:
single £90–£135
double £120–£180
premium double £190–£210

Awards/Recognition: 2 AA Rosettes 2008-2009

Location: B3315, 1.23 miles; A30, 2.67 miles; Penzance, 3.3 miles; Lands End, 10.9 miles

Attractions: Coastal walk to Lamorna Cove; Minack Theatre in Porthcurno; Cape Cornwall; St Michaels Mount

Described by Dylan Thomas as "the most beautiful village in England", Mousehole is remarkably unspoilt and with a charm of its own. Within this vibrant community and nestled between rolling headlands is the charming Old Coastguard Hotel. Here the lush sub-tropical gardens lead down to the sea, beach and rock pools. Many of the hotel rooms have panoramic views over Mounts Bay. Cool, contemporary furnishings of cream and black create a relaxed and refreshing ambience. While away the hours watching little fishing boats and yachts drift across the coastline from one of many bedroom balconies or explore endless Cornish coastal paths and bridleways, hidden coves and villages. Delectable daily changing menus feature locally sourced dishes and fresh fish from nearby Newlyn fish market.

THE ROSEVINE

ROSELAND, PORTSCATHO, CORNWALL TR2 5EW
Tel: 0845 365 2678 **International:** +44 (0)1872 580206 **Fax:** 01872 580230
Web: www.johansens.com/rosevine **E-mail:** info@rosevine.co.uk

Our inspector loved: *Absolutely everything, Tim and Hazel have introduced their own mark quite beautifully.*

Price Guide: (closed 4th Jan - 6th Feb 2009)
apartment/suite nightly £150–£335
apartment/suite weekly £995–£2,300

Location: A3078, 0.7 miles; St Mawes, 6 miles; A390, 11 miles; Newquay Airport 28 miles

Attractions: Roseland Peninsula; Falmouth Maritime Museum; St Mawes; Lost Gardens of Heligan

With the friendliness of a family home, The Rosevine is a privately owned house a short stroll from a great beach on the Cornish Roseland Peninsula. An idyllic retreat for families and couples who love a more informal place to stay. Split into 12 apartments and suites, each with small kitchen, dining and sitting areas and either 1 or 2 bedrooms. You have the independence, freedom and flexibility of renting an apartment, with all the facilities that you would find in a great small hotel. There's a cosy drawing room with woodburner, a play room with essentials such as Xbox, DVD library, toy cupboard, and an indoor swimming pool. If you wish to take a break from cooking, food is served downstairs in the dining room or order from the house deli menu for delivery to your apartment. Standing within 2 acres, relax on the top lawn or head to the lower field to enjoy the trampoline, playhouse and outdoor games.

ROSE-IN-VALE COUNTRY HOUSE HOTEL

MITHIAN, ST AGNES, CORNWALL TR5 0QD
Tel: 0845 365 2306 **International:** +44 (0)1872 552202 **Fax:** 01872 552700
Web: www.johansens.com/roseinvalecountryhouse **E-mail:** reception@rose-in-vale-hotel.co.uk

Our inspector loved: The tranquility of the setting and the warmth of the welcome.

Price Guide:
single from £80
double/twin from £135
suite £260

Awards/Recognition: 1 AA Rosette 2007-2008

Location: A3075, 1.4 miles; A30, 2.3 miles; Newquay Airport, 15 miles

Attractions: Local Beaches; Eden Project; Lost Gardens of Heligan; Various National Trust Gardens

A few miles inland from St Agnes you descend into a pretty wooded valley and find The Rose-in-Vale, a welcoming Georgian Cornish country house hotel surrounded by charming grounds. Owners, James and Sara Evans are extremely hospitable and there is a genuine desire to ensure that you have all you need. A light and very spacious dinning room is the setting for a carefully thought-out menu which works with the seasons and features an impressive 'surf & turf' option letting you enjoy the best of local meat and freshly caught seafood. Comfortable bedrooms throughout and The Rose Suite comes with a four-poster bed and the indulgence of a double Jacuzzi bath and a double twelve-jet walk in shower! Outside relax by the swimming pool, in the hot tub or simply find a quite corner by the duck pond.

THE PHEASANT

BASSENTHWAITE LAKE, NR COCKERMOUTH, CUMBRIA CA13 9YE
Tel: 0845 365 2643 **International:** +44 (0)17687 76234 **Fax:** 017687 76002
Web: www.johansens.com/pheasantcumbria **E-mail:** info@the-pheasant.co.uk

Our inspector loved: *The comfort and Olde World ambience and charm of this award winning traditional inn.*

Price Guide:
single £80–£100
double/twin £150–£200

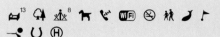

Awards/Recognition: Condé Nast Johansens Most Excellent Inn Award 2008;1 AA Rosette 2007-2008

Location: A66, 0.5 mile; M6 jct 40, 25 miles; Keswick, 6 miles; Cockermouth, 6 miles

Attractions: Bassenthwaite Lake; Lake District National Park; Wordsworth House

This 500 year old hotel is rightly proud of its heritage – it has remained truly British in the classical sense. There is a charm and peacefulness about the place and set in 40 acres of gardens and woodlands just a few yards from Bassenthwaite Lake makes it ideal for exploring this beautiful unspoilt northern part of the Lake District. The bar is testament to a bygone era with traditional wood-panelling and highly polished walls. The beamed dining room serves delicious traditional Cumbrian specialties as well as delicate fine dishes which are influenced by the seasons and local produce. Several lounges invite you to curl up with a good book and relax. Charming bedrooms combine light colours and textures with antiques and personal touches.

CROSBY LODGE COUNTRY HOUSE HOTEL

HIGH CROSBY, CROSBY-ON-EDEN, CARLISLE, CUMBRIA CA6 4QZ
Tel: 0845 365 3253 **International:** +44 (0)1228 573618 **Fax:** 01228 573428
Web: www.johansens.com/crosbylodge **E-mail:** info@crosbylodge.co.uk

Our inspector loved: Philippa Sedgwick's wine warehouse in the courtyard, selling quality wines and home-made produce.

Price Guide:
single £90–£115
double £160–£210

Location: A689, 0.5 mile; M6 jct 44, 3.5 miles; Brampton 4, miles; Carlisle, 4.5 miles

Attractions: Hadrians Wall; Historic City of Carlisle; Scottish Borders; Lake District

Crosby Lodge is a Grade II listed mansion skilfully converted into a country hotel amidst pastoral countryside close to the Scottish Lowlands, Hadrian's Wall and the Lake District. Spacious interiors are elegantly furnished and reflect the superb comfort and service created by Michael and Patricia Sedgwick. Most of the bedrooms have antique and half-testers beds. The 2 bedrooms situated in the converted stables are ideal if you want to take your dog. In The Lodge restaurant, the head chef and his team create dishes from traditional English recipes - and also continental cuisine, matched by an extensive wine list. Tables are set with cut glass and silver cutlery, complementing the surroundings. Crosby Lodge makes a superb venue for weddings, parties, business and social events. Closed 24 December to 16 January.

WEST VALE COUNTRY HOUSE & RESTAURANT

FAR SAWREY, HAWKSHEAD, AMBLESIDE, CUMBRIA LA22 0LQ
Tel: 0845 365 2795 **International:** +44 (0)1539 442 817 **Fax:** 01539 445 302
Web: www.johansens.com/westvale **E-mail:** enquiries@westvalecountryhouse.co.uk

Our inspector loved: The delicious dinner cooked by Glynn, the owner in this charming small hotel

Price Guide:
single £80-£98
double £110-£145
junior suite £153-£165

Awards/Recognition: 2 AA Rosettes 2007-2008

Location: On the B5285; M6 jct 36, 16 miles; Hawkshead, 2 miles; Windermere Ferry, 1 mile

Attractions: Windermere; Hawkshead with Beatrix Potter; Langdale; Grizdale Forest

In the heart of the Lake District National Park this late 19th century former Victorian gentleman's residence is on the edge of a tranquil village, well associated with Beatrix Potter who wrote her much loved stories at "Hilltop," just a few minutes' walk away. Carefully restored with captivating views of Grizedale Forest and The Old Man of Coniston, the AA and Visit Britain 5 Star West Vale exudes the grace of a bygone age with traditional touches such as a complimentary decanter of sherry awaiting you in your bedroom. The bedrooms are well appointed and fresh fruit and complimentary slippers are provided in the de luxe rooms and junior suites. Excellent classical cuisine is served in the award winning restaurant where fresh local fresh produce is used whenever possible. Special breaks available. Closed January.

THE WHEATSHEAF @ BRIGSTEER

BRIGSTEER, KENDAL, CUMBRIA LA8 8AN
Tel: 0845 365 2734 **International:** +44 (0)15395 68254
Web: www.johansens.com/brigsteer **E-mail:** wheatsheaf@brigsteer.gb.com

Our inspector loved: This delightful village inn, specialising in traditional English cuisine with a modern twist.

Price Guide:
single from £75
double from £85

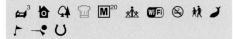

Location: A591, 2 miles; M6 jct 36, 6 miles; Kendal, 3 miles

Attractions: Sizergh Castle; Gateway to The lakes; Morecambe Bay; Damson growing region of the Lyth Valley

Tucked away in the Lakeland village of Brigsteer, at the foot of Scout Scar, with its stunning panoramic views and on the edge of a damson-growing region of Lyth Valley, The Wheatsheaf is an impressive food lead country inn. There's a traditional feel though a recent refurbishment has given it a contemporary twist with polished oak floors and handcrafted bistro style furniture. Menus are based around the impressive seasonal abundance of locally sourced produce, fish from around Morecambe bay and flavoursome game and meat much of which is reared themselves in conjunction with local farmers Their own fruit, vegetables & herbs complement the finest of local ingredients and is aided by an excellent wine list and local cask ales that will leave you more than satisfied. 3 double bedrooms are upstairs for those lucky enough to stay over after an excellent evening of hospitality and have the chance to explore this beautiful area.

HIPPING HALL

COWAN BRIDGE, KIRKBY LONSDALE, CUMBRIA LA6 2JJ
Tel: 0845 365 1859 **International:** +44 (0)15242 71187 **Fax:** 015242 72452
Web: www.johansens.com/hippinghall **E-mail:** info@hippinghall.com

Our inspector loved: *The delicious and imaginative dinner in the 15th-century banqueting hall.*

Price Guide: (including dinner)
single from £160
double £210–£305
exclusive use from £3000

Location: A65, 100yds; Kikby Lonsdale, 2 miles; M6 Jct 36, 8 miles

Attractions: Lake District; Yorkshire Dales; Eden Valley; Trough of Bowland

New owners in 2005 and a sensitive restoration, has regenerated the 300 year old Hipping Hall and rediscovered its old English charm. The use of bold fabrics and striking colours create vibrant interiors with an atmosphere of stylish elegance. Dinner is served in the magnificent 15th-century oak beamed banqueting hall, where you can experience the unique modern cuisine of Head Chef, Jason Birkbeck whose excellent reputation is based on dishes using the finest locally sourced ingredients. These include roast breast of quail, ballotine of reared Lincolnshire rabbit, roast short loin of lamb and fillet of line caught Sea Bass. The beautifully designed bedrooms are light and airy. All have handmade beds, exposed beams and either large walk-in showers or baths; many overlook the pretty gardens.

FAYRER GARDEN HOUSE HOTEL

LYTH VALLEY ROAD, BOWNESS-ON-WINDERMERE, CUMBRIA LA23 3JP
Tel: 0845 365 3292 **International:** +44 (0)15394 88195 **Fax:** 015394 45986
Web: www.johansens.com/fayrergarden **E-mail:** lakescene@fayrergarden.com

Our inspector loved: Dining in the redesigned restaurant overlooking Lake Windermere.

Price Guide: (including 5-course dinner)
single £85–£140
standard £150–£200
lake view £214–£300

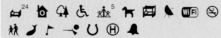

Awards/Recognition: 2 AA Rosettes 2008-2009

Location: A5074, 0.25 miles; A591, 8 miles; M6 jct 36, 16 miles; Windermere, 2.5 miles

Attractions: Lake Windermere; Lake District National Park and Visitor Centre; Beatrix Potter; Blackwell Arts and Crafts House

A lovely Victorian house in spacious gardens and grounds. Its hard to find such wonderful views over Lake Windermere at such excellent value for money. The garden is full of gorgeous colours and a terrace enviably positioned to catch all the afternoon sun. Menus change daily and use local produce such as fish, game and poultry – whatever is in season. The wine list is excellent and again, very reasonably priced. Many of the bedrooms benefit from the views, some with four-posters and some leading directly onto the garden. There is much to entertain you nearby, with the Windermere Steamboat Museum, boating from Bowness Pier, golf at Windermere Golf Club and The Beatrix Potter attraction amongst the favourites. Closed the first 2 weeks of January.

BROADOAKS COUNTRY HOUSE

BRIDGE LANE, TROUTBECK, WINDERMERE, CUMBRIA LA23 1LA
Tel: 0845 365 3201 **International:** +44 (0)1539 445566 **Fax:** +44 (0)1539 488766
Web: www.johansens.com/broadoaks **E-mail:** info@broadoakscountryhouse.co.uk

Our inspector loved: *This charming secluded hotel with beautiful views over the troutbeck Valley.*

Price Guide:
single £70–£160
double £90–£210

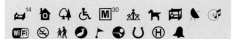

Location: M6 jct 36, 18 miles; A591, 0.5 mile; Windermere, 1.5 miles; Ambleside, 4 miles

Attractions: Lake District National Park; Lake Windermere; Beatrix Potter Centre; Brockhole Visitors Centre & Holehead Gardens

A striking vista across the Troutbeck Valley and Lake Windermere makes Broadoaks a delightful retreat for those exploring the picturesque Lake District. Here you will find warm English hospitality, period styling, personal touches and many impressive original features. Furnishings in the bedrooms are mindful of the graceful building's Victorian past, some featuring four-poster or antique brass bedsteads. A favourite room is the elegant music room complete with Bechstein piano, an open fireplace and barrel vaulted ceiling. Here you can enjoy a pre-dinner cocktail before dinner in the light and elegant dining room. Daily and signature dishes show creativity for winning combinations of seasonal textures, tastes and flavours. This secluded hotel with is spectacular views is just the sort of place you can curl up with a good book or enjoy outside pursuits such as fishing and clay pigeon shooting in the grounds.

THE CROWN INN

RIGGS LANE, MARSTON MONTGOMERY, DERBYSHIRE DE6 2FF
Tel: 0845 365 3608 **International:** +44 (0)1889 590 541
Web: www.johansens.com/crowninn **E-mail:** info@thecrowninn-derbyshire.co.uk

Our inspector loved: Its location set in the delightful unspoilt South Derbyshire countryside, yet everything close-by.

Price Guide:
double from £60
twin from £75
family rooms from £85

A pretty inn standing at the southern edge of the Peak District, an area of outstanding natural beauty, in the small delightful hamlet of Marston Montgomery. The inn has been completely refurbished and updated yet retains its original charm and character. The restaurant has a strong local reputation as a popular and intimate venue for both lunch and dinner, serving simple British dishes and using largely local produce. An excellent range of beer is to be found in the cosy bar whilst the elevated terrace and garden area provides a beautiful space in which to enjoy long summer days and mild evenings. The seven guestrooms are unfussy and individually decorated. Closed Christmas Day and New Years Day.

Awards/Recognition: 1 AA Rosette 2007-2008

Location: A 515, 2 miles; A52, 5 miles; A50, 2 miles; East Midlands Airport, 24 miles

Attractions: Uttoxeter Race Course; Peak District; Chatsworth House; Sudbury Hall (NT)

EAST LODGE COUNTRY HOUSE HOTEL

ROWSLEY, NR MATLOCK, DERBYSHIRE DE4 2EF
Tel: 0845 365 3278 **International:** +44 (0)1629 734474 **Fax:** 01629 733949
Web: www.johansens.com/eastlodgecountryhouse **E-mail:** info@eastlodge.com

Our inspector loved: The very flexible all day menu avalible at the hotel. Eat what you want, when you want

Price Guide:
single from £125
double/twin from £125

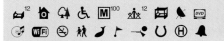

Awards/Recognition: Condé Nast Johansens Readers' Award 2008; Derbyshire Restaurant of the Year 2007-2008; 2 AA Rosettes 2008-2009

Location: Chesterfield, 8 miles; Sheffield, 9 miles; Derby, 21 miles; Manchester, 37 miles

Attractions: Chatsworth House; Haddon Hall; Peak District National Park; Cromford Mill World Heritage Site

A glorious tree-lined driveway guides you from the Peak District National Park to this elegant country house hotel. As you enter the reception you're enveloped by the warm, hospitable atmosphere that has been effortlessly created by the Hardman Family and their excellent team, who ensure every visit is memorable. The traditional and modern fuse together, with Broadband availability, luxurious bathrooms, a romantic garden room and terrace all merely adding to the charm of this award-winning property. Outside, David Hardman has created splendid gardens. The use of floodlight in the evening is enchanting and the 10 acres of grounds provide tranquil wanders. Beyond, fishing on the River Derwent, within the Chatsworth Estate, can be arranged. This is the nearest hotel to historic Chatsworth House.

DANNAH FARM COUNTRY HOUSE

BOWMAN'S LANE, SHOTTLE, NEAR BELPER, DERBYSHIRE DE56 2DR
Tel: 0845 365 3262 **International:** +44 (0)1773 550273/550630 **Fax:** 01773 550590
Web: www.johansens.com/dannah **E-mail:** slack@dannah.co.uk

Our inspector loved: *The luxurious and secluded spa cabin with hot tub is a must during your stay.*

Price Guide:
double (single occupancy) from £75
double/twin from £150
suite from £195

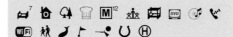

Experience the joys of rural living with the comforts of home at this unique 18th-century Georgian farmhouse. Brimming with character, its bedrooms overlook rolling pastures and pretty gardens and are beautifully furnished. All are different, some with four-poster beds, private sitting rooms, wet rooms and double spa-baths. Aromas of freshly baked bread waft from the kitchen to whet your appetite for breakfast, cooked to order using free range eggs and locally sourced produce. The Spa facilities situated in "The Leisure Cabin", can be booked for exclusive use with any of the rooms. These private facilities are tucked out of sight and feature a huge Canadian Spa hot-tub set on a private terrace, a sauna, steam shower and luxurious sitting room, overlooking farmland into the distance. Dannah has been awarded "Highly Commended, 5 Yellow Star", from the AA, putting it in the top 10% of guest accommodation in the country.

Location: A517, 2 miles; M1, 16 miles; A50, 18 miles; East Midlands Airport, 20 miles

Attractions: Peak District; Chatsworth House; Haddon Hall; Crich Tramway Museum

DONINGTON MANOR HOTEL

HIGH STREET, CASTLE DONINGTON, DERBY, DERBYSHIRE DE74 2PP
Tel: 0845 365 3916 **International:** +44 (0)1332 810 253 **Fax:** 01332 850330
Web: www.johansens.com/doningtonmanorhotel **E-mail:** stay@doningtonmanorhotel.co.uk

Our inspector loved: *The peace of the garden view rooms. Some have a private terrace and garden access.*

Price Guide:
classic from £70
superior from £90
suite from £110

Awards/Recognition: 1 AA Rosette 2007–2008

Location: A50, 2 miles; M1, 3 miles; Derby City Centre, 9 miles; East Midlands Airport, 3 miles

Attractions: Donington Race Park; Chatsworth House; Alton Towers; Nottingham City

In a green leafy village close to Derby and its excellent links through the heart of England, you'll find a friendly, and very enthusiastic team at this 18th-century coaching inn. The main house has preserved its original architectural features and the relaxed atmosphere has made it a popular meeting place for both locals and travelling guests. Bedrooms are a welcome mix of cosy and simple and grand and imposing where little touches such as Roberts radios and Aveda bathroom products make you feel right at home. The bar is a lively place to start the evening, before adjourning to Sage restaurant for its modern European food served in light airy surroundings and a happily unpretentious atmosphere. Sunday lunch is renowned as a family affair, so booking is a must.

THE PLOUGH INN

LEADMILL BRIDGE, HATHERSAGE, DERBYSHIRE S30 1BA
Tel: 0845 365 2647 **International:** +44 (0)1433 650319 **Fax:** 01433 651049
Web: www.johansens.com/ploughinnhathersage **E-mail:** sales@theploughinn-hathersage.co.uk

Our inspector loved: *The central courtyard, a real sun trap and relaxing place to enjoy a well-earned drink after a day's walking.*

Price Guide:
double/twin from £90

Location: A619, 4 miles; A623, 6 miles; M1 Jct 29, 20 miles; Sheffield, 11 miles

Attractions: Chatsworth House; Haddon Hall; Blue John Mine and Caves; Eyam Village

The Plough is a traditional 16th-century English inn with low beams, open fireplaces and ancient thick stone walls. Set in its own 9 acres of lush green lawns and bright flowers that lead to the edge of the river Derwent, you are well placed to enjoy walks in the spectacular Derbyshire countryside. Attentive staff will make sure you are well looked after, and excellent food can be enjoyed within the cool, whitewashed walls of the restaurant. An area rich in seasonal produce inspires both classical and more modern dishes. Rooms have been tastefully restored using local materials and feature exposed beams and brickwork. Downstairs the main bar offers a range of hand-pulled ales which can also be enjoyed on a sunny day in the cobbled court yard or out on the decking.

THE TURTLEY CORN MILL

AVONWICK, DEVON TQ10 9ES

Tel: 0845 365 3921 **International:** +44 (0)1364 646100 **Fax:** 01364 646101
Web: www.johansens.com/turtleycornmill **E-mail:** mill@avonwick.net

Our inspector loved: *This beautifully tucked away little secret that is so very accessible.*

Price Guide:
single £90
double £90-£110

Location: Just off the B3372; A38, 5 miles; Totnes, 8 miles; Plymouth, 10 miles

Attractions: Totnes; Exeter; Plymouth; Dartmoor

Turtley has had many guises. It began life as a corn mill, then was a famous chicken hatchery before becoming a pub in the 1970s. A complete refurbishment in 2005 makes the most of light and space and has resulted in a delightful, secluded gem set amid 6½ acres of lawns and woodland walks. The 4 bedrooms, 3 with spacious showers and 1 with a bath are kitted out with king-sized beds, lovely linens and flat-screen TVs, not to mention the Laurence Lewellyn Bowen wall hangings. Menus change daily, and are dependent on the locally sourced ingredients that feature so heavily on them. The accompanying wine list and selection of beers are all well priced options that will appeal to a variety of tastes.

THE EDGEMOOR

HAYTOR ROAD, BOVEY TRACEY, SOUTH DEVON TQ13 9LE
Tel: 0845 365 3224 **International:** +44 (0)1626 832466 **Fax:** 01626 834760
Web: www.johansens.com/edgemoor **E-mail:** reservations@edgemoor.co.uk

Our inspector loved: The picture postcard exterior followed by the character and welcome within.

Price Guide:
single from £95
double £140-£160

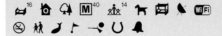

Location: B3387; A382, 1 mile; A38, 3 miles; Exeter, 17.5 miles

Attractions: Dartmoor National Park; Castle Drogo; Exeter Cathedral; Jeremy Leach Pottery

Once a 19th-century school and now a delightful country house hotel the building oozes warmth and character in a peaceful location. There is a strong sense of style running throughout the house and its individual contemporary and classic bedrooms. A beautifully light dining room that is both elegant and unpretentious offers inventive menus making the most of the abundance of local seasonal West Country produce. More informal dining takes place in the bar which offers a wide range of cask ales and whiskies, some rather weird and marvellous. Whether it is peace and quiet you are after or an active break new owners Simon, Heather and Morten delight in ensuring you make the most of your time - for car enthusiasts hire a Morgan, or there's moorland riding, fishing, mountain biking and more uniquely Letterboxing - a local game started in 1854 where using clues, walkers find cunningly hidden boxes concealing messages from previous walkers to find.

DEVON - CHAGFORD

MILL END

DARTMOOR NATIONAL PARK, CHAGFORD, DEVON TQ13 8JN
Tel: 0845 365 2062 **International:** +44 (0)1647 432282 **Fax:** 01647 433106
Web: www.johansens.com/millend **E-mail:** info@millendhotel.com

Our inspector loved: This truly delightful tucked away little gem - an absolute getaway.

Price Guide: (exclusive use price on request)
single £90–£125
double/twin £90–£175
suite £175–£220

Awards/Recognition: 2 AA Rosettes 2006-2007

Location: On the A382; A30, 3.66 miles; M5 jct 31, 19 miles; Newton Aboot, 16 miles

Attractions: Chagford; Castle Drogo; Rosemoor Gardens; Eden Project

Gleaming white under slate grey tiles, Mill End is an idyllic hideaway in Dartmoor's National Park, surrounded by a beautiful English garden with colourful borders that run down to the River Teign. Built in the mid 1700s as a flour mill, you will find little corner nooks, paintings and old photographs that imbue a feeling of seclusion, enhanced by the smell of wood smoke and polished wood. The delightful bedrooms feature lovely fabrics and attractive local hand-crafted furniture. The elegant dining room offers you the delightful cuisine of Head Chef, Christophe Ferraro and his young team who's menus include; crab risotto with chilli and lemon grass froth followed by slow roasted fillet of beef with truffle potato and marrow soufflé and a carpaccio of pineapple with coconut ice cream and warm malibu jelly.

THE WHITE HOUSE

CHILLINGTON, KINGSBRIDGE, DEVON TQ7 2JX

Tel: 0845 365 4615   **International:** +44 (0)1548 580505   **Fax:** 01548 581196
Web: www.johansens.com/whitehousedevon   **E-mail:** frontofhouse@whitehousedevon.com

Our inspector loved: The whole experience - I just did not want to leave!

Price Guide:
double £155-£175 (Thursday to Saturday minimum 2-night stay)
exclusive house hire from £2,150 for a two night stay

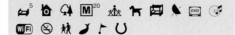

An all-encompassing relaxed atmosphere prevails at The White House. Positioned between the 2 picturesque estuaries of Salcombe and historic Dartmouth, this Georgian house has been lovingly restored. Beautifully designed with the concept of space, you can quietly curl up in a cosy corner, chat by the fireside, lounge on the terrace, or should you book the screening room, enjoy relaxing on a beanbag and savour a tub of ice cream. Large handmade beds dominate the delightful bedrooms, which are complete with crisp linen and bathrooms filled with local hand-blended bath products. Breakfasts are unhurried and lunches and dinners can be long and leisurely, allowing you to enjoy the simple luxury of great food in great company.

Location: A379, 0.5 miles; A38 Devon Expressway, 20 miles; M5 Jct 31, 37 miles; Exeter Airport, 45 miles

Attractions: Salcombe; Dartmouth; Slapton Sands & Ley; Dartmoor

KINGSTON HOUSE

STAVERTON, NEAR TOTNES, DEVON TQ9 6AR
Tel: 0845 365 1937 **International:** +44 (0)1803 762 235 **Fax:** 01803 762 444
Web: www.johansens.com/kingstonhouse **E-mail:** info@kingston-estate.co.uk

Our inspector loved: *Once arriving not wanting to leave.*

Price Guide:
single £110–£120
double £190
suite £200–£225

Location: A384, 2 miles; A38, 5.5 miles; M5 jct 31, 24 miles; Totnes, 4 miles

Attractions: Exeter; Dartmoor National Park; River Dart; Dartmouth

Offering some of the dreamiest accommodation in the country, the Kingston Estate nestles amongst rolling hills and valleys, bounded by Dartmoor and the sea. Kingston House and its superb self-contained cottages have been restored by the Corfields without losing a drop of 18th-century charm. In the main house 3 striking period suites are reached by one of the finest examples of a marquetry staircase in England. The bedrooms have original panelling and shutters, fine plasterwork and profusion of wall paintings. Soak up the atmosphere of crackling log fires in winter, summer drinks on the terrace, and candlelight glittering on sparkling crystal in the elegant dining room. Here you are as welcome as if it were Elizabeth and Michael Corfields' own private house party. Plenty of flexible space for weddings, meetings and gatherings.

BRIDGEHOUSE BEAMINSTER

PROUT BRIDGE, BEAMINSTER, DORSET DT8 3AY
Tel: 0845 365 2408 **International:** +44 (0)1308 862200 **Fax:** 01308 863700
Web: www.johansens.com/bridgehousebeam **E-mail:** enquiries@bridge-house.co.uk

Our inspector loved: *The mix of contemporary and traditional design and the terrific al fresco dinning.*

Price Guide:
single £76
double/twin £116–£200

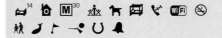

Awards/Recognition: 1 AA Rosettes 2006-2007

Location: On the A3066; A356, 7 miles; M5 jct 25, 22 miles; Exeter, 42 miles

Attractions: Jurassic Coast; Abbotsbury; Chesil Beach; Lyme Regis

This beautiful old West Dorset retreat partly dates back to the 13th century but today its attentive staff create a memorable experience. The bedrooms, some with stone fireplaces and garden views, are spacious. The gardens, surrounded by an ancient stone wall, are a suntrap, ideal for lunches or candle-lit dinners. The oldest room is a quiet bar with a quaint atmosphere and an impressive range of drinks. A large inglenook fireplace in the lounge is the perfect place to enjoy a drink before dinner or earlier an afternoon tea. Seasonal menus include daily à la carte specials of delicious fresh organic cuisine such as the acclaimed medallions of pork served with fresh figs and stilton sauce. The addition of a new brasserie style restaurant offers a great new dining option. A healthy breakfast is served in the conservatory overlooking the gardens that are floodlit at night.

THE GRANGE AT OBORNE

OBORNE, NR SHERBORNE, DORSET DT9 4LA
Tel: 0845 365 2506 **International:** +44 (0)1935 813463 **Fax:** 01935 817464
Web: www.johansens.com/grangesherborne **E-mail:** reception@thegrange.co.uk

Our inspector loved: *The Dorsetshire village setting in a beautiful corner of hidden England.*

Price Guide:
single from £90
double from £109
four-poster from £150

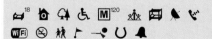

Location: A30, 0.25 mile; M27 lct 2, 45 miles; Sherborne, 1.5 miles; Bristol, 54 miles

Attractions: Stourhead House and Gardens; Stonehenge; The Cerne Abbas Giant; Shaftesbury;

This 200-year-old house nestles peacefully in formal gardens, just 1.5 miles from historic Sherborne. Guests are welcomed by owners Jennifer and Jon Fletcher, and can relax in each of the 18 well-appointed and spacious bedrooms. Dinner is served in a most pleasant atmosphere, overlooking the attractive floodlit gardens. The restaurant specialises in both international and traditional cuisine. For those planning an event or occasion the hotel can provide a service for up to 120 guests, and is also suited to conferences and business meetings. This quiet haven is a most ideal escape from city life, and guests can unwind with horse riding, fishing or simply taking in the local scenery.

CHANNELS LODGE

BELSTEADS FARM LANE, LITTLE WALTHAM, CHELMSFORD, ESSEX CM3 3PT
Tel: 0845 365 3918 **International:** +44 (0)1245 441547 **Fax:** 01245 442032
Web: www.johansens.com/channelslodge **E-mail:** info@channelslodge.co.uk

Our inspector loved: The way the stylish and contemporary furnishings harmonise with the traditional features of the building.

Price Guide:
single £80-£110
double £115-£155

This beautifully converted 15th-century farmhouse and barn is a cool and calm oasis within the elevated grounds of Channels Golf Club. Choose from spacious and airy bedrooms such as Birch, Cedar or Chestnut or seriously spoil yourself with a stay in one of the suites. Full of character, some rooms have high ceiling beams and stand alone baths, while all have TVs and DVD players, complimentary goodies, soft duvets and comfy robes and slippers. The attractive Brasserie is located in the Golf Club, another renovated period building, or there is the Waltham Bistro at the sister club Regiment Way Golf Centre, only a short drive away. A serious contender if you are looking to host a function in a very special setting.

Location: A130, 1.5 miles; A414, 5 miles; Stansted Airport, 20-min drive; M11 Jct 8, 20-min drive

Attractions: Constable Country; The East Coast; Roman Garrision Town of Colchester; Chelmsford, Home of Essex County Cricket

BIBURY COURT

BIBURY COURT, BIBURY, GLOUCESTERSHIRE GL7 5NT
Tel: 0845 365 3035 **International:** +44 (0)1285 740337 **Fax:** 01285 740660
Web: www.johansens.com/biburycourt **E-mail:** info@biburycourt.com

Our inspector loved: Walking along the river and through the gardens of this lovely country house.

Price Guide:
Single from £135
Double from £160
Suite £240

Awards/Recognition: 2 AA Rosettes 2007-2008

Location: Just off B4425; A40, 8.5 miles; Cirencester, 7 miles; Cheltenham, 22 miles

Attractions: Stow-on-the-Wold; Bourton-on-the-Water; Arlington Row; Hidcote Manor Gardens

Charles II and during the reign of George III, the Prince Regent, are said to have visited here. Dating from Tudor times, the main house was built in 1663 by Sir Thomas Sackville. Following generations of illustrious owners, it became a hotel in 1968. Set in 6 acres on the outskirts of Bibury, which William Morris called "the most beautiful village in England" Bibury Court is run as a country house focusing on good food and wine in informal and pleasurable surroundings. You can enjoy log fires in the cooler months and there are some lovely panelled rooms to explore, with fine detail and antique furniture. Many of the bedrooms have four-posters, all have private bathrooms and for those who like greater privacy there is the Sackville suite.

THE DIAL HOUSE

THE CHESTNUTS, HIGH STREET, BOURTON-ON-THE-WATER, GLOUCESTERSHIRE GL54 2AN
Tel: 0845 365 2463 **International:** +44 (0)1451 822244 **Fax:** 01451 810126
Web: www.johansens.com/dialhouse **E-mail:** info@dialhousehotel.com

Our inspector loved: The stylish decoration throughout and great food.

Price Guide:
single £120
double £140–£180
four poster £180-£220

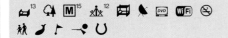

Location: A429, 0.65 miles; A40, 5 miles; Cheltenham, 19.5 miles

Attractions: Stow-on-the-Wold; Warwick Castle; Shakespeare country; Cheltenham town and racecourse

Feel that you're stepping into a period drama at this beautiful family-run hotel, built in 1698 of Cotswold stone in an unspoiled village where the little River Windrush flows down the main street under "toy town" bridges. Exuding sophisticated English country style, The Dial House is filled with large inglenook fireplaces, exposed timber beams, monks' chairs, poor boxes, secret cupboards, water wells and stone arches. There is so much you'll find memorable, and every bedroom has gorgeous details from hand-painted wallpaper to lavish big beds, deep baths and exquisite fabrics. Mouth-watering cuisine is served in intimate dining rooms where like the rest of the hotel innovative style and high standards reign.

BEAUMONT HOUSE

56 SHURDINGTON ROAD, CHELTENHAM, GLOUCESTERSHIRE GL53 0JE
Tel: 0845 365 3912 **International:** +44 (0)1242 223311 **Fax:** 01242 520044
Web: www.johansens.com/beaumonthouse **E-mail:** reservations@bhhotel.co.uk

Our inspector loved: *The two themed bedrooms, "Out of Africa" and "Out of Asia."*

Price Guide:
single from £65
double from £86
themed room/suite from £144

Location: A46; Cheltenham, 1 mile; Cheltenham Railway Station, 0.75 miles; M5 jct 1/11a, 3 miles

Attractions: Cotswolds; Cheltenham Racecourse; Sudeley Castle; Gloucester

At Beaumont House you are encouraged to feel at home and help yourself to fresh coffee or cappuccino from the bean to cup coffee machine, or a drink from the honour bar in the sitting room. This immaculate 1860s house reveals two themed bedrooms: the "Out of Africa," with all-slate tiled walls and rustic canopy, and the "Out of Asia" complete with serene Buddha statue. The remaining guest rooms are well presented and feature complimentary wireless broadband access and flat-screen TVs. Breakfast is taken in the Garden room with its floor to ceiling windows overlooking the pretty garden. Whilst room service is on hand for an evening meal on week nights you will find an excellent selection of restaurants and bars close by.

LYPIATT HOUSE

LYPIATT ROAD, CHELTENHAM, GLOUCESTERSHIRE GL50 2QW
Tel: 0845 365 2051 **International:** +44 (0)1242 224994 **Fax:** 01242 224996
Web: www.johansens.com/lypiatt **E-mail:** stay@lypiatt.co.uk

Our inspector loved: *The warm welcome and comfortable hospitality. An ideal spot for visiting Cheltenham's stylish shops in Montpellier.*

Price Guide:
single £70–£90
double/twin £80–£110

Location: On the A40; M5 jct 11, 2.6 miles

Attractions: Cotswolds; Cheltenham Racecourse; Rococo Gardens, Painswick; Moreton-in-Marsh

Staying at this hotel in the fashionable Montpellier district gives you a great location for exploring Cheltenham's main shopping areas, theatres and interesting corners. Lypiatt House has a stunning contemporary décor and a homely atmosphere, all of which set off its Victorian style perfectly. In the sunny drawing room large windows and warm colours give a spacious, light ambience The bedrooms are also generously sized and nicely done while a substantial full English breakfast will ensure you're set up for the day. The 'honesty' bar is a welcome touch and allows you to concoct a drink to your own standards before heading out to dinner. With no restaurant on site yet a plethora of good eateries nearby the team will be happy to make reservations for you.

NEW INN AT COLN

COLN ST-ALDWYNS, NEAR CIRENCESTER, GLOUCESTERSHIRE GL7 5AN
Tel: 0845 365 3754 **International:** +44 (0)1285 750651 **Fax:** 01285 750657
Web: www.johansens.com/newinnatcoln **E-mail:** info@thenewinnatcoln.co.uk

Our inspector loved: *My amazingly comfy bed and the great food.*

Price Guide:
single £75–£120
double £120–£180
suite from £180

Awards/Recognition: 2 AA Rosettes 2008-2009

Location: A417, 3 miles; A429, 8 miles; M4/M5, 20 miles; Cheltenham, 23 miles

Attractions: Cirencester; Burford; Bibury; Stow on the Wold

This quaint inn hidden beneath a bright carpet of green creeper has recently undergone an extensive refurbishment. Original features, including oak beams in the bedrooms and an open fire, mix well with contemporary facilities including flat-screen TVs and sleek furniture. In the summer you can enjoy a glass of Pimms on the large south-facing terrace or take a stroll in the orchard. The British menu, including pan roast halibut and chocolate fondant, is simplicity at its best. Located in the heart of the Cotswolds between Burford and Cirencester, there is plenty to keep you entertained, including fishing, golf, boating, antique shopping, and of course Cheltenham Racecourse is only 23 miles away. Deservedly they have been named an AA top 200 hotel. The new boardroom, available for hire by the hour or day, is fully equipped with audio-visual equipment and is ideal for private working lunches, meetings and presentations.

THE REDESDALE ARMS

HIGH STREET, MORETON-IN-MARSH, GLOUCESTERSHIRE GL56 0AW
Tel: 0845 365 1873 **International:** +44 (0)1608 650308 **Fax:** 01608 651843
Web: www.johansens.com/redesdalearms **E-mail:** info@redesdalearms.com

Our inspector loved: The lovely new executive bedrooms and the buzzy atmosphere throughout.

Price Guide:
single from £65
double from £85
executive from £105

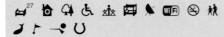

Awards/Recognition: 1 AA Rosette 2008–2009

Location: On A429; On A44 (Fosse Way); Stratford-upon-Avon, 10 miles

Attractions: Cotswolds; Snowshill Manor; Hidcote Manor Garden; Stow-on-the-Wold

Dating back to 1650, the Redesdale Arms remains a busy inn at the centre of this bustling market town. Its traditional atmosphere has touches of the contemporary, and the emphasis is on relaxation, fine food and a good local ale. Menus mix modern international cooking with British favourites, drawing widely on locally grown vegetables and Cotswold meats. There is a daily fish list, and local game features heavily in winter. Mixing the old with the new, bedrooms stand where the original inn and stables used to be, mingling original beams and quaint passages with bold fabrics, satellite TV and Gilchrist & Soames toiletries. The new executive rooms are especially spacious, and 2 feature whirlpool baths. At the centre of the Cotswolds, this is an ideal spot from which to explore.

LOWER BROOK HOUSE

BLOCKLEY, NR MORETON-IN-MARSH, GLOUCESTERSHIRE GL56 9DS
Tel: 0845 365 2045 **International:** +44 (0)1386 700286 **Fax:** 01386 701400
Web: www.johansens.com/lowerbrookhouse **E-mail:** info@lowerbrookhouse.com

Our inspector loved: *My room, Colebrook. A wonderful stay with great hosts, Julian & Anna*

Price Guide:
single £80–£175
double £95–£175

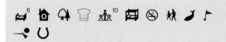

Location: On the B4479; A44, 1.5 miles; Broadway, 8.5 miles

Attractions: Hidcote Manor and Gardens; Snowshill Manor; Sudeley Castle; Broadway Tower

Blockley is a village within a designated Area of Outstanding Natural Beauty and perhaps one of the Cotswold's best kept secrets. Characterised by wisteria covered cottages, dovecotes, and a meandering babbling brook this lovely 17th-century house stands serenely at its heart. The brook once provided power for 12 mills, 6 of which now give their names to the hotel's charming guest rooms. Owners, Julian and Anna, have taken every care to ensure you feel totally at ease in this idyllic setting. The large, deep open fireplace in the relaxing lounge is a favorite spot for a social chat or just to curl up with a good book. Homemade biscuits in your room, big fluffy bathrobes, sumptuous breakfasts and imaginative dinner menus make this a place you'd like to keep all to yourself.

THE MILL AT GORDLETON

SILVER STREET, HORDLE, NR LYMINGTON, NEW FOREST, HAMPSHIRE SO41 6DJ
Tel: 0845 365 2597 **International:** +44 (0)1590 682219 **Fax:** 01590 683073
Web: www.johansens.com/themillatgordleton **E-mail:** info@themillatgordleton.co.uk

Our inspector loved: *A delicious lunch on the terrace overlooking the Mill pond, one of Hampshire's very special places.*

Price Guide:
single from £90
double/Twin £130
balcony from £150

Location: A337, 2 miles; M27 jct 1, 12 miles; Lymington, 3 miles; Southampton, 23 miles

Attractions: New Forest; Lymington and Harbour; Exbury Gardens; Beaulieu and Bucklers Hard

Tucked away between the New Forest National Park and the sea lies this idyllic ivy-clad 17th-century rural hideaway owned and run by Liz Cottingham. Immaculately restored to its former glory, the Mill was the winner of Condé Nast Johansens Most Excellent Value for Money Award 2005. The landscaped gardens exude rustic charm, and visitors weary of their hectic urban lifestyles will certainly relax here to the sound of the mill pond with its charming sluice gates and well fed ducks. The restaurant has a most welcoming atmosphere serving an excellent choice of imaginative dishes. On warm sunny days you can sit outside but be sure to book well in advance! The bedrooms have been recently refurbished with delightful bathrooms.

THE NURSE'S COTTAGE RESTAURANT WITH ROOMS

STATION ROAD, SWAY, LYMINGTON, HAMPSHIRE SO41 6BA
Tel: 0845 365 2609 **International:** +44 (0)1590 683402
Web: www.johansens.com/nursescottage **E-mail:** nurses.cottage@lineone.net

Our inspector loved: *The attentive service from Tony Barnfield and a very delicious dinner.*

Price Guide: (including dinner)
single £90
double/twin £170–£190

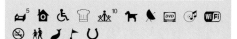

Location: A337, 3.5 miles; M27 jct 1, 11 miles; Lymington, 4 miles; Bournemouth, 13 miles

Attractions: New Forest National Park; ArtSway Gallery ; Beaulieu National Motor Museum; Exbury Gardens and Bucklers Hard

The motto 'good things come in small packages' is certainly true of this charming little hotel, where the cosy, ground-floor bedrooms are named after Sway's successive District Nurses, who lived here until 1983. Chef/Proprietor Tony Barnfield's innovative pampering of guests cannot fail to impress: extras in the bedroom include a flatscreen TV, dvd, Beaulieu chocolates, biscuits and fruit bowl and, in a small fridge, New Forest Spring Water, fresh organic milk, fruit juices and snacks. The kitchen brigade caters for guests in the smart Conservatory Restaurant, open to non-residents for breakfast and dinner. The seasonally-changing menu includes such British classics as cottage pie alongside guinea fowl in a tarragon white wine sauce, one of several house specialities. Over 60 bins comprise the award-winning Wine List and the numerous other accolades range from Best Breakfast in Britain to Excellence in Commitment to the Interests of Disabled People.

LANGRISH HOUSE

LANGRISH, NEAR PETERSFIELD, HAMPSHIRE GU32 1RN
Tel: 0845 365 1986 **International:** +44 (0)1730 266941 **Fax:** 01730 260543
Web: www.johansens.com/langrishhouse **E-mail:** frontdesk@langrishhouse.co.uk

Our inspector loved: *This very traditional English country house hotel steeped in a fascinating family history.*

Price Guide:
single £80–£100
double £116–£155
suite £155–£170

Awards/Recognition: 2 AA Rosette 2007-2008

Location: A272, 0.5 miles; Petersfield, 3 miles; Portsmouth, 15 miles; Heathrow, 53 miles

Attractions: Uppark; Hinton Ampner; Portsmouth Dockyard and HMS Victory; Goodwood

Capture the full traditional country house experience here at Langrish House. Extended by the present owners forbears in 1842 it opened as a hotel in 1979 and remains very much a family home, expertly run by Nigel and Robina Talbot-Ponsonby. Family portraits, antiques and heirlooms grace the rooms, and 14 acres of mature grounds include a picturesque lake. Individually decorated bedrooms with thoughtful touches give you ample opportunity to soak up the peace and quiet. Frederick's Restaurant affords glorious views of the lawns and rambling countryside, whilst its menus feature fresh regional produce, such good food has won the house AA recognition. Langrish House is an ideal venue for wedding receptions and business conferences offering dining facilities for up to 100 people.

THE OLD HOUSE HOTEL

THE SQUARE, WICKHAM, HAMPSHIRE PO17 5JG

Tel: 0845 365 3951 **International:** +44 (0)1329 833049 **Fax:** 01329 833672
Web: www.johansens.com/oldhousehotel **E-mail:** enquiries@oldhousehotel.co.uk

Our inspector loved: The pretty dining room leading out onto the walled garden terrace.

Price Guide:
double £90-£165
cottage from £350

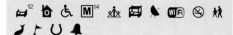

Awards/Recognition: 2 AA Rosettes 2008-2009

Location: A32, 1 miles; M27, 5 miles; Southampton, 11 miles; Southampton Airport, 10 miles

Attractions: Historic Dockyard Portsmouth; Mary Rose; Isle of Wight; New Forest

Beautifully twisted ivy grows lusciously around this stunning Georgian grade II listed building, which is ideally set in the middle of Wickham Village Square. Having been recently and sympathetically restored, it now offers elegant double bedrooms complete with original fireplaces and pretty tiled bathrooms. In the evening, you could enjoy a drink in the beamed bar, followed by a sensational, award-winning meal; all locally and freshly produced. The restaurant features a large conservatory, which opens out to the gardens when the weather is fine. If you are after total privacy the Garden Rooms and Anchorage Cottage are a short walk through the enchanting grounds.

AYLESTONE COURT

AYLESTONE HILL, HEREFORD, HEREFORDSHIRE HR1 1HS
Tel: 0845 365 3022 **International:** +44 (0)1432 341891 **Fax:** 01432 267691
Web: www.johansens.com/aylestonecourt **E-mail:** enquiries@aylestonecourthotel.com

Our inspector loved: The friendly welcome and relaxed feel.

Price Guide:
single from £75
double from £95
family from £120

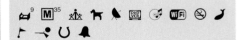

Location: On the A4103; Hereford Town Centre, 1 mile

Attractions: Hay on Wye; Ludlow; Ross-on-Wye; Ledbury

This handsome Georgian town house has been restored and extended to create an inviting, homely environment. The 9 non-smoking bedrooms are individual and combine original features with modern comforts. Take pre-dinner drinks in the lounge bar before going through to AC's restaurant or the light and airy Orangery. During warm summers meals may be eaten outside in the garden or patio areas. The flexible nature of the ground floor rooms means intimate breakfast meetings right through to corporate functiions can be well looked after. Two delightful rooms are licensed for civil weddings and can hold a maximum of 60 people for buffets whilst the walled garden and patio areas provide the perfect backdrop for photographs. Aylestone Court is conveniently located for Hereford's town centre as well as its train station.

MOCCAS COURT

MOCCAS, HEREFORDSHIRE HR2 9LH
Tel: 0845 365 2071 **International:** +44 (0)1981 500 019 **Fax:** 01981 500 095
Web: www.johansens.com/moccas **E-mail:** info@moccas-court.co.uk

Our inspector loved: A truly unique property and a real treat if you want to stay somewhere different.

Price Guide:
double/twin £140-£215
dinner (not available Sunday & Monday night) £40

Location: B4352, 1 mile; A438, 4.34 miles; A49, 10.47 miles; Hereford, 10.8 miles

Attractions: Hay on Wye; Mappa Mundi, Hereford Cathedral; Ludlow; The Black and White Trail

Moccas Court sits proudly on terraced banks above the River Wye, affording sensational sweeping views of the river and historic deer park. Expect an exceptional experience when staying here; personal touches, elegance and the welcoming atmosphere of a private English country house. Beautiful large bedrooms are classically styled; details include fresh flowers, antiquities and bathroom candles. At 7.30pm guests meet in the library for drinks before dining in the gorgeous Adam designed 'Round Room', with its exquisite hand-painted wallpaper enhanced by soft candlelight. Ben Chester-Master uses his natural culinary talent to create classical yet unpretentious 'set' menus, inspired by seasonal ingredients and a knowledge of guest's own likes and dislikes. Ben takes great care in sourcing ingredients daily; locally grown, reared and known to him. This is a very special place indeed. Closed occasionally between February and March

THE CHASE HOTEL

GLOUCESTER ROAD, ROSS-ON-WYE, HEREFORDSHIRE HR9 5LH
Tel: 0845 365 3741 **International:** +44 (0)1989 763161 **Fax:** 01989 768330
Web: www.johansens.com/chasehotel **E-mail:** res@chasehotel.co.uk

Our inspector loved: The extensive conference and banqueting rooms and lovely grounds, right in the heart of beautiful Ross-on-Wye.

Price Guide:
single £90–£135
double/twin £110–£155
four poster £175–£195

Awards/Recognition: 1 AA Rosette 2008-2009

Location: Town Centre, 3-min walk; A40, 0.25 mile; M50 jct 4, 1 mile; Hereford, 16 miles

Attractions: Forest of Dean; Wye Valley and River Wye; Hereford Cathedral; Gloucester Cathedral

A Georgian house that sits proudly within 11 acres of grounds and landscaped gardens in the picturesque countryside of Herefordshire. The owners have retained many of the original features, including an impressive staircase and in Harry's Restaurant the ornate plaster covings have been made a striking feature against the more contemporary, pale silk drapes and cream and tan colour scheme. Comfortable bedrooms each have their own character and the four-posters in the original Georgian house have wonderful high ceilings. In such a beautiful setting, with versatile meeting rooms and so many outdoor pursuits close at hand The Chase knows how to organise private and company events. Team building could include white water rafting, hill walking, ballooning and caving. Though for the less energetic there is antiquing and gentle river walks.

WILTON COURT HOTEL

WILTON, ROSS-ON-WYE, HEREFORDSHIRE HR9 6AQ
Tel: 0845 365 2809 **International:** +44 (0)1989 562569 **Fax:** 01989 768460
Web: www.johansens.com/wiltoncourthotel **E-mail:** info@wiltoncourthotel.com

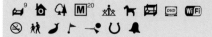

Our inspector loved: *Great bedrooms, great food and the loveliest of settings right on the River Wye.*

Price Guide:
single £80–£125
double £95–£145
suite £125–£165

Awards/Recognition: 2 AA Rosettes 2008-2009

Location: Off the B4260; A40, ½ mile; Ross on Wye, ½ mile

Attractions: Wye Valley and Royal Forest of Dean; Hereford Cathedral; Hay-on-Wye; Tintern Abbey

You can see how much care and personal effort has been put into making this an enchanting hotel by it's owners Helen and Roger Wynn, both previously trained under the auspicious eye of renowned luxury hotels. Leaded windows, stone mullions, walled gardens with mature shrubs and sloping lawns down to the banks of River Wye make this a delight. Bedrooms all have views and having recently been refurbished offer plenty of charm. The cosy bar with its fire in winter has been cleverly styled using artifacts from the Wynn's many travels. The bright conservatory Mulberry Restaurant, highly commended for "Restaurant of the Year" and "Breakfast of the Year" in the "Flavours of Herefordshire Awards" 2008, has 2 AA Rosettes and weather permitting you can eat al fresco. Sporting enthusiasts will be in their element with local activities including canoeing, fishing on the River Wye, walking, horse riding, claypigeon shooting, ballooning, tennis, cycling and golf.

GLEWSTONE COURT

NEAR ROSS-ON-WYE, HEREFORDSHIRE HR9 6AW
Tel: 0845 365 1782 **International:** +44 (0)1989 770367 **Fax:** 01989 770282
Web: www.johansens.com/glewstonecourt **E-mail:** glewstone@aol.com

Our inspector loved: Relaxed and charming, you could just kick off your shoes and sink into one of the comfy sofas with a good book.

Price Guide: (closed for Christmas)
single £55-£80-£95
double £95-£115-£135

Location: A40, 1 mile; M50, 3 miles; Hereford, 14 miles

Attractions: Wye Valley, area of outstanding natural beauty; Royal Forest of Dean; Brecon Beacons; Hereford Cathedral and the Mappa Mundi

Refreshing and unstuffy, Glewstone Court's eclectic antiques, works of art and bric-a-brac epitomise the relaxed and hospitable style of owners, Christine and Bill Reeve-Tucker. The comfortable atmosphere permeates the bedrooms where you'll find a hospitality tray with delicious homemade biscuits, and soft bathrobes. A finalist for the Restaurant of the Year and Breakfast of the Year in the "Flavours of Herefordshire", Christine's food is innovative and prepared from good, fresh local ingredients; organic and free-range whenever possible. Herefordshire is marvellous walking country and although you're secluded here, you're still only 3 miles from Ross-on-Wye. Alternatively, relax by the log fires, or on fine days, laze in the garden. Places of interest nearby include Hay-on-Wye, the Welsh Marches, Hereford Cathedral with the Mappa Mundi, and the Brecon Beacons.

KICK & DICKY

WELLPOND GREEN, STANDON, HERTFORDSHIRE SG11 1NL
Tel: 0845 365 3907 **International:** +44 (0)1920 821424
Web: www.johansens.com/kickanddicky **E-mail:** kickanddicky@btinternet.com

Our inspector loved: *The terraced garden with water features.*

Price Guide:
single from £65
double from £85

Location: On A120, 1 mile; Stansted Airport, 20-min drive

Attractions: Cambridge; Hatfield House; Horse Racing at Newmarket; County Town of Hertford

The intriguing name of this historic inn, "Kick & Dicky," refers to the farmer who historically raced his carts and ponies in this unspoiled hamlet surrounded by the peace and quiet of the countryside yet within minutes of major routes. The inn itself is very much a "food led" country pub that offers simple, pleasant and welcoming bedrooms. There are relaxing views over the panoramic Hertfordshire farmland, and another feature of this warm, informal establishment is that it is very female friendly, recognising that many business women travel alone. Well renowned, and rightly so, the restaurant offers various menus, à la carte to lunch specials, accompanied by intriguing wines at sensible prices. You can request the restaurant for private use, which is the perfect venue for parties, receptions, or just a good night out.

The White House and Lion & Lamb Bar & Restaurant

SMITHS GREEN, DUNMOW ROAD, TAKELEY, BISHOP'S STORTFORD, HERTFORDSHIRE CM22 6NR
Tel: 0845 365 2736 **International:** +44 (0)1279 870257 **Fax:** 01279 870423
Web: www.johansens.com/whitehousestansted **E-mail:** info@whitehousestansted.co.uk

Our inspector loved: The quiet dappled garden surrounding the house.

Price Guide:
single from £60
double from £75

Location: Just off B1256; M11 jct 8, 3 miles; Great Dunmow, 4.4 miles; Bishops Stortford, 5.3 miles

Attractions: Cambridge; Newmarket Racecourse; Constable Country; Audley End House

Situated in an acre of gardens this 15th-century Grade II listed country manor house offers excellent accommodation. Following a refurbishment, the comfortable bedrooms have state-of-the-art bathrooms and double aspect windows creating a light and airy feel. First-class dining is available at The Lion & Lamb; free transport is offered for the 2-minute drive. Open fires in the traditional restaurant provide warmth on chilly days, whilst soft lighting and beautiful old blackened oak beams create an intimate atmosphere. Service is professional but relaxed, with an emphasis on superb food, prepared with fresh ingredients and fish from Billingsgate, and accompanied by fine wines. A most unusual country-style room with its own terrace and garden is available for functions and meetings for up to 25 people.

AUBERGE DU LAC

BROCKET HALL, WELWYN, HERTFORDSHIRE AL8 7XG
Tel: 0845 365 3756 **International:** +44 (0)1707 368888 **Fax:** 01707 368898
Web: www.johansens.com/aubergedulac **E-mail:** auberge@brocket-hall.co.uk

Our inspector loved: *The idyllic setting on the edge of the lake and view of the beautiful grounds beyond.*

Price Guide: (per person)
3 course (midweek lunch) £29.50
2 course (á la carte) £45

Awards/Recognition: 2 AA Rosettes 2007–2008

Location: A1(M) junction 4, 5-min drive; Luton Airport, 20-min drive

Attractions: Shaws Corner; Hatfield House; St Albans; Knebworth

Dating back to 1760, this former Hunting Lodge is situated on the Brocket Hall Estate. A distinctive and captivating venue in which to host a special occasion: anniversary, birthday, dinner party, wedding or even a small VIP meeting in one of the four beautiful private rooms. In an idyllic lakeside setting with expansive views over the 543 acre Estate, Auberge du Lac has been delightfully and comfortably updated and great care has been taken to retain the traditional atmosphere and many original features. A strong emphasis has been placed on fine dining which is complemented by an excellent wine cellar. Award winning Executive Chef, Phil Thompson, is renowned for his passion, creativity and enthusiasm for culinary adventure. As a special treat they offer a Dining Package, which includes an overnight stay in Melbourne Lodge.

WINTERBOURNE COUNTRY HOUSE

BONCHURCH VILLAGE ROAD, BONCHURCH, ISLE OF WIGHT PO38 1RQ
Tel: 0845 365 2813 **International:** +44 (0)1983 852 535 **Fax:** 01983 857 529
Web: www.johansens.com/winterbourne **E-mail:** info@winterbournehouse.co.uk

Our inspector loved: Its spacious and stylish bedrooms, and a sun-trap swimming pool to while away the sunny hours.

Price Guide:
single from £65
double/twin £110–£190

Location: A3055, 1 mile; Ventnor, 2 miles; Cowes (Southampton) Ferry Terminal, 17 miles; Fishbourne (Portsmouth) Ferry Terminal, 18miles

Attractions: Walking on St Boniface Down; Isle of Wight Glass; Carisbrooke Castle; Osborne House

Obviously the perfect antidote to writers' block, Charles Dickens worked on "David Copperfield," while staying here in July 1849 and wrote to his wife, "I have taken a most delightful and beautiful house - cool, airy, everything delicious" You'll still find a house of charm and character, with many of the original features. The lawns sweep down to the bay and in summer the gardens blaze with colour. There's a secluded swimming pool, sun terrace, gently flowing stream and via a private path you reach the shingle and sand beach. Winterbourne has several lovely restaurants close by and as they only provide breakfast you will be happily advised on where to dine, though a pre-dinner drink on the terrace is highly recommended.

THE PRIORY BAY HOTEL

PRIORY DRIVE, SEAVIEW, ISLE OF WIGHT PO34 5BU
Tel: 0845 365 2649 **International:** +44 (0)1983 613146 **Fax:** 01983 616539
Web: www.johansens.com/priorybayiow **E-mail:** enquiries@priorybay.co.uk

Our inspector loved: *The food here, which just gets better and better under new Head Chef Carlos Garcia-Rodriguez.*

Price Guide:
single from £70
double £120-£270
suite £250-£375

Awards/Recognition: 1 AA Rosette 2008-2009

Location: A3055, 2 miles; Ryde, 3.5 miles; Cowes (Southampton) Ferry Terminal, 10.6 miles; Fishbourne (Portsmouth) Ferry Terminal, 6.1 miles

Attractions: Ventnor Botanic Garden; Osborne House; Carisbrooke Castle; Sailing at Seaview and Bembridge

For centuries this beautiful site has been used by Medieval monks, Tudor farmers and Georgian gentry, and now thanks to its current owners you can experience the buildings as a splendid hotel. A carved, arched stone entrance leads to delightful, flower-filled gardens and thatched tithe barns, and inside, public rooms are framed by tall windows and heavy curtains. Each of the 18 comfortable bedrooms has views over the grounds, and all are individually furnished. The two dining rooms and terraces serve superb cuisine masterminded by Alexis Gauthier, celebrated Chef Patron of Roussillon, the hotel's Michelin starred London restaurant. For those who want to stretch their legs, the outdoor pool, adjoining 6-hole golf course, tennis courts and neighbouring woodlands are certain to keep all active and entertained. Coastal paths also pass by the gate.

RYLSTONE MANOR

RYLSTONE GARDENS, SHANKLIN, ISLE OF WIGHT PO37 6RG
Tel: 0845 365 2318 **International:** +44 (0)1983 862806 **Fax:** 01983 862806
Web: www.johansens.com/rylstonemanor **E-mail:** rylstone.manor@btinternet.com

Our inspector loved: Chef Patron Michael's delicious dinners, making best use of local fare.

Price Guide: (including dinner)
single £72–£100
double £158–£214

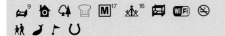

Location: A3055, 0.25 mile; Shanklin, 0.5 mile; Cowes (Southampton) Ferry Terminal, 12 miles; Fishbourne (Portsmouth) Ferry Terminal, 10 miles

Attractions: Osborne House; Ventnor Botanic Gardens; Godshill Old Village; Carisbrooke Castle

Carole and Michael Hailston are the proud owners of this delightful manor house hidden away in 4½ acres of peaceful mature gardens on the edge of Shanklin. You can catch a glimpse of the sea from some of the charming bedrooms and the stylish day rooms are just the thing for a good book and afternoon tea. Of course in good weather you will probably wish to be outside for much of the day and from the clifftop you will be able to enjoy stunning views of Shanklin Bay and a 2-minute walk leads to the promenade and beach. The restaurant menu changes daily and is complemented by a well thought out wine list which includes some interesting local vintages.

THE HAMBROUGH

HAMBROUGH ROAD, VENTNOR, ISLE OF WIGHT PO38 1SQ
Tel: 0845 365 2517 **International:** +44 (0)1983 856333 **Fax:** 01983 857260
Web: www.johansens.com/thehambrough **E-mail:** info@thehambrough.com

Our inspector loved: This boutique hotel with its splendid views and truly outstanding food.

Price Guide:
single from £80
double £100–£200

Awards/Recognition: 2 AA Rosettes 2008-2009

Location: A3055, 0.25 mile; Shanklin, 3.8 miles; Cowes (Southampton) Ferry Terminal, 15 miles; Fishbourne (Portsmouth) Ferry Terminal, 15miles

Attractions: Osborne House; Carisbrooke Castle; Bonchurch Pottery; Botanic Gardens; Sailing

This stylish delightful hotel, high above the harbour, at the southern end of Ventnor Bay, has stunning views of the coastline, and scenic views of St Boniface Down. Two of the seven newly presented bedrooms have balconies upon which you can relax and sip a cooling drink or evening aperitif whilst watching the world drift by. The decor is minimalist throughout, the bedrooms feature flat screen TV's and DVD players - even an espresso machine. The bathrooms are a joy with underfloor heating and de luxe baths and showers. Take a coffee break, sundowner cocktail or an after dinner nightcap in the bar. The arrival of Michelin starred Chef-Patron Robert Thompson will take the food at The Hambrough and the Isle of Wight to new heights.

THE WHITE CLIFFS HOTEL

HIGH STREET, ST MARGARET'S-AT-CLIFFE, DOVER, KENT CT15 6AT
Tel: 0845 365 4026 **International:** +44 (0)1304 852229 **Fax:** 01304 851880
Web: www.johansens.com/whitecliffs **E-mail:** mail@thewhitecliffs.com

Our inspector loved: *The fresh, informal and relaxed atmosphere - and all the goodies to buy.*

Price Guide:
single £49-£89
double £89-£99
4 poster room £129

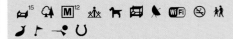

Awards/Recognition: 1 AA Rosette 2008-2009

Location: A258, 2 miles; M20 jct 12, 5 miles; Dover, 4 miles; Gatwick Airport, 70 miles

Attractions: Dover Castles; The Cathedral City of Canterbury; The White Cliffs; Shopping in Calais

This former village inn, with its own rose-filled walled garden, offers a warm and inviting atmosphere to those seeking a delightful base to explore the intriguing landscape of England's emblematic White Cliff coastline. In the heart of St Margaret's-at-Cliffe, this contemporary hotel boasts an informal and relaxed approach to looking after guests however not diminishing the service that this well versed team deliver. The 15 bedrooms are individually appointed some with striking wall paper and panelled four poster beds. Modern comforts include goose down quilts, DVD players and free WiFi Internet access. After a day spent enjoying bracing walks along the cliffs or by the sea, you can enjoy a sumptuous meal created by Gavin Oakley and his team at The Bay Restaurant, many of whom trained at the award winning sister property, Wallett's Court.

WALLETT'S COURT HOTEL & SPA

WEST CLIFFE, ST MARGARET'S-AT-CLIFFE, DOVER, KENT CT15 6EW
Tel: 0845 365 2784 **International:** +44 (0)1304 852424 **Fax:** 01304 853430
Web: www.johansens.com/wallettscourt **E-mail:** mail@wallettscourt.com

Our inspector loved: *The standard of guest comfort - enjoy being pampered in the unique treatment cabins in the wood.*

Price Guide:
single £109–£139
double £129–£169
suite £199

Awards/Recognition: 3 AA Rosettes 2008-2009

Location: A2, 1 mile; M2 jct7, 30 miles; Dover, 3 miles; Gatwick Airport, 73 miles

Attractions: Dover Castle; White Cliffs of Dover; Canterbury Cathedral; Leeds Castle

This Grade II listed house was found in ruins in the late 70's by the Oakley family, who thankfully picked it up and put it back on its feet. In the main house the Jacobean staircase leads to one of the three traditional 4-poster bedrooms and across the courtyard there are 14 contemporary rooms housed in converted Kentish hay barns. On top of excellent hospitality there is a spa complete with hydrotherapy pool and treatment cabins set in the woods. The restaurant is deservedly popular locally and local ingredients are important - try the St Margaret's Bay lobster or Romney Marsh lamb. You can practice clay pigeon shooting with a professional or have a round of golf atop the White Cliffs or simply relax here for a day or two before heading over to France.

ROMNEY BAY HOUSE HOTEL

COAST ROAD, LITTLESTONE, NEW ROMNEY, KENT TN28 8QY
Tel: 0845 365 2305 **International:** +44 (0)1797 364747 **Fax:** 01797 367156
Web: www.johansens.com/romneybayhouse

Our inspector loved: The comfort and informality, combined with Chef Patron's excellent food.

Price Guide:
single from £65
double £90–£160

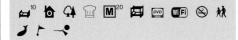

Winner of the Condé Nast Johansens Most Excellent Coastal Hotel in 2006, this spectacular house mixes the historic Kent coastline with a dash of 1920's Hollywood glamour. Built for the infamous American actress and journalist Hedda Hopper, there is access to the beach, croquet lawn and golf course, while a 5-minute drive to Lydd Airport means you can fly to Le Touquet and back in no time. The chef-patron and his wife both with London hotel/restaurant backgrounds, create delicious dishes for sea-air enhanced appetites and also provide wonderful cream teas on the terrace. Upstairs, comfortable bedrooms are furnished with antiques. You can relax in the drawing room or survey the irresistible panoramic views through the telescope in the first-floor library.

Awards/Recognition: Condé Nast Johansens Most Excellent Coastal Hotel 2006

Location: A259, 2 miles; M20 jct 11, 11 miles; Channel Tunnel, 10 miles; Gatwick Airport, 77 miles

Attractions: Dover Castle; Canterbury Cathedral; Ancient Rye; Sissinghurst /Great Dixter Gardens

THE ROYAL HARBOUR HOTEL

NELSON CRESCENT, RAMSGATE, KENT CT11 9JF
Tel: 0845 365 4853 **International:** +44 (0)1843 591514 **Fax:** 01843 570443
Web: www.johansens.com/royalharbour **E-mail:** info@royalharbourhotel.co.uk

Our inspector loved: *The sun-trap paved herb garden.*

Price Guide:
single from £78
double £98–£218

Location: A256, 1 mile; A255, 2.5 miles; A299, 2.5 miles; M2 (A2), 16.5 miles; Kent International Airport, 3.5 miles

Attractions: Pugin's home – The Grange; Ferry service to Ostende; Fishing and Yachting Harbour; Blue Flag sandy beach

A Regency townhouse overlooking Ramsgate harbour is where owner James Thomas, previously GM of a fine London boutique hotel, has put his mark. With an eye for detail, he has given the Royal Harbour a unique style - traditional yet eclectic; with fine art, quirky memorabilia and books in abundance. A record player with stacks of old vinyls awaits your attention in the snug. Lovely gestures of hospitality include a cheese board and hot drinks put out for guests returning late. Rooms vary in size, most enjoying marina views. Some feature beautiful teak four-poster beds, including the Royal Harbour Suite, which boasts a working fireplace. In the basement - a screening room - where guests can watch films when the local film production team are not in residence. While guests dine at one of the local restaurants a hearty breakfast greets you each morning.

LITTLE SILVER COUNTRY HOTEL

ASHFORD ROAD, ST MICHAELS, TENTERDEN, KENT TN30 6SP
Tel: 0845 365 2032 **International:** +44 (0)1233 850321 **Fax:** 01233 850647
Web: www.johansens.com/littlesilver **E-mail:** enquiries@little-silver.co.uk

Our inspector loved: *The commitment to every guest's comfort - including the needs of less able visitors.*

Price Guide:
single from £60
double/twin from £95
suites from £150

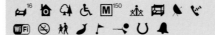

Location: On the A28; M20 jct 9, 12 miles; Tenterden, 0.5 miles; Gatwick Airport, 52 miles

Attractions: Sissinghurst and Great Dixter Gardens; Ancient Rye; Leeds and Bodiam Castles; Canterbury Cathedral

An unexpected find in the Weald of Kent, you'll discover that this wood framed Tudor-style hotel welcomes you with friendly hospitality and service. An excellent choice for weekends and longer breaks, weddings and celebrations. Especially attractive is the Kentish oast-house inspired octagonal hall with stained-glass windows, which can accommodate up to 150 guests. The beamed lounge's blazing log fires bring warmth and pleasure to a grey winter's day. Individually furnished bedrooms and suites deliver complete comfort, some with four-poster beds, Spa baths, and views across the gardens. 2 rooms are particularly suitable for wheelchair users. Good food is never far away, with breakfast, morning coffee, lunch, afternoon tea and dinner served in the Oaks restaurant.

NUMBER ONE SOUTH BEACH

4 HARROWSIDE WEST, BLACKPOOL, LANCASHIRE FY4 1NW
Tel: 0845 365 3759 **International:** +44 (0)1253 343900 **Fax:** 01253 343900
Web: www.johansens.com/numberone **E-mail:** info@numberonesouthbeach.com

Our inspector loved: *The relaxed and homely environment in this sumptuous boutique-style hotel.*

Price Guide:
single £85-£100
double £140-£155
suite £170-£180

Location: A584, 50 yards; M55 junction 3, 1.5 miles; M6 junction 4, 14 miles; Blackpool International Airport, 1 mile

Attractions: Pleasure Beach - Blackpool; Blackpool Illuminations; Blackpool Tower; 4 International Championship Golf Courses

This is considered by many to be the ultimate boutique hotel experience. A typical seaside hotel that has been completely renovated, redesigned and refurbished without losing any of its appeal and attraction to Blackpool lovers, this is a small oasis of luxury with a relaxed and homely environment. You will love the choice of beautifully designed and decorated bedrooms with their uninterrupted views of the sea, South Beach Promenade, Mirrorball, Solaris Gardens and the famed Blackpool Illuminations. Each room has a king-size bed (some four poster), 42" plasma TV with Sky and Sky Sports, CD, DVD and full bathroom en suite with whirlpool bath, 17" SplashTV, power shower and music system. The stylish restaurant offers a high standard of cuisine complemented by a cellar that will please all tastes. Choose to have pre or post-dinner drinks in the distinctive bar or lounge.

Brooklands Country Retreat & Health Spa

CALDER HOUSE LANE, GARSTANG, LANCASHIRE PR3 1QB
Tel: 0845 365 4623 **International:** +44 (0)1995 605162 **Fax:** 01995 601203
Web: www.johansens.com/brooklandsretreat **E-mail:** info@brooklandsretreat.co.uk

Our inspector loved: Being pampered at this small, secluded spa retreat.

Price Guide: (per person including breakfast, lunch, dinner and 3 spa treatments)
single from £212
double from £212
suite from £247
master suite from £275

Tucked away in a tranquil setting Brooklands has built up an excellent reputation over 25 years as a luxurious retreat for day breaks and weekend getaways. The beautiful 19th-century country house is privately owned and offers 11 individual suites. You can be as active as you like when it comes to using the health spa and fitness facilities, as staff will happily devise a gym programme for you to follow during your stay. Or if you prefer to exercise at a more leisurely pace, why not relax by the indoor pool, soak in the hydrotherapy pool or enjoy a country walk around the landscaped grounds. They offer some excellent residential courses and breaks exclusively designed to rejuvenate and invigorate the body. Plenty of beauty treatments are also available, and you can finish off your day at the newly opened Thai bistro.

Location: B6430, 200 yards; A6, 2 miles; M6 jct 32, 10 miles; Garstang, 2 miles

Attractions: Trough of Bowland; Lake District; Ribble Valley; Manchester

FERRARI'S RESTAURANT & HOTEL

THORNLEY, LONGRIDGE, PRESTON, LANCASHIRE PR3 2TB
Tel: 0845 365 3293 **International:** +44 (0)1772 783148 **Fax:** 01772 786174
Web: www.johansens.com/ferraris **E-mail:** info@ferrariscountryhouse.co.uk

Our inspector loved: *The Italian hospitality and friendliness at this family run hotel.*

Price Guide:
single £50–£100
double/twin £70–£120

Location: B5269, 1.5 miles; M6 jct 31a, 15-mins drive; Longridge, 1.5 miles; Preston, 25-mins drive

Attractions: Ribble Valley; Clitheroe; Preston; Blackpool

This impressive house was built by the Earl of Derby in 1830 as a shooting lodge, and today it's a family owned affair, with Susan Ferrari and daughter Luisa overseeing the kitchen and restaurant. Dishes are a combination of traditional English and Italian cooking, including Loin of Lamb of Rosemary and Insalata di Gamberi. The Ferraris pride themselves on a personalised wedding service, working together with each couple to provide the perfect day. Comfortable bedrooms are individually styled, some have Jacuzzis and half-tester Tudor beds, and many feature antique furniture and garden views. You're spoilt for choice with places to visit as the historic market town of Clitheroe and its famous Norman castle are on the doorstep, as well as the natural beauty of rural Lancashire.

THE CROWN HOTEL

ALL SAINTS PLACE, STAMFORD, LINCOLNSHIRE PE9 2AG
Tel: 0845 365 2451 **International:** +44 (0)1780 763136 **Fax:** 01780 756111
Web: www.johansens.com/crownstamford **E-mail:** reservations@thecrownhotelstamford.co.uk

Our inspector loved: The way in which the mix of traditional and modern work so well.

Price Guide:
single from £85
double from £100

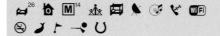

Location: A1, 1 mile; Peterborough, 13.5 miles

Attractions: Burghley House; Belvoir Castle; Rutland Water; Rockingham Raceway

Owned and managed by a lively, enthusiastic brother and sister team, The Crown Hotel lies in the heart of this attractive stone built town, a popular setting for many acclaimed English period dramas. They have cleverly kept key traditional elements - stone walls, beams and original floors and blended them with fresh contemporary colours, wallpaper and fabrics. Early evening the bar is a popular meeting place for locals and in summer you can relax in the side courtyard. The restaurant makes the best use of Lincolnshire's farming heritage - succulent meat and tasty seasonal vegetables are accompanied by excellent wines and real ales. A meeting room is also available off the courtyard with plenty of parking at the back. A great base when exploring this beautiful part of England.

TREE TOPS COUNTRY HOUSE RESTAURANT & HOTEL

SOUTHPORT OLD ROAD, FORMBY, NR SOUTHPORT, MERSEYSIDE L37 0AB
Tel: 0845 365 2759 **International:** +44 (0)1704 572430 **Fax:** 01704 573011
Web: www.johansens.com/treetopscountryhouse **E-mail:** sales@treetopsformby.fsnet.co.uk

Our inspector loved: *The light and airy restaurant and the open air swimming pool.*

Price Guide:
single £63–£78
double £105–£130

Location: A565, 300yds; M57 jct 7, 16 miles; Southport, 5 miles; Liverpool, 18 miles

Attractions: Formby & Ainsdale Beaches; Southport; Liverpool Albert Dock; Numerous Championship Golf Cources

Set in 5 acres of lawns and woodland, Tree Tops is the former Dower House of Formby Hall and still retains the elegance of another age. The house has been fully restored by Lesley Winsland over the past 26 years. Spacious accommodation is available in well-appointed en-suite lodges. An outdoor heated swimming pool has direct access to the richly decorated Cocktail Lounge. Dark leather seating and subtle lighting all contribute to the overall ambience, complemented by welcoming and efficient staff. The restaurant and conservatory have been refurbished, cleverly incorporating some 21st-century ideas. Menus offer a wonderful blend of traditional and modern, English and international cuisine. Table d'hôte, à la carte and lunchtime snacks are available, using only the freshest of local produce.

FELBRIGG LODGE

AYLMERTON, NORTH NORFOLK NR11 8RA
Tel: 0845 365 2853 **International:** +44 (0)1263 837588 **Fax:** 01263 838012
Web: www.johansens.com/felbrigglodge **E-mail:** info@felbrigglodge.co.uk

Our inspector loved: *The secluded and intimate luxury - a place to unwind.*

Price Guide:
suite £150-£200

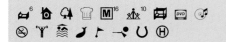

Location: A140, 2 miles; M11, 80 miles; Sheringham, 5 miles ;Holt, 7 miles; Norwich, 21 miles

Attractions: North Norfolk Coast; Blickling Hall; Norfolk Broads; Felbrigg Hall

Deep in a beautiful North Norfolk woodland setting six delightful suites offer a real sense of peace, privacy and charm. For those determined to hibernate this is the place. All of the rooms are personally and well appointed and the spacious Oak Pavilion has a lovely valuted ceiling and open fire. The Ivy restaurant is open and friendly rather like the dining car on the Orient Express! Philip Lomax cooks according to the seasons. Dinner is at 7pm from Sunday to Thursday and 7.30pm on Friday and Saturdays and guests must confirm ahead. Dee Dee is an excellent concierge whose local knowledge can help you plan your day. One favourite activity is an early morning walk along Cromers promenade just 2½ miles away to watch the crab fishermen bring ashore their famous catch.

THE KINGS HEAD HOTEL

GREAT BIRCHAM, KING'S LYNN, NORFOLK PE31 6RJ
Tel: 0845 365 2567 **International:** +44 (0)1485 578 265 **Fax:** 01485 578 635
Web: www.johansens.com/kingsheadbircham **E-mail:** welcome@the-kings-head-bircham.co.uk

Our inspector loved: *Eating lunch in the bright contemporary bar taking in the local atmosphere.*

Price Guide:
superior from £125
deluxe from £150
executive from £165

Awards/Recognition: 1 AA Rosettes 2008-2009

Location: On the B1153; A148, 4 miles; King's Lynn, 14 miles; Norwich airport, 37 miles

Attractions: Sandringham; Burnham Market; Holkham Hall; Houghton Hall

Tall red brick chimneys and decorative gables are just two attractive features of this white-faced, Grade II Listed Victorian hotel in the heart of North Norfolk. Others include a comfortable atmosphere, stylish modern décor and spacious bedrooms. Bathrooms are particularly luxurious, and you might find that the gorgeous homemade Norfolk toiletries make it into your bag and home with you. Just as tempting are the innovative and unfussy restaurant menus which are inspired by local and seasonal ingredients. On warm days you can eat outside in the pretty courtyard. A contemporary bar offers light meals and snacks alongside local and guest ales. Stately homes galore in the surrounding area and nature lovers can head to bird sanctuaries and miles of unspoilt sandy beaches.

TITCHWELL MANOR HOTEL

TITCHWELL, KING'S LYNN, NORFOLK PE31 8BB
Tel: 0845 365 2861 **International:** +44 (0)1485 210221 **Fax:** 01485 210104
Web: www.johansens.com/titchwellmanor **E-mail:** margaret@titchwellmanor.com

Our inspector loved: *The large new conservatory restaurant which compliments this spacious and elegant coastal hotel*

Price Guide:
double £70-£170

Awards/Recognition: 2 AA Rosettes 2007-2008

Location: On the A149; Brancaster, 1 mile; King's Lynn, 23 miles; Norwich Airport, 40 miles

Attractions: Burnham Market; Titchwell RSPB Reserve; Holkham Hall

Once a Victorian gentlemen's club, Titchwell Manor is now one of those wonderful and rare hotels that manages to capture the period feeling of an older residence with the stylish and contemporary luxury that we all love. Always warm and welcoming, the hotel now has 25 bedrooms and the latest 13 are stunning - built around a central courtyard herb garden, where the wonderful aromas inspire the names of the rooms themselves. The conservatory dining room uses an impressive list of local fare - be it mussels and lobsters from Brancaster Staithe, Cromer crabs or Holkham venison - and a log fire burns in the lounge during the winter months. The surrounding scenery is simply stunning and a walk on Norfolk's beautiful golden beaches is an absolute must at any time of the year.

THE OLD RECTORY

103 YARMOUTH ROAD, NORWICH, NORFOLK NR7 0HF
Tel: 0845 365 2614 **International:** +44 (0)1603 700772 **Fax:** 01603 300772
Web: www.johansens.com/oldrectorynorwich **E-mail:** enquiries@oldrectorynorwich.com

Our inspector loved: The relaxing feel of this beautiful Georgian home.

Price Guide:
single £85-£110
double £115-£145

Awards/Recognition: 2 AA Rosettes 2007-2008

Location: A47, 2 miles; Norwich, 2 miles; Norwich Airport, 4 miles

Attractions: Whitlingham Country Park; Norwich Cathedral; Sandringham

The promise of a warm welcome and personal service will draw you to this Wisteria clad Grade II listed Georgian house. Set in an acre of mature gardens on the outskirts of Norwich overlooking the Yare Valley the spacious bedrooms and elegant Drawing Room offer a great place to relax. Chris and Sally Entwistle understand hospitality and are the proud winners of a Green Tourism Business Scheme Award for 2007. The tempting dinner menu is changed daily, and if you must talk business the Wellingtonia Room and Conservatory, overlooking the pool terrace and gardens, provide a unique venue for meetings, private lunches or dinners. To escape, the Dowagers Cottage in the grounds is a comfortable self-contained option.

BROAD HOUSE

THE AVENUE, WROXHAM, NORFOLK NR12 8TS
Tel: 0845 365 4856 **International:** +44 (0)1603 783567 **Fax:** 01603 782033
Web: www.johansens.com/broadhouse **E-mail:** info@broadhousehotel.co.uk

Our inspector loved: *The total commitment of the owners to make this the finest hotel in Norfolk.*

Price Guide:
double from £130
suite from £190

An idyllic old English home in a tranquil rural location, 7 miles from Norwich and along side the Norfolk Broads, which are well worth a little exploration. The coast just 12 miles away and fishing, golf and country walks all conveniently nearby. This is a charming retreat, originally a 18th century Queen Anne Estate House which in its role as a boutique hotel has been stylishly decorated with great care and attention to detail. The 14 rooms all have there own personality and enjoy views of the extensive grounds and gardens surrounding the grade II listed building. The owners' admirable aim is to source all of their products from Norfolk, from soaps to puddings. The effect: a very unique and genuine Norfolk experience.

Location: Just off the B1140; A1151, 0.7 miles; Norwich, 7 miles

Attractions: The Norfolk Broads; Wroxham Barns & Belwiderwood; Norwich Cathedral; North Norfolk Coast & Beaches

BRAUNSTON MANOR

HIGH STREET, BRAUNSTON, NEAR DAVENTRY, NORTHAMPTONSHIRE NN11 7HS
Tel: 0845 365 3256 **International:** +44 (0)1788 890267 **Fax:** 01788 891515
Web: www.johansens.com/braunstonmanor **E-mail:** info@BraunstonManor.com

Our inspector loved: *The immaculate bedrooms and the glorious situation.*

Price Guide:
single £80
double £100
four poster £130

Location: A45, 1-min drive; M45, 5-min drive; Daventry, 5-min drive; Birmingham International Airport, 30-min drive

Attractions: The Canals and Marina; Coventry Cathedral; Silverton Raceway; Braunston Village

Idyllically languishing amidst attractive gardens and parklands that sweep down to the canal with its own private mooring, this wonderfully restored and maintained 400-year-old Tudor manor house overflows with eye-catching local artworks, antiques and authentic period details. This beautiful hotel has been in the same family for over a hundred years and you will see many personal items that allude to the surrounding canals and the owner's love of skiing, making it a truly unique and engaging property. After a few short steps across a courtyard, you will discover 4 charming bedrooms housed in restored little cottages. 6 more uniquely styled bedrooms can be found in the main building. Although the hotel does not serve dinner, the manor's own pub is just around the corner and serves delicious meals.

WAREN HOUSE HOTEL

WAREN MILL, BAMBURGH, NORTHUMBERLAND NE70 7EE
Tel: 0845 365 2785 **International:** +44 (0)1668 214581 **Fax:** 01668 214484
Web: www.johansens.com/warenhouse **E-mail:** enquiries@warenhousehotel.co.uk

Our inspector loved: Strolling in the delightful gardens and dining in the candle-lit restaurant.

Price Guide:
single £90–£143
double £120–£175
suite £168–£223

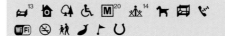

Location: B1342, 200yds; A1, 2 miles; Bamburgh, 3 miles; Alnwick, 15 miles

Attractions: Bamburgh Castle; Holy Island & Farne Islands; Alnwick Gardens; Budle Bay Wildlife Sanctuary

"To visit the North East and not to stay here, would be foolish indeed", so says one of many complimentary entries in the hotel's visitors' book. This delightful, traditional country house will meet all your expectations. Set in 6 acres of gardens and woodland on the edge of Budle Bay Bird Sanctuary overlooking Holy Island and close to majestic Bamburgh Castle. Antique furnishings and immaculate decor create a warm ambience. Choose from a daily changing menu and complementary fine wines in the candle-lit dining room surrounded by family portraits. Owners Anita and Peter don't cater for under 14s, so peace and tranquility are assured even in the summer months. Dogs are welcome by prior arrangement. There is a boardroom for executive meetings and special breaks are available.

THE OTTERBURN TOWER

OTTERBURN, NORTHUMBERLAND NE19 1NS
Tel: 0845 365 3748 **International:** +44 (0)1830 520620 **Fax:** 01830 521504
Web: www.johansens.com/otterburntower **E-mail:** info@otterburntower.com

Our inspector loved: The bridal suite has leaded windows, beautiful views, a panelled fireplace and a king size four-poster bed.

Price Guide:
single £65
double £130–£230
suite £230

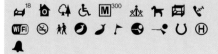

Location: A696, 100yds; A68, 2 miles; A 1 M, 26 miles; Newcastle Airport, 25 miles

Attractions: Alnwick Castle & Gardens; Hadrians Wall; Kielder Water & Forest Park

Standing regally at the heart of a 32 acre estate in the Redesdale valley this magestic building dates back to the 11th century ; founded by a cousin of William the Conqueror. Painstakingly restored, the building retains stunning original features, from oak panelling, leaded panes and stained glass. The 18 stylish and unique rooms include The Library Room, featuring a beautiful four poster bed, panelling and well-stocked bookshelves. Admire the extensive terraced lawns and flower-abundant gardens from the Morning Room. Dining at the Otterburn Tower is a delight, with all ingredients for the imaginative dishes supplied by either Longwitton Farm, covering over 3000 acres to the south-east of the hotel and run by the hotel owner's son, John Goodfellow Junior, or other locally accredited sources. The hotel owns a stretch of the river Rede, and the chefs take full advantage of the fresh trout and salmon in season.

THE ORCHARD HOUSE

HIGH STREET, ROTHBURY, NORTHUMBERLAND NE65 7TL
Tel: 0845 365 3726 **International:** +44 (0)1669 620 684 **Fax:** 01669 620 684
Web: www.johansens.com/orchardhouse **E-mail:** info@orchardhouserothbury.com

Our inspector loved: The elegant, inviting and flower-filled drawing room..

Price Guide:
single £88-£148
double £88-£170

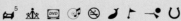

Location: B6341, 20yds; A697, 6 miles; A1, 7 miles; Alnwick, 11 miles

Attractions: Cragside Hall; Alnwick Castle & Gardens; Cheviot Hills; Northumberland National Park

A striking grey stone, grade II listed Georgian House situated on the High Street in the pretty town of Rothbury. The stylish, contemporary bedrooms are fragranced with fresh flowers and feature beds dressed with sumptuous duck down duvets and crisp white Egyptian linen. Canapés, chocolates and champagne breakfasts can all be arranged for extra indulgence. The drawing room, furnished with antiques and filled with fresh flowers, is elegant, warm and inviting; wile away your evening here and enjoy the bar service. The Orchard House does not cater for dinner, however the owners will gladly recommend local restaurants. Be sure to savour the lavish breakfast, with its emphasis on local organic produce, both hearty traditional and contemporary dishes are offered, and the extensive sideboard will also keep you busy!

GREENWOOD LODGE

5 THIRD AVENUE, SHERWOOD RISE, NOTTINGHAM, NG7 6JH
Tel: 0845 365 2891 **International:** +44 (0)115 962 1206 **Fax:** 0115 962 1206
Web: www.johansens.com/greenwoodlodge **E-mail:** pdouglas71@aol.com

Our inspector loved: *An oasis of quiet stuffed with immaculate Victoriana and theatrical mementos.*

Price Guide:
single £45–£60
double £75–£95

Location: City Centre, 1 mile; A610, 2 miles; M1 jct 26, 6 miles; East Midlands Airport, 30-min drive

Attractions: Nottingham Castle; Lace Market; Theatre; National Arena Ice Rink

Greenwood Lodge enjoys a quiet, secluded location in the heart of a conservation area, yet is conveniently just 1 mile from Nottingham city centre. Built in 1834, the lodge is set in a mature courtyard garden, filled with lovingly tended shrubs and trees. Immaculately maintained throughout, the lodge features antique furniture and paintings and retains a sense of traditional refinement as well as home-from-home charm. The attractive rooms are individually decorated in fresh colour schemes and feature antique furniture and paintings. Three feature striking four poster beds. A notable breakfast menu is served in the airy conservatory and whilst lunch or dinner are not provided guests are given plenty of recommendations for eating out close by. Of course you may just be happy to curl up in the beautiful lounge with a drink and a good book.

COCKLIFFE COUNTRY HOUSE HOTEL

BURNTSTUMP COUNTRY PARK, BURNTSTUMP HILL, NOTTINGHAMSHIRE NG5 8PQ
Tel: 0845 365 3237 **International:** +44 (0)115 968 0179 **Fax:** 0115 968 0623
Web: www.johansens.com/cockliffe **E-mail:** enquiries@cockliffehouse.co.uk

Our inspector loved: The White Room, the scintillating new ground floor Bridal Suite.

Price Guide:
single from £75
double £95–£150

Awards/Recognition: 1 AA Rosette 2008-2009

Location: Off the A614, 2 miles; M1 jct 26, 9 miles; Nottingham, 7 miles; East Midlands, 23 miles

Attractions: Nottingham Castle; Sherwood Forest; Southwell Minster; Newstead Abbey

For those who have never found Cockliffe Country House nor sought it out, you may be surprised to discover that it has sat secluded from the hustle and bustle of both Nottingham and Mansfield for over 300 years. It is hard to imagine a rustic idyll nestling peacefully, yet conveniently, between the A60 and A614 but seemingly miles from anywhere. Owners Dane and Jane Clarke became enchanted by this secret hideaway 15 years ago and have combined their flair for innovative style and cuisine. Each of the 11 bedrooms has their own personality nurtured by Jane's use of fabric, antiques and colour. Undeniably unique, with a resolute approach to the customer as individual, you will discover a quality rarely found in many hotels. Complemented by an alluring ambience and gastronomy nurtured by a talented team - with skills gained in Michelin starred kitchens and mutual passion and dedication - Cockliffe leaves a lasting impression.

LANGAR HALL

LANGAR, NOTTINGHAMSHIRE NG13 9HG
Tel: 0845 365 1983 **International:** +44 (0)1949 860559 **Fax:** 01949 861045
Web: www.johansens.com/langarhall **E-mail:** info@langarhall.co.uk

Our inspector loved: *The distinctly different styles of all the bedrooms but a favourite is Edwards with views over the meadow with sheep (and emus!).*

Price Guide:
single £80–£125
double/twin £95–£210
suite £210

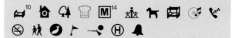

Awards/Recognition: Nottingham Restaurant Award - Best Out of Town Restaurant 2008

Location: A52, 4 miles; A46, 5 miles; Nottingham, 12 miles; East Midlands Airport, 30 min-drive

Attractions: Belvoir Castle; Trent Bridge cricket; Nottingham Castle; Stilton cheese making

Combining the charm of a traditional private home and good country living Langar Hall stands quietly secluded, overlooking parkland where sheep graze among ancient trees. The family home of Imogen Skirving, its site is historic, and the house itself dates back to 1837. Today, bedrooms are delightful with lovely views of the gardens and moat, the restaurant - very popular locally - serves English dishes of local meat, poultry, game, fish, and garden vegetables in season. Beyond the croquet lawn you can get lost in a romantic network of medieval fishponds teeming with carp. Further afield, the hotel is perfect for cricket at Trent Bridge, trips to Belvoir Castle and visits to the academics at Nottingham University. Dogs can also enjoy the Hall's comforts by prior arrangement.

BURFORD HOUSE

99 HIGH STREET, BURFORD, OXFORDSHIRE OX18 4QA
Tel: 0845 365 3914 **International:** +44 (0)1993 823151 **Fax:** 01993 823240
Web: www.johansens.com/burfordhouse **E-mail:** stay@burfordhouse.co.uk

Our inspector loved: *The character and personality of this charming town house hotel.*

Price Guide: (room only)
single from £110
double from £165
joining family suite upon request

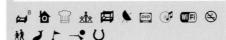

Location: A40, 0.5 miles; M40, 15 miles; Oxford, 21 miles; Heathrow Airport, 62 miles

Attractions: Oxford; Blenheim Palace; Hidcote Manor Garden; Sudeley Castle

A handsome 17th-century landmark that sits on this Cotswold stone High Street, Burford House is well-loved by its owners and guests alike. Ian Hawkins and Stewart Dunkley searched for 2 years to find their dream hotel and have now enhanced this highly regarded elegant, welcoming retreat. They retained many of the dedicated, local staff, and today the atmosphere is truly lovely. Bedrooms in classic Farrow & Ball tones are filled with antique furniture, sumptuous beds and linens, and gleaming bathrooms with plenty of character. You can indulge in fantastic breakfasts and afternoon teas or drinks in one of 2 intimate sitting rooms. Stewart enjoys creating delicious menus using the finest fresh local organic produce available, thus giving guests the chance to sample some of the delights of the region. Dinner is served on Thursday, Friday and Saturday evenings and the rest of the week you will be recommended a choice of local eateries close by.

BURFORD LODGE HOTEL & RESTAURANT

OXFORD ROAD, BURFORD, OXFORDSHIRE OX18 4PH
Tel: 0845 365 3215 **International:** +44 (0)1993 823354
Web: www.johansens.com/burfordlodge **E-mail:** info@burfordlodge.com

Our inspector loved: *The warm welcome of this friendly hostelry on the edge of the Cotswolds.*

Price Guide:
single £98
double/twin £118
suite £140

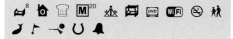

Location: A40, 50 yds; M40, M5, M4, 25 miles; Burford, 0.50 miles; Birmingham, 52 miles

Attractions: Oxford; Cheltenham; Cotswolds; Blenheim Palace

Reminiscent of its beginnings as a comfortable country residence, this Victorian hotel underwent a remarkable refurbishment. Owners Graham and Paula Cox have taken great care to blend traditional style with modern amenities, mixing power showers with Victorian style sit-in baths. The popular restaurant serves a seasonal menu with plenty of fresh fish delivered daily from the coast. The chocolate fountain is certain to be a hit with the youngsters, and for the adults the menu offers the chance to cook their own food at your table on volcanic stones. The ideal mid-week getaway destination, Burford is a delightful village with many antique and craft shops in its high street. And is also the perfect base for travelling to Oxford or Cheltenham, exploring the Cotswolds or playing a round of golf at the Burford Golf Course.

THE LAMB INN

SHEEP STREET, BURFORD, OXFORDSHIRE OX18 4LR
Tel: 0845 365 2576 **International:** +44 (0)1993 823155 **Fax:** +44 (0)1993 822228
Web: www.johansens.com/lambinnburford **E-mail:** info@lambinn-burford.co.uk

Our inspector loved: This informal, relaxed yet eclectic traditional inn bursting with character - don't miss the flower packed secret garden

Price Guide:
single £145-£165
double £165-£195
suite £195-£255

Awards/Recognition: 2 AA Rosettes 2008-2009

Location: A40, 1 mile; M40, 20 miles; Burford, 30yds; Birmingham Airport, 50 miles

Attractions: Cotswold Tours; Cheltenham Racecourse; Cotswold Wildlife Park; Sherbourne Estate(NT)

Walk into The Lamb Inn and instantly recapture something of the 14th-century - flagged floors, antiques, and the flicker of log fires on gleaming copper, brass and silver. Cleverly amongst the traditional elements is a complementary tone of the contemporary, in particular in the stunning Allium suite which adds an indulgent feel. The attractive bar invites you into its sumptuous sofas and overstuffed chairs. Bar meals and the more formal award winning restaurant specialise in fresh fish and in summer you can eat outside in the pretty walled garden. Located near the heart of Burford you might like to browse through antiques shops or laze by the waters of the River Windrush. You're within easy reach of Oxford, Cheltenham, Stow-on-the-Wold and many other quintessential Cotswold villages. The Lamb can be either for romance, business or as an ideal venue for a house party if getting together with friends or family for a special occasion.

THE NUT TREE INN

MURCOTT, KIDLINGTON, OXFORDSHIRE OX5 2RE
Tel: 0845 365 3789 **International:** +44 (0)1865 331253
Web: www.johansens.com/nuttreeinn **E-mail:** imog79@hotmail.com

Our inspector loved: The wonderful enthusiasm and energy of Mike and Imogen which makes this friendly 'locals' inn such a success.

Price Guide:
starters £6.95–£9
main £14–£24
dessert £5.50–£7.50
set menu mon-fri (lunch) and mon-thurs (evening)
2 course £15; 3 course £18

Awards/Recognition: 2 AA Rosettes 2007-2008; Michelin Rising Star 2008/2009

Location: A34, 6 miles; M40 jct 9, 6 miles; Oxford, 10 miles

Attractions: Oxford; Bicester Shopping Village; Boarstal Duck Decoy; Nature Reserve

The Nut Tree Inn with its thatched roof and village pond effortlessly and unaffectedly combines a country pub atmosphere with the informal sophistication of a great restaurant. Savour real ale from the cask before sampling the fabulous modern British cuisine. Previously, owner Mike was the youngest holder of a Michelin Star and you can therefore expect some wonderfully creative dishes with seasonal flavours used to their best. Its all about uncomplicated but delicious cooking; home smoked salmon, homemade breads and ice-cream along with succulent meats from their own reared Dexter Cattle. With all these exceptional ingredients it is great value with menus starting from £14. During the summer, dine at the inviting al fresco dining area in the company of the Gloucester Old Spot Tamworth pigs stabled nearby. The Inn is planning on providing bedrooms later in the year but until then staff will happily recommend nearby accommodation.

WESTON MANOR

WESTON-ON-THE-GREEN, OXFORDSHIRE OX25 3QL
Tel: 0845 365 2798 **International:** +44 (0)1869 350621 **Fax:** 01869 350901
Web: www.johansens.com/westonmanor **E-mail:** reception@westonmanor.co.uk

Our inspector loved: The sense of stepping back in time as soon as you approach the manor and enter the panelled reception.

Price Guide:
single from £99
double from £121
suite from £180

You'll pass through imposing wrought-iron gates and tall grey stone pillars before reaching the impressive entrance to this manor house, once ancestral home of the Earls of Abingdon and Berkshire and owned by Henry VIII. Many bedrooms, 16 in the coach-house, have antique furniture, while all have garden views. The magnificent vaulted, oak-panelled Baronial Hall with its Rosette-awarded menus, overlooks the beautiful grounds and creates a feeling of aristocratic grandeur. If you are planning a family celebration, a wedding of any size or a get together with friends or colleagues there is plenty of flexibility with seven private meeting rooms including the stunning Osborn Suite. If you're feeling brave why not visit for an exciting murder mystery weekend, hosted at the hotel throughout the year.

Awards/Recognition: 2 AA Rosettes 2008-2009

Location: A34, 0.5 mile; M40 jct 9, 2 miles; Oxford, 10 miles; Heathrow Airport, 52 miles

Attractions: Bicester shopping village; Blenheim Palace; Gateway to Cotswolds; Oxford

THE GOOSE

BRITWELL SALOME, WATLINGTON, OXFORDSHIRE OX49 5LG
Tel: 0845 365 1938 **International:** +44 (0)1491 612304 **Fax:** 01491613945
Web: www.johansens.com/thegoose **E-mail:** info_thegoose@btconnect.com

Our inspector loved: *The setting, friendliness of staff and Chef Ryan's passion for food.*

Price Guide: (open Tuesdays and Saturdays for lunch and dinner. Sundays for lunch. Closed Sunday Evenings.)
lunch menu 2 courses £14.50, 3 courses £17.50
dinner menu 2 courses £18.50, 3 courses £23.50

Awards/Recognition: 2 AA Rosettes 2008–2009

Location: A4074, 4 miles; M40, 4 miles; Watlington, 2 miles; Heathrow Airport, 35 miles

Attractions: River walks; Marlow; Henley; Reading

This handsome red brick building with its blend of contemporary interiors and original features provides a great stop off whilst touring the Oxfordshire countryside. Decidedly not stuffy or pretentious, The Goose is more friendly and welcoming and Mary, the restaurant manager, is a delight. Head Chef Ryan Simpson enthusiastically creates modern French-inspired menus with unsurprisingly top-notch ingredients including home-grown apples, pears and herbs, bantam eggs from a local farm and produce from a gamekeeper just 2 miles away. The superbly balanced flavours of each course are complemented with a great choice of wines, local ales and ciders. there is an area available for private parties and an attactive patio for al fresco occasions. If you're tempted to stay in the area longer, there are good B&Bs or hotels nearby and you can breakfast at The Goose before a day's races at Ascot!

DUKE OF MARLBOROUGH COUNTRY INN

WOODLEYS, WOODSTOCK, OXFORD OX20 1HT
Tel: 0845 365 3273 **International:** +44 (0)1993 811460 **Fax:** 01993 810165
Web: www.johansens.com/dukeofmarlborough **E-mail:** sales@dukeofmarlborough.co.uk

Our inspector loved: This friendly inn – A good stopping off point for leisure and business.

Price Guide:
single £70
double/twin £85–£110

Location: A44, 20yds; M40, 6 miles; Woodstock, 1 mile; Heathrow Airport, 60 miles

Attractions: Blenheim Palace; Woodstock; Stratford Upon Avon; Cotswold Tours

This friendly, traditional English inn, situated on the A44 is just a few minutes from the pretty town of Woodstock. A good location for business stays, stopovers or when visiting the area. You will find the accommodation in a separate building, designed to reflect its rural setting and its' 13 bedrooms are spacious and comfortable. With a focus on good service and hospitality, the Duke of Marlborough serves thoughtfully prepared seasonal dishes in the pub style restaurant and the menus make good use of locally sourced produce. The menu also offers chefs specials – wholesome steaks with a choice of delicious sauces whilst other dishes include fish, vegetarian options and a childrens menu. The welcoming bar offers an extensive wine list and a selection of real ales. The beer garden and patio provides a safe and secure area for youngsters when the weather is fine.

NICK'S RESTAURANT

LORD NELSON'S HOUSE, 11,MARKET PLACE, OAKHAM, RUTLAND LE15 6DT
Tel: 0845 365 3924 **International:** +44 (0)1572 723199
Web: www.johansens.com/nicksrestaurant **E-mail:** info@NicksRestaurant.co.uk

Our inspector loved: *The food but also the Lady Emma Hamilton Room and its view over the "secret garden."*

Price Guide:
single from £60
double from £60
suite from £85

Awards/Recognition: 2 AA Rosettes 2008-2009; Top Table Gold Award 2008

Location: A6003, 1 mile; M1 jct 21, 40-min drive; Oakham, on-site; East Midlands Airport, 45-min drive

Attractions: Rutland Water; Oakham; Burghley House; Belvoir Castle

There will be plenty to remember about your dinner and stay at this wonderful tucked away Grade II listed building with its Nelsonian associations in the historic county of Rutland. Owner Simon McEnery and head chef Dameon Clarke are constantly developing the menus to capture the best of the superb local produce to tantalise guests with textures, delicate aromas and combinations of flavours. Fresh crab, salmon and swordfish all take pride of place, along with traditional roasts on Sundays. The wine list will impress even the most picky cognoscenti and the service is impeccable. For those fortunate enough to stay after diner there are four truly individual bedrooms including the elegant Lady Emma Hamilton and the nautical Lord Horatio Nelson Room. This is a great little hide away not only to enjoy great food but from which to explore a beautiful part of the country.

BARNSDALE LODGE

THE AVENUE, RUTLAND WATER, NEAR OAKHAM, RUTLAND LE15 8AH
Tel: 0845 365 3028 **International:** +44 (0)1572 724678 **Fax:** 01572 724961
Web: www.johansens.com/barnsdalelodge **E-mail:** enquiries@barnsdalelodge.co.uk

Our inspector loved: *Enjoying the food in the conservatory and trying to spot the free roaming chickens outside (fresh eggs for breakfast!).*

Price Guide:
single from £65
double/twin from £80
superior from £105

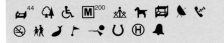

Awards/Recognition: 1 AA Rosette 2007-2008

Location: A606, 0.9 miles; A1, 7.5 miles; Oakham, 3 miles; East Midlands Airport, 42 miles

Attractions: Oakham; Vale of Belvoir; Rutland Water; Burghley House

Overlooking Rutland Water, surrounded by green hills and standing at the head of a tree-lined avenue, this former 17th-century farmhouse, built of local stone is an idyllic retreat for those wishing to escape. Fully restored and converted, you will find every comfort available. The furnishings and décor are superb and the well appointed bedrooms offer relaxation; 2 have been specifically designed for disabled guests, some are interconnecting and many offer panoramic views south over Rutland Water. The talented kitchen brigade offers an inspirational new bistro-style menu using organic and local produce, free-range eggs from the Gainsborough Estate and damson jam from the orchards, complemented by a cellar of fine wines. A multitude of water sports can also be arranged.

THE LAKE ISLE HOTEL & RESTAURANT

16 HIGH STREET EAST, UPPINGHAM, RUTLAND LE15 9PZ
Tel: 0845 365 2573 **International:** +44 (0)1572 822951 **Fax:** 01572 824400
Web: www.johansens.com/lakeislehotel **E-mail:** info@lakeisle.co.uk

Our inspector loved: *Sitting by the cosy fire perusing and trying the extensive wine list.*

Price Guide:
standard £75
superior £100

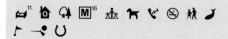

Awards/Recognition: 2 AA Rosettes 2007-2008

Location: Just off A6003; A43, 13 miles; Melton Mowbray, 20 min-drive; East Midlands Airport, 40 min-drive

Attractions: Rutland Water; Uppingham School; Burghley House; Oakham

There has been plenty of praise poured on owners Richard and Janine Burton whose charming, warm and hospitable natures have ensured a large, regular following. You'll appreciate over 350 years of character at The Lake Isle Hotel & Restaurant. Entered from a quiet courtyard, downstairs a log fire for cold nights and upstairs a relaxing lounge overlooking the pretty High Street of this charming town famous for Uppingham School. Food and wine are taken very seriously here and under the disciplined eye of chef Stuart Mead the restaurant offers imaginative seasonal menus, and a wine list ranging from regional labels to old clarets. Monthly wine dinners are great fun and to save you from driving you can simply roll upstairs to a comfortable night's sleep.

Pen-Y-Dyffryn Country Hotel

RHYDYCROESAU, NEAR OSWESTRY, SHROPSHIRE SY10 7JD
Tel: 0845 365 2106 **International:** +44 (0)1691 653700 **Fax:** 01978 211004
Web: www.johansens.com/penydyffryn **E-mail:** stay@peny.co.uk

Our inspector loved: *The rural location and stunning views at this peaceful haven.*

Price Guide:
single £86
double £115–£170

Awards/Recognition: 2 AA Rosettes 2007-2008

Location: A 5, 4 miles; Oswestry 3 miles; Chester, 28 miles; Shrewsbury, 20 miles

Attractions: Erddig (NT); Powis Castle (NT); Chirk Castle (NT); Lake Vyrnwy

Enjoying breathtaking Welsh mountain views from high on the last hill in Shropshire, this captivating former Condé Nast Johansens Best Value for Money award-winning hotel, offers you the chance to totally relax and unwind. Built in 1845 as a Georgian rectory for a Celtic scholar, the Grade II listed property now happily rests in the hands of owners Miles and Audrey Hunter, who provide a well-established discreet service and cosy atmosphere. All bedrooms, some of which have Jacuzzis or spa baths, overlook the attractive terraced gardens, while 4 rooms in the coach-house have private patios. Chef David Morris - awarded 2 AA Rosettes - creates menus from local, often organic, produce. Peruse the exciting wine list with many organic wines alongside non-alcoholic organic drinks. Chester and Shrewsbury are nearby and the local area offers hill walking, riding, golf, and trout fishing.

THE INN AT GRINSHILL

THE HIGH STREET, GRINSHILL, NEAR SHREWSBURY, SHROPSHIRE SY4 3BL
Tel: 0845 365 4634 **International:** +44 (0)1939 220410 **Fax:** 01939 220327
Web: www.johansens.com/theinnatgrinshill **E-mail:** info@theinnatgrinshill.co.uk

Our inspector loved: *The charming village ambience and contemporary bedrooms.*

Price Guide:
single £60-£100
double £120-£160

Location: A49, 0.5 miles; M54 jct 7, 9 miles; M6 jct 15, 30 miles; Shrewsbury, 7 miles

Attractions: Chester; Hawkstone Park Historic Follies and Golf Courses; Ironbridge; West Midlands Shooting Ground

A perfect package, this inn combines contemporary restaurant and luxurious accommodation along with the ethos of a traditional country pub. Whether you're a thirsty walker, dressed-to-the-nines or accompanied by a canine companion, you're assured of a warm welcome here. Civilised yet down-to-earth and buzzy, the Elephant and Castle bar offers real ales, an open fire and hearty meals. Dining in the restaurant is a gourmet experience, and chefs seek out local artisan suppliers to create their menus. Ever-changing dishes might include fillet of bass, chicken panang or chateaubriand, and the cheese selection is mightily impressive. You can't fail to relax in the elegant, unfussy bedrooms, and if you just want to unwind in front of a film you'll find TVs cleverly tucked behind gorgeous hand-made mirrors.

SOULTON HALL

NEAR WEM, SHROPSHIRE SY4 5RS
Tel: 0845 365 2356 **International:** +44 (0)1939 232786 **Fax:** 01939 234097
Web: www.johansens.com/soultonhall **E-mail:** enquiries@soultonhall.co.uk

Our inspector loved: This charming historic hall and family home.

Price Guide:
single from £65
double £100–£122
exclusive use from £1500

Location: On the B5065; A49, 2 miles; Shrewsbury, 10 miles; M54 jct 7, 18 miles

Attractions: Chester; Ironbridge; Castles of North Wales; Hawkstone Country Park

Dating from the 15th and 17th centuries, this imposing Tudor manor with magnificent pillared courtyard stands in 550 acres of parkland. Owners, the Ashton family are descendants of the first protestant Lord Mayor of London who bought Soulton Hall in 1556, and have restored the property whilst retaining many of its unique features in the 6 spacious bedrooms; 4 in the main building and 2 in the nearby Carriage House. The converted Soulton Court was built in 1783 as stables and its stone-flagged floor, and beams make it an ideal venue for private dining, weddings and conferences. Ann Ashton exercises her skills in traditional English cooking, specialities might include, hand-raised game pie and butter baked salmon served with saffron oil. Game from the estate in season and fruit from the garden.

COMPTON HOUSE

TOWNSEND, AXBRIDGE, SOMERSET BS26 2AJ

Tel: 0845 365 3243 **International:** +44 (0)1934 733944 **Fax:** 01934 733945
Web: www.johansens.com/comptonhouse **E-mail:** info@comptonhse.com

Our inspector loved: The extensive countryside views and exquisite decor.

Price Guide:
single from £75
double/twin from £100

Location: On the A371; M5 jct 21, 10 miles; Bristol, 18.3 miles; Bristol Airport, 9 miles

Attractions: Cheddar Gorge; Wells Cathedral; Bath; Glastonbury

This impressive 17th-century, Grade II listed manor house is situated in historic Axbridge, at the foot of the Mendip Hills, commanding spectacular views over the Somerset Levels to Glastonbury Tor. Surrounded by an expansive and secluded lawned garden, Compton House dates back to Elizabethan times and oak panelling, elegant mouldings and wonderful fireplaces feature throughout. Enthusiastic owners, Patricia and Robert Tallack, whose interest is routing local walks, have continually pursued excellence, earning the hotel a reputation for comfort, hospitality and service. The generous bedrooms have many original features, and Patricia uses Fairtrade and West Country produce for the superb dishes served in the attractive dining room, following apèritifs, if desired, on the sun-catching terrace. Exclusive use for house parties, meetings and weddings can be arranged.

WOODLANDS COUNTRY HOUSE HOTEL

HILL LANE, BRENT KNOLL, NR BRISTOL, SOMERSET TA9 4DF
Tel: 0845 365 3242 **International:** +44 (0)1278 760232 **Fax:** 01278 769090
Web: www.johansens.com/woodlandshotel **E-mail:** info@woodlands-hotel.co.uk

Our inspector loved: *The cosy bar and friendly atmosphere.*

Price Guide:
single £69-£99
double £99-£135
suite £155

Location: A38, 3 miles; M5 jct 22, 5 miles; Bristol, 24 miles

Attractions: Glastonbury Tor; Cheddar Gorge; Wookey Hole; Somerset Levels; Bath

In a magnificent rural setting of Somerset close to both Cheddar Gorge and the unspoilt beach at Brean Sands you'll find Woodland Country House Hotel. Owners, Peter and Glenda Botes are incredibly attentive hosts and genuinely believe nothing is too much trouble for their guests. The bedrooms are individual, comfortable and classically decorated and all have fantastic country views. Food is an important element of any stay here whether for breakfast or dinner and the kitchen takes pride in locally sourcing organic and seasonal produce. After a day using the hotel's bicycles or visiting nearby attractions such as the Mendip Hills and Bath, you'll deserve a delicious cream tea or before dinner head to the cosy bar for an aperitif. Woodlands has a tranquil home-from-home ambience and in such a picturesque setting you can see why you leave so relaxed.

BELLPLOT HOUSE HOTEL

HIGH STREET, CHARD, SOMERSET TA20 1QB
Tel: 0845 365 3033 **International:** +44 (0)1460 62600 **Fax:** 01460 62600
Web: www.johansens.com/bellplothouse **E-mail:** info@bellplothouse.co.uk

Our inspector loved: *The central location and homely feel of this family run hotel.*

Price Guide:
single from £109
double from £122
all exclusive use from £1300

Location: On the A30; A358, 1 miles; M5 jct 25, 12 miles; Honiton, 14 miles

Attractions: Forde Abbey; Barrington Court (NT); Lyme Regis; Exeter

Bellplot House is a delightful Georgian bolthole, full of lovely period features and décor that reflects its 1729 beginnings. You arrive to a very warm welcome from Betty and Dennis Jones who take pride in ensuring all their guests have all they need. The 7 spacious bedrooms are named after the female deed holders who once owned Bellplot and feature crisp white linens, high speed WIFI internet connections and all the facilities demanded by today's traveller. Breakfast is a feast of excellent local ingredients which will set you up for a day of exploring both this historic town, birthplace of the inventor of powered flight, John Stringfellow and the beautiful surrounding countryside. A lovely feature that makes you feel quite at home is the honesty bar where you can mix yourself a drink before heading out to one of the many good restaurants in Chard.

THREE ACRES COUNTRY HOUSE

THREE ACRES, BRUSHFORD, DULVERTON, SOMERSET TA22 9AR
Tel: 0845 365 2751 **International:** +44 (0)1398 323730
Web: www.johansens.com/threeacres **E-mail:** enquiries@threeacrescountryhouse.co.uk

Our inspector loved: The warm welcome and beautifully appointed rooms.

Price Guide:
single £60–£75
double/twin £90–£120
exclusive use £650 maximum 12

Location: B3222, 0.5 miles; A396, 1.3 miles; M5 jct 27, 17.6 miles; Dulverton, 2 miles

Attractions: Exmoor National Park; Wimbleball Lake; Knightshayes Court(NT); 4X4 Off-road Safari

You may have to look carefully but on the edge of Exmoor hidden by trees is the peaceful Three Acres. The house has been decorated with relaxation in mind, spacious rooms, generous sofas, log fires and a bar that leads onto a sun terrace. Bedrooms are individually styled and have plenty of personal character. There is no morning rush for breakfast, which includes delicious daily specials using fresh local produce. Lunch and dinner are not catered for however owners Edward and Julie recommend excellent restaurants, cafés and pubs close at hand, although for exclusive use dinner can be provided by prior arrangement. The unspoilt Dulverton's art galleries and antique shops are also nearby. Country sports and activities can be arranged including fishing, shooting, hunting and 4x4 off-road safari.

BINHAM GRANGE

OLD CLEEVE, NEAR MINEHEAD, SOMERSET TA24 6HX
Tel: 0845 365 1806 **International:** +44 (0)1984 640056
Web: www.johansens.com/binhamgrange **E-mail:** mariethomas@btconnect.com

Our inspector loved: *The tranquil setting, beautiful gardens and Marie Thomas' incredible home-made cakes and traditional cuisine. An experience not to be missed!*

Price Guide:
blue room from £100
abbey room from £140

Location: A39, 1.3 miles; M5 jct 23, 24 miles; Dunster, 4.6 miles; Minehead, 6.5 miles

Attractions: Steam Train to Taunton; Cleeve Abbey; Exmoor; Hestercombe Gardens

As soon as you arrive at this delightful Jacobean farmhouse, you'll find yourself captivated by the sense of total peace and tranquillity. Inside there are many striking original features including an original Jacobean frieze, Tudor alabaster arches and beautiful solid oak doors. The Exmoor Restaurant is a destination in its own right from lunches and teas on the terrace with its far reaching views to dinner served in the Great Hall. Working with the seasons and an extraordinary wealth of local produce Marie and daughter Victoria create delicious menus with occasional hints of their cooking experiences of Italy and Morocco. From your bedroom you can gaze across the beautiful gardens with a traditional orchard that leads to the landscapes beyond. Many little personal touches are dotted around to make you feel welcome, good books to browse through, fresh flowers to brighten up the room and authentic antiques to create a warm, opulent atmosphere.

FARTHINGS COUNTRY HOUSE HOTEL & RESTAURANT

HATCH BEAUCHAMP, NEAR TAUNTON, SOMERSET TA3 6SG
Tel: 0845 365 3290 **International:** +44 (0)1823 480664 **Fax:** 01823 481118
Web: www.johansens.com/farthings **E-mail:** info@farthingshotel.co.uk

Our inspector loved: *The warmth and character of this traditional country house.*

Price Guide:
single £110
double/twin £130
suite £175

Awards/Recognition: 1 AA Rosette 2007-2008

Location: A358, 1.5 miles; M5 jct 25, 4 miles; A303, 4.6 miles; Taunton, 7.6 miles

Attractions: Exmoor; Montacute House; Cheddar Gorge; Forde Abbey

Overlooking the village green of peaceful Hatch Beauchamp in the heart of Somerset, it's hard to believe that the hotel is only 5 miles from Taunton and the M5. Relaxing and informal, you can enjoy drinks and canapés in the garden on a warm summer's evening, and log fires in the cosy lounge or bar in winter. The AA 3 Star, Farthings is privately owned with tasteful bedrooms, and the family and staff are on hand with locally sourced food, cooked and presented in the AA Rosette-awarded restaurant. There are many attractions in the area such as Barrington Court, Montacute House, Hestercombe Gardens and West Somerset Railway. Wells Cathedral, Cheddar Gorge, Longleat Safari Park and the cities of Exeter and Bristol are all easily accessible.

BINDON COUNTRY HOUSE

LANGFORD BUDVILLE, WELLINGTON, SOMERSET TA21 0RU
Tel: 0845 365 3037 **International:** +44 (0)1823 400070 **Fax:** 01823 400071
Web: www.johansens.com/bindoncountryhouse **E-mail:** stay@bindon.com

Our inspector loved: *The perfect location to spend time with family and friends, with the added benefit of having it all to yourselves.*

Price Guide: (excusive use based on 24 adults on a self catering basis.)
midweek £1,250 per night, minimum 2 nights stay
weekend £4,500 (Friday-Sunday inclusive)

Location: B3187, 1 miles; M5 jct 26, 5 miles; Wellington, 3 miles; Taunton, 11 miles

Attractions: Cothay Manor; Hestercombe; Wells

Draped with curtains of Wisteria, enhanced with magnificent Baroque gables, and surrounded by 7 acres of glorious Somerset landscape, this 17th-century Gothic mansion oozes grace, comfort and informal splendour. For exclusive use only Bindon is a place where relaxation comes easily and everything can be tailored to your needs. For that very special wedding, family get-together, friends' reunion, celebration or prestigious corporate gathering, team building and training. All 12 bedrooms are sumptuously furnished and the business and leisure facilities include an excellent games room with computer games, pool and card table. Service is as attentive and discreet as you desire and you have award-winning dining under the direction of a Master Chef. If you prefer to cook yourself you have full access to the hotel's kitchens and barbecue areas, however its hard to resist the fully-catered hotel-style breakfast, lunch and dinner service.

BERYL

WELLS, SOMERSET BA5 3JP
Tel: 0845 365 3034 **International:** +44 (0)1749 678738 **Fax:** 01749 670508
Web: www.johansens.com/beryl **E-mail:** stay@beryl-wells.co.uk

Our inspector loved: The welcoming log fire and homely surroundings.

Price Guide:
single £65–£85
double £85–£130

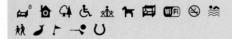

Location: B3139, 0.36 miles; A371, 2.16 miles; Bath, 21 miles

Attractions: Wells Cathedral; Cheddar Caves & Gorge; Longleat House; Roman Baths

This 19th-century, 5 Star, Gothic mansion is a real treasure, set in 13 acres of parkland and gardens, which have been skillfully restored. Beryl is tastefully furnished with antiques and offers you hospitality of the highest order. Holly Nowell and her daughter Mary-Ellen are charming hostesses, and take pride in the great attention to detail evident throughout the house. Guests are invited to use the honesty bar in the Green Room or enjoy drinks and wines on the lawn in summer. Holly and Mary-Ellen, who with her husband run a jewellery boutique in the Coach House, are happy to organise group bookings and make reservations for overnight guests at the many first-class restaurants and pubs situated nearby. The bedrooms have interesting views and offer every comfort. Take a dip in Beryl's outdoor pool from May to September.

KARSLAKE COUNTRY HOUSE AND COTTAGE

HALSE LANE, WINSFORD, EXMOOR NATIONAL PARK, SOMERSET TA24 7JE
Tel: 0845 365 1935 **International:** +44 (0)1643 851242 **Fax:** 01643 851242
Web: www.johansens.com/karslake **E-mail:** enquiries@karslakehouse.co.uk

Our inspector loved: *The beautiful English countryside making this a haven of peace and tranquility. Coupled with fabulous home cuisine, what more could you ask for.*

Price Guide:
single £55-£70
double £75-£110
exclusive use half board £1000

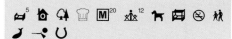

Awards/Recognition: 1 AA Rosette 2007-2008

Location: A396, 1.66 miles; A361, 19 miles; M5 jct 27, 25 miles

Attractions: Salmon and Trout Fishing; Exmoor Pony Centre; Dunster Castle; Tarr Steps

This 15th-century Malthouse was subsequently named after Sir John Burgess Karslake, a prominent lawyer and MP during the 1860s. Nestling in the wooded hills of Exmoor, Karslake is ideally located for exploring Devon's coasts or why not try an Exmoor jeep safari or one of the beautiful guided walks. Owners Nick and Juliette Mountford have devoted themselves to this oasis, where views of the Exe Valley and the hotel's garden can be seen from 3 of the 5 bedrooms. The four-poster room offers total luxury. The accredited restaurant uses seasonal, local produce, and homemade bread, jams and marmalades at breakfast. The bar is well stocked, and also has a wide range of great English wines. Packed lunches can be provided if you wish to explore the countryside. Relaxation treatments such as aromatherapy, lymphatic drainage massage and cranio-sacral therapy are provided by Karslake's health therapist.

DUNSLEY HALL HOTEL

DUNSLEY ROAD, KINVER, SOUTH STAFFORDSHIRE DY7 6LU
Tel: 0845 365 3908 **International:** +44 (0)1384 877077 **Fax:** 01384 877871
Web: www.johansens.com/dunsleyhallkinver **E-mail:** info@dunsleyhallhotel.co.uk

Our inspector loved: Walking around the Victorian walled gardens full of flowers, fruit and vegetables.

Price Guide:
single from £110
double £125-£230

Location: A449, 800yds; M5 jct 3, 20 miles; Wolverhampton, 15 miles; Birmingham, 20 miles

Attractions: Kinver Edge National Trust; Severn Valley Railway; Black Country Museum; Worcester Cathedral; Ironbridge

Tucked away as a private house for over 100 years, Dunsley Hall Hotel only opened its doors to paying guests in November 2007. Part dating back to the late 13th century, the quintessential English country manor atmosphere remains, along with the original 15th-century timber frames and roaring log fires. You can hide away from prying eyes by using the house and grounds exclusively, or simply escape the children for a couple of nights of romance and relaxation. Individually designed rooms have en-suite shower facilities and pampering toiletries, and some have antique brass beds or four posters. The restaurant aims to be the best in the area, and presents seasonal food that is locally sourced whenever possible, with many vegetables and fruits, including figs and peach trees grown in the Victorian walled garden.

THE MANOR AT HANCHURCH

NEWCASTLE ROAD, STOKE-ON-TRENT, STAFFORDSHIRE ST4 8SD
Tel: 0845 365 4618 **International:** +44 (0)1782 643 030 **Fax:** 01782 643 714
Web: www.johansens.com/themanorathanchurch **E-mail:** info@themanorathanchurch.co.uk

Our inspector loved: *The luxury and seclusion of this small hotel that is so conveniently located.*

Price Guide:
single £100-£350
double £100-£350

Location: M6 jct 15, 1 mile; A519, 200 metres; Stoke-on-Trent, 5 miles; Stafford, 14 miles

Attractions: Alton Towers; The Potteries & Wedgewood; Trentham Gardens & Stapeley Water Gardens

As you sweep up the driveway through the striking grounds you get an idea of the high levels of service and standards that await you at this impressive Neo-tudor manor. Recently refurbished to extremely high specifications and with a sharp eye for detail this is both a place to relax and a place to indulge in luxurious surroundings. The bedrooms are sumptuous and totally individual, complete with todays modern gadgets and comforts. Dining is an important element of the experience; in the restaurant an inspired contemporary menu focuses on local produce and on Sunday's includes a traditional roast whilst after a day exploring the Staffordshire countryside you can enjoy a home-made cream tea. The Manor at Hanchurch would be an excellent choice for a house party and most certainly for a wedding. Due to the nature of the property children under 12 are not allowed.

CLARICE HOUSE

HORRINGER COURT, HORRINGER ROAD, BURY ST EDMUNDS SUFFOLK IP29 5PH
Tel: 0845 365 3235 **International:** +44 (0)1284 705550 **Fax:** 01284 716120
Web: www.johansens.com/clarice **E-mail:** bury@claricehouse.co.uk

Our inspector loved: *The informal, friendly atmosphere.*

Price Guide:
single £65–£90
double/twin £100–£115

Awards/Recognition: 1 AA Rosette 2007-2008

Location: On the A143; A14, 2.3 miles

Attractions: Cambridge; Ely; Newmarket Racecourse

Clarice House is a residential spa within a beautifully refurbished neo-Jacobean mansion set in 20 acres of Suffolk countryside and ancient woodland. The excellent restaurant is open to residents and non-residents and for those choosing to stay for bed and breakfast, the bedrooms are comfortable and well-appointed. A variety of Spa Break packages include dinner and full use of the spa facilities, The hi-tech gym includes personal programme management and a team of dedicated instructors who offer daily classes. A 20-metre indoor swimming pool leads into a spa bath, steam room and sauna. The suite of beauty salons offers a wide range of indulgent treatments from the more traditional to holistic treatments such as reflexology, reiki and Indian head massage.

THE CORNWALLIS COUNTRY HOTEL & RESTAURANT

BROME, EYE, SUFFOLK IP23 8AJ
Tel: 0845 365 4603 **International:** +44 (0)1379 870326 **Fax:** 01379 870051
Web: www.johansens.com/cornwallis **E-mail:** reservations@ohiml.com

Our inspector loved: *The fine dining restaurant: dramatic, intimate and exceptional.*

Price Guide:
single from £95
double from £115

Awards/Recognition: 1 AA Rosette 2007–2008

Location: On A140; Diss, 2-min drive; Ipswich, 30-min drive; Bury St Edmunds, 30-min drive

Attractions: Suffolk Coast; Bury St Edmunds; Bressingham Gardens and Steam Museum

The long avenue of mature lime trees that greets you as you arrive at this pretty 16th-century dower house promises a romantic setting, and the tranquil topiary gardens and surrounding woodland do not disappoint. The house has clung on to many of its interesting original features; an intriguing script above the stairwell, oak panelling, working fireplaces and in the Tudor bar, serving cask ales, a 30-foot deep well. The oldest areas have low beams and quaint sloping floors, while the later Victorian addition features loftier spaces. All bedrooms are unique. The Lexington Restaurant prides itself on its cuisine, inspired by the excellent local Suffolk produce. Lighter but equally delicious meals can be enjoyed in the Lunchoen garden and on most Saturday's a farmer's market is held in the walled garden.

THE ANGEL HOTEL

MARKET PLACE, LAVENHAM, SUFFOLK CO10 9QZ

Tel: 0845 365 1802 **International:** +44 (0)1787 247388 **Fax:** 01787 248344
Web: www.johansens.com/angellavenham **E-mail:** angel@maypolehotels.com

Our inspector loved: The Grade I listed, wonderful plaster ceiling in the resident's lounge that dates back to the 1700s.

Price Guide:
single from £70
double from £85

Awards/Recognition: 1 AA Rosette 2008-2009

Location: On A1141; A14 jct 44, 15-min drive; Sudbury, 7 miles; Ipswich, 19 miles

Attractions: Bury St Edmunds; Newmarket; Constable Country; Gainsboroughs House in Sudbury

A traditional English country inn that was first licensed in 1420 and with heaps of historic charm is believed to be the oldest in Lavenham. Of course much has changed over the years but you can still spot many original features that bring character to the interiors and work well with today's modern comforts. Bedrooms also echo the period - some with beams and a fresh country style decor. The wood-beamed pub is ideal for enjoying Suffolk ale and the comforts of local chatter by a warm fireside. Eat more formally in the restaurant, al fresco in the shady garden or privately in the snug - all serving a menu inspired by local produce transformed by a young innovative team. Guests have the added advantage of exclusive use of a private lounge with views over the square and Guildhall.

THE WESTLETON CROWN

THE STREET, WESTLETON, NEAR SOUTHWOLD, SUFFOLK IP17 3AD
Tel: 0845 365 2731 **International:** +44 (0)1728 648777 **Fax:** 01728 648239
Web: www.johansens.com/westletoncrown **E-mail:** info@westletoncrown.co.uk

Our inspector loved: The fresh, contemporary decor of the bedrooms.

Price Guide:
single from £90
double/twin £110–£170

Awards/Recognition: 2 AA Rosettes 2008-2009; Suffolk Dining Pub of the Year 2008- Good Pub Guide

Location: On the B1125; A12, 3.9 miles; Southwold, 7 miles; Aldeburgh, 8 miles

Attractions: Dunwich Heath (NT); Snape Maltings and Music Festival; Minsmere RPSB Bird Reserve; Southwold Pier

You'll be very happy to drop your bags at this historic coaching inn that dates back to the 12th century. Bedrooms, some located in converted stables and cottages, are furnished in a fresh country style, and each is named after a species of bird - you'll spot them in the lovely canvas photographs. Hearty breakfasts, light meals in the bar or more elegant dining in the restaurant and conservatory are all created with passion and served by the efficient team that prides itself on making sure you're happy. A range of local ales in the bar is always tempting. You're close to the Suffolk Heritage Coast and its unspoiled heathlands, nature reserves, beaches and wild salt marshes, as well as the quintessential English seaside towns of Aldeburgh and Southwold.

THE CROWN INN

THE GREEN, PETWORTH ROAD, CHIDDINGFOLD, SURREY GU8 4TX
Tel: 0845 365 3252 **International:** +44 (0)1428 682255 **Fax:** 01428 683313
Web: www.johansens.com/crownchiddingfold **E-mail:** enquiries@thecrownchiddingfold.com

Our inspector loved: The new owners have done an outstanding job on this pub! It is an absolute little gem.

Price Guide:
single from £100
double £125–£200

An idyllic English pub, The Crown nestles in a quiet corner of the picture-perfect village green of Chiddingfold. Totally refurbished by the new owners, the olde world charm of the property has been lovingly maintained and sympathetically blended with a more sophisticated and contemporary décor. Beautiful stained-glass windows provide a stunning backdrop to the large dining rooms, whilst the downstairs bar has a more informal ambience. There is a passion for food at The Crown and using excellent seasonal ingredients they serve "proper pub food" complemented by an excellent extensive selection of wines and real ales. The bedrooms have all been completely refurbished, and their stunning ancient beams and gently sloping floors create a romantic and welcoming haven. Within an hour's drive of London there can be few better locations for a weekend break - or even just a cracking Sunday lunch!

Location: On the A283; Guildford, 13.5 miles; London Waterloo, 40-min train/metro

Attractions: Petworth House; Ramster Gardens; Lurgashall Winery

PRIDE OF THE VALLEY

TILFORD ROAD, CHURT, FARNHAM, SURREY GU10 2LH
Tel: 0845 365 3791 **International:** +44 (0)1428 605799 **Fax:** 01428 605875
Web: www.johansens.com/prideofthevalley **E-mail:** reservations@prideofthevalleyhotel.com

Our inspector loved: *The recent refurbishment downstairs that is so welcoming and fashionable.*

Price Guide:
single from £95
double from £120

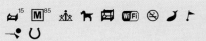

Location: A3 Hindhead, 3 miles; Farnham, 4.5 miles; London Waterloo, 45-min train ride; Gatwick and Heathrow Airports, 55-min drive

Attractions: Winkworth Arboretum and Devil's Punchbowl; Birdworld; Guildford Shopping; Classic Car Museum By Appointment

Set in the picture-book village of Tilford, Pride of the Valley is currently the subject of a stylish and meticulous refurbishment. By combining leather, wood and seagrass materials, a warm and inviting atmosphere is being created throughout this fantastic find. Traditional elements that reflect the property's locality in the heart of the Surrey countryside remain carefully incorporated. The large bar area is a great place to relax and enjoy an informal lunch after a long walk, while during the evenings Chef David Terrell serves locally sourced produce whenever possible in the modern and elegant restaurant. The quirky bedrooms are comfortable and will soon reflect the more sophisticated design that features downstairs. They host some entertaining classic car days, champagne tasting evenings and gourmet dinners throughout the year.

The Mill House Hotel

MILL LANE, ASHINGTON, WEST SUSSEX RH20 3BX
Tel: 0845 365 2598 **International:** +44 (0)1903 892426 **Fax:** 01903 893846
Web: www.johansens.com/millhousehotelashington **E-mail:** info@millhousehotelsussex.co.uk

Our inspector loved: The friendly welcome and informal atmosphere.

Price Guide:
single from £59
double from £92
suite from £125

Just to the north of Worthing and convenient for South Downs' walking and countryside, you will find this enchanting Grade II listed small hotel. Many features demonstrate its 17th-century origins and the cottage presentation is delightful. Simple bedroom provision offers a quiet night's rest, and the ground floor has interesting antiques and a lovely inglenook fireplace with log fires on colder days. The sheltered garden is ideal for enjoying the summer sun with a glass of Pimms. Chef Patron Kim Johnson prepares excellent food, using locally sourced Sussex produce that is complemented by a good wine list; all served with traditional, attentive service. The meeting room will accommodate up to 48 people, and is perfect for small conferences, weddings and private dining.

Location: A24, 0.5 miles; M23 Jct 11, 20 miles; Worthing, 12 miles; London Gatwick, 28 miles

Attractions: South Downs; Thakeham House; Regency Brighton; Arundel Castle

EPISODE HOTEL

64 UPPER HOLLY WALK, ROYAL LEAMINGTON SPA, WARWICKSHIRE CV32 4JL
Tel: 0845 365 3764 **International:** +44 (0)1926 883777 **Fax:** 01926 330467
Web: www.johansens.com/epsiode **E-mail:** leamington@episodehotels.co.uk

Our inspector loved: *The brilliant contemporary décor and design in this beautiful Regency building.*

Price Guide:
single £75-£145
double £90-£160

Location: A452, 1 mile; M40 exit 15, 10-min drive; Birmingham International Airport, 25-min drive

Attractions: Warwick Castle; Stratford-upon-Avon; Kenilworth Castle; NEC

Drop your luggage and accept the warm welcome at this lovely Regency town house hotel in the heart of Leamington Spa, the healthy mineral waters town on the River Leam that Queen Victoria made "royal" after a visit in 1838. Impressive on the outside and gorgeous on the inside, this up-to-date, chic boutique stopover offers striking décor and stunning furnishings within classic surrounds. The restaurant is equally fabulous where diners are able to enjoy modern British cooking with what is described as "a sprinkling of Continental style and technique." And for those who take pleasure from an appetizer or after dinner nightcap there's a champagne and cocktail terrace on which to relax and reminisce over the day's activities.

THE GEORGE HOTEL

HIGH STREET, SHIPSTON-ON-STOUR, WARWICKSHIRE CV36 4AJ
Tel: 0845 365 3762 **International:** +44 (0)1608 661453 **Fax:** 01608 661453
Web: www.johansens.com/georgeshipston **E-mail:** info@thefabulousgeorgehotel.com

Our inspector loved: The atmospheric main bar and dining area.

Price Guide:
single £75-£145
double £90-£160

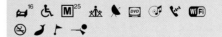

Location: Just off the A3400; Stratford-upon-Avon, 20-min drive; M40 exit 15, 30-min drive; Birmingham International Airport, 45-min drive

Attractions: Stratford-upon-Avon; The Cotswolds; Oxford; Banbury

The number of coaching inns in the High Street of this historic sheep market town located on the fringe of the Cotswolds is testament to Shipston-on-Stour's importance as a stopover during an era of horse-drawn travel. The George is one of these inns: beautifully maintained, early 18th century and boasting a winter warming 15th-century fireplace in its welcoming bar. Queen Victoria, before her crowning, is reputed to have used the facilities here and had her horses changed outside the property during one of her cross-country journeys. She would hardly recognise The George today. Sensitively transformed into a chic boutique hotel it has dramatic and striking décor and furnishings, stylish bedrooms, fine food and a welcome befitting royalty!

BEECHFIELD HOUSE

BEANACRE, WILTSHIRE SN12 7PU

Tel: 0845 365 3031 **International:** +44 (0)1225 703700 **Fax:** 01225 790118
Web: www.johansens.com/beechfieldhouse **E-mail:** reception@beechfieldhouse.co.uk

Our inspector loved: *The warm welcome and relaxed hospitality at this handsome Victorian house set in beautiful grounds.*

Price Guide:
single from £95
double from £125
family from £150
feature from £150

Location: On the A350; M4 jct 17, 15-min drive; Lacock, 2 miles; Bath, 11 miles

Attractions: Bath; Lacock; Longleat House; Stonehenge

A privately owned country house hotel, within easy reach of Bath, the Cotswolds and everything this delightful region has to offer. Whether you are going to visit the surrounding attractions or to just switch off, you will find something to help you unwind. The terrace and outdoor heated pool are gorgeous in the summer, whilst in the winter the open fires are as warm as the welcome. A relaxing candlelit dinner can be enjoyed from an ever changing menu offering a wide variety of dishes, many created from locally sourced and home grown produce. Walk around the beautiful grounds or pamper yourself in the in-house beauty treatment centre with their natural 'Pure Fiji' product range. All bedrooms are comfortable and well appointed with kingsize beds and the latest digital LCD TVs. Crisp Eqyptian cotton sheets, fluffy towels and Molton Brown goodies add to the sense of indulgence. The coach house rooms are all newly refurbished and include disabled access rooms.

WIDBROOK GRANGE

WIDBROOK, BRADFORD-ON-AVON, NEAR BATH, WILTSHIRE BA15 1UH
Tel: 0845 365 2805 **International:** +44 (0)1225 864750/863173
Web: www.johansens.com/widbrookgrange **E-mail:** stay@widbrookgrange.co.uk

Our inspector loved: The home-from-home relaxing feel throughout.

Price Guide:
single £95–£120
double £120–£130
four poster £140
family rooms from £160.50

Awards/Recognition: 1 AA Rosette 2008-2009

Location: Off the A363; Bradford-on-Avon, 1.3 miles; M4 jct 18, 19 miles; Bath, 6.8 miles

Attractions: Bath; Longleat; Laycock Abbey Stonehenge

Widbrook Grange is an elegant 250 year old Georgian AA three star country house hotel peacefully located in 11 acres of grounds and rolling countryside on the outskirts of medieval Bradford-on-Avon, only 20 minutes from the historic city of Bath and from Longleat House and Safari Park. There are wonderful country walks from the hotel and spacious grounds in which children can play in safety. Service is attentive yet unobtrusive and it has an informal intimate relaxing atmosphere with peaceful gardens, cosy lounges and log fires on cold winter nights. Its award winning restaurant serves fine modern European cuisine complemented by an interesting selection of New and Old World wines. The spacious and tastefully decorated bedrooms in the main house, courtyard and garden include romantic four posters, family rooms and rooms with facilities for disabled guests. There is a heated indoor swimming pool, a gym and meeting rooms.

THE CASTLE INN

CASTLE COMBE, WILTSHIRE SN14 7HN
Tel: 0845 365 2894 International: +44 (0)1249 783030 Fax: 01249 782315
Web: www.johansens.com/castleinn E-mail: enquiries@castle-inn.info

Our inspector loved: *The new stylish bedrooms and the location in the most picturesque of villages.*

Price Guide:
single £69.50-£150
double £110-£175

Location: M4 jct 17, 5 miles; A420, 1 mile; Chippenham Railway Station, 6 miles

Attractions: Bath; Lacock; Bradford on Avon

A charming country hotel nestling in a wooded Cotswold valley and conveniently located for historic Bath. Castle Combe often referred to as the "Prettiest Village in England" is intriguingly also home to a renowned classic race circuit. Here little has changed architecturally since the 15th century and every property is now a listed monument. The famous Castle Inn stands in the market place, and has been lovingly restored to preserve and enhance its matchless charm. The guest rooms are tastefully decorated with antique furniture and rich fabrics, in a manner in keeping with a building that retains many of its original features. The ambient restaurant, relaxed garden room and cosy bar offer a range of tempting menus to suit every taste, from five course indulgence to light bar snacks.

STANTON MANOR HOTEL & GALLERY RESTAURANT

STANTON SAINT QUINTIN, NEAR CHIPPENHAM, WILTSHIRE SN14 6DQ

Tel: 0845 365 2364 **International:** +44 (0)1666 837552 **Fax:** 01666 837022
Web: www.johansens.com/stantonmanor **E-mail:** reception@stantonmanor.co.uk

Our inspector loved: *The informal and relaxed atmosphere, you are made to feel like an old friend.*

Price Guide:
single £110–£115
double £140–£190
double superior deluxe £220

Awards/Recognition: 1 AA Rosette 2008-2009

Location: A429, 1 mile; M4 jct 17, 1 mile; Chippenham, 5 miles; Bath, 17 miles

Attractions: Thermae Bath Spa; Stourhead Garden and House; Longleat; Tewkesbury Abbey

Listed in the Domesday-book and whilst more recently rebuilt in 1840, the original Dovecot still exists. There is a very clever and comfortable mix of the traditional and contemporary. Magnificent Tudor fireplaces and stone flooring blend with strong bold modern fabrics. Bedrooms are spacious, 4 have four-poster beds, some a private patio and some ideal for families. Owners Robert and Linda Davis take great care with the detail and they have an obvious love of the East which shows in the art lining the walls of the elegant Gallery restaurant. You can buy the art and all proceeds go to support a children's orphanage in Vietnam. Head Chef Paul Hudson, winner of the South West Chef of the Year 2008, and his team are creative in their interpretation of British cuisine using seasonal local ingredients. A super location not far from the M4, at the gateway to the Costwolds.

The Lamb at Hindon

HIGH STREET, HINDON, WILTSHIRE SP3 6DP
Tel: 0845 365 2574 **International:** +44 (0)1747 820 573 **Fax:** 01747 820 605
Web: www.johansens.com/lambathindon **E-mail:** info@lambathindon.co.uk

Our inspector loved: *The buzzy atmosphere of a true traditional inn.*

Price Guide:
single £70
double/twin £99–£135

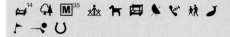

Location: Just off B3089; A303, 1.2 miles; Salisbury, 19 miles

Attractions: Longleat; Stonehenge; Cranborne Chase; Old Wardour Castle

A 12th century public house that by the 1870's was considered a 'favourable' stop for coaches travelling between London and the West Country. Its characterful interiors with rich colours, flagstone floors, tartan fabrics and wooden beams are in keeping with its sense of history. Some of the charming and spacious bedrooms have four-posters, and there are ample corners thoughout for you to relax in, including the Whisky & Cigar Bar and the cosy Snug. A Scottish flavour influences food, with ingredients sourced whenever possible from local or Scottish suppliers. Rare wines from the award-winning Boisdale selection make an appearance, and in addition to real ales the malt whisky menu is reputedly the largest in Wiltshire.

THE PEAR TREE INN

THE PEAR TREE, TOP LANE, WHITLEY, WILTSHIRE SN12 8QX
Tel: 0845 365 1746 **International:** +44 (0)1225 709131
Web: www.johansens.com/peartreewhitley **E-mail:** peartreeinn@maypolehotels.com

Our inspector loved: The cosy feel of this lovely country pub with log fires and tastefully designed, well-equipped bedrooms.

Price Guide:
single £95
double £125

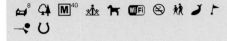

A cool, rustic chic flows through this cosy pub with its dreamy blend of quintessential English heritage and Gallic inspiration. The modern, neutrally decorated bedrooms include 2 family rooms and 4 stable rooms complete with their own entrances and which are ideal for those with canine companions. Molton Brown toiletries, flatscreen TVs and Broadband and WiFi complete the luxurious feel. The success of the food here boils down to the balance of a laidback country pub ambience and the fine dining ethos from the kitchen. Vegetables from local Bromham growers are used, however, the chefs do occasionally look further afield for such key ingredients as lemons from the Amalfi Coast for a zesty tart and a good list of international wines. 4 acres of gardens surround the inn, and there is ample space for a marquee.

Location: B3353, 0.5 miles; A365, 0.5 miles; A350, 2 miles

Attractions: Bath; Lacock; Castle Combe; Bristol

ROYAL FORESTER COUNTRY INN

CALLOW HILL, NEAR BEWDLEY, WORCESTERSHIRE DY14 9XW
Tel: 0845 365 2865 **International:** +44 (0)1299 266286
Web: www.johansens.com/royalforester **E-mail:** contact@royalforesterinn.co.uk

Our inspector loved: *The prominence on the menu of produce (including wine) from "Local Food Heroes"*

Price Guide:
single from £55
double from £79

Location: On the A456; M5 jct 6, 18 miles; Bewdley, 2 miles; Birmingham International Airport, 55-min drive

Attractions: Bewdley; Severn Valley Steam Railway; Witley Court; Shelsley Walsh Hill Climb

This beautifully refurbished and modernized old inn has origins dating back to 1411. The charming restaurant is a "meandering-shape" with old floors and walls which showcase murals of Wyre Forest scenes and characters from over a 100 years ago. Great emphasis is put on creating seasonal menus and building a complementary wine list, needless to say it is a popular spot for resident and non-residents alike, the surprisingly moderate rates are an added bonus. The 7 bedrooms, named after fruits, have been styled with rich fabrics and bold colours and as you would expect come with all the 21st century gadgets a modern guest would require. Opposite, the ancient and alluring Wyre Forest is ideal for riding or walking and the hotel can arrange stabling and livery.

RIVERSIDE HOTEL AND RESTAURANT

THE PARKS, OFFENHAM ROAD, NEAR EVESHAM, WORCESTERSHIRE WR11 8JP
Tel: 0845 365 3607 **International:** +44 (0)1386 446200 **Fax:** 01386 49755
Web: www.johansens.com/riversiderestaurant **E-mail:** info@theparksoffenham.freeserve.co.uk

Our inspector loved: The delightful river views and the delicious food and ambience in the restaurant.

Price Guide:
single £62.95–£74.95
double £89–£119
superior king £99–£139

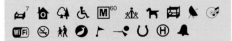

Awards/Recognition: 2 AA Rosettes 2008-2009

Location: A46, 2-min drive; M40, 20-min drive; Evesham, 5-min drive; Birmingham International, 30-min drive

Attractions: Broadway; Stratford Upon Avon; Warwick Castle; Evesham Country Park (opposite the hotel)

The Riverside Hotel is an 18th century manor house which continues to triumph in its superb position perched high above the River Avon within the original Evesham Abbeys 12th century deer parks. Its also blazing a trail for "low food miles" organic produce supplied direct by local farms with the owners hens leading the way in providing fresh eggs from the restaurant. Dining here is a real treat with the hotel winning many awards for its delicious food, be sure to look out for special events such as Italian and Greek nights, guest chef appearances and summertime barbecues on decks overlooking the river. The bedrooms are all individually interior designed, some with jacuzzi baths, all with fabulous views overlooking the river. The hotel has its own private moorings from which you can fish from the decks or hire a cruise boat to explore the River Avon.

THE OLD RECTORY

IPSLEY LANE, IPSLEY, NEAR REDDITCH, WORCESTERSHIRE B98 0AP
Tel: 0845 365 2615 **International:** +44 (0)1527 523000 **Fax:** 01527 517003
Web: www.johansens.com/oldrecipsley **E-mail:** ipsleyoldrectory@aol.com

Our inspector loved: *This hidden jewel. All the bedrooms - especially No 4 "Chapel" and its startling shower cum massager.*

Price Guide:
single from £87
double/twin from £112

Location: A435, 2 miles; M42 jct 3, 7 miles; Redditch, 3 miles; Birmingham International, 13 miles

Attractions: Stratford-upon-Avon; Warwick Castle; The Cotswolds; Birmingham Bullring

The great-grandson of Sir Christopher Wren 'modernised' The Old Rectory in 1812 whilst living in the house for 40 years. The property has endured over 500 years of history and the Domesday Book lists a building on this site which borders the Roman built Icknield Street. Today you can experience warm and relaxed hospitality. The bedrooms are all quite different; one is reputedly haunted, others have exposed beams and one has a barrel ceiling. Take dinner in the conservatory where menus offer dishes prepared on the premises, using the freshest seasonal produce. Coffee and liqueurs may be enjoyed in the snug or lounge, whilst the beautiful gardens with their rhododendrons, Portuguese laurel, old oak, cedar, silver birch and weeping ash trees, beckon to be explored.

THE WHITE LION HOTEL

HIGH STREET, UPTON-UPON-SEVERN, NEAR MALVERN, WORCESTERSHIRE WR8 0HJ
Tel: 0845 365 2738 **International:** +44 (0)1684 592551 **Fax:** 01684 593333
Web: www.johansens.com/whitelionupton **E-mail:** info@whitelionhotel.biz

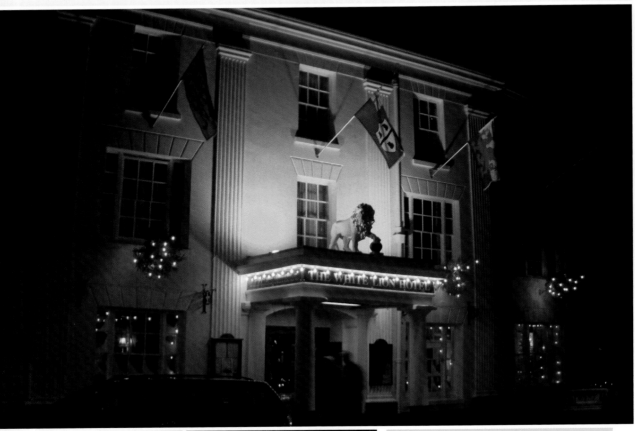

Our inspector loved: The relaxing lounge - giving onto the High Street - a staging post between the locals' bar and the delights of the restaurant.

Price Guide:
single from £70–£90
double from £99
four-poster from £125

Awards/Recognition: 1 AA Rosette 2006-2007

Location: On the A4104; A38, 1.5 miles; M5 jct 7, 8 miles; Worcester, 11 miles

Attractions: Worcester; Malvern Hills; Ledbury; Tewkesbury Abbey

In his 1749 novel, "The History of Tom Jones", Henry Fielding described the hotel as "the fairest Inn on the street" and "a house of exceedingly good repute", so owners Jon and Chris Lear have taken him at his word, upholding a tradition of hospitality, good food & drink. Bedrooms from various periods date back to 1510 - again, with literary aspirations, the Rose Room and Wild Goose Room are named in a Fielding book. The award-winning Pepperpot Brasserie serves fine dishes with flair and plenty of seasonal influence. As a member of CAMRA – supporters for Real Ale the bar is appropriately stocked for aficionados and each summer hold their own mini-beer festival. Other great days out locally include The Three Counties Show Ground and The Upton jazz festival.

KILHAM HALL

DRIFFIELD ROAD, KILHAM, DRIFFIELD, EAST YORKSHIRE YO25 4SP
Tel: 0845 365 3285 **International:** +44 (0)1262 420466
Web: www.johansens.com/kilhamhall **E-mail:** enquiries@kilhamhall.co.uk

Our inspector loved: *The complimentary afternoon tea on arrival, with home-made cake or scones. This really is a luxurious home-from-home.*

Price Guide:
double from £130

Location: Coast, 8 miles; Beverley, 18 miles; York, 32 miles; M62, 38 miles; Humberside Airport, 42 miles

Attractions: Burton Agnes Hall; Sledmere House; Flamborough Head and East Coast; The City of York

A picture-perfect country house approached by a shingle driveway, Kilham Hall is the ideal if you like attention to detail without the fuss of a full service hotel. Joanne Long delights in personally welcoming her guests and for those arriving between 4pm-6pm there is a sumptuous complimentary home-made tea in the elegant drawing room. The 2 bedrooms and 1 suite are packed with modern classic design features perfectly fusing old world charm with contemporary chic. The beds and baths have a "wow" factor! Most gorgeous is the suite split over 2 floors; accessed by a spiral staircase and offers a romantic double spa bath. A delicious breakfast is served around a large table laden with home-made and locally sourced produce. There is no restaurant but plenty of local choice for dinner, however start the evening off with a glass of complimentary wine in the conservatory or on warm nights on the terrace overlooking the heated outdoor pool and croquet lawn.

THE AUSTWICK TRADDOCK

AUSTWICK, VIA LANCASTER, NORTH YORKSHIRE LA2 8BY
Tel: 0845 365 2396 **International:** +44 (0)15242 51224 **Fax:** 015242 51796
Web: www.johansens.com/austwick **E-mail:** info@austwicktraddock.co.uk

Our inspector loved: The immediate feel of the character and charm of this beautifully furnished country house hotel.

Price Guide:
single £80–£120
double/twin £140–£190

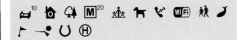

Awards/Recognition: 1 AA Rosette 2007-2008

Location: A65, 1 mile; M6 jct 36, 30 miles; Settle, 4 miles; Kirkby Lonsdale, 12 miles

Attractions: Ingleborough Cave; The 3 peaks of Whernside, Pen-y-ghent, Ingleborough; Settle; Yorkshire Dales

Set in 2 acres of peaceful, landscaped gardens in the heart of the Yorkshire Dales National Park is this fine Georgian country house hotel and restaurant, oozing character, charm and the friendliest of hospitality. Here you are surrounded by some of the most sensational limestone scenery in Europe, including several magnificent caves with dazzling stalagmites and stalactites. You can relax after walking and sightseeing tours in the comfortable bar and lounge, warmed in winter by open log fires. Bedrooms are individually designed and beautifully furnished with English antiques. The restaurant won Organic Restaurant of the Year 2006 and Chef, John Pratt, produces excellent modern, seasonal and local British cuisine, complemented by an extensive wine list. Special breaks are available on request.

George and Dragon Inn

AYSGARTH, NORTH YORKSHIRE DL8 3AD
Tel: 0845 365 4609 **International:** +44 (0)1969 663358 **Fax:** 01969 663773
Web: www.johansens.com/georgeanddragon **E-mail:** www.info@georgeanddragonaysgarth.co.uk

Our inspector loved: *Choosing a local beer in the the cosy bar before enjoying a delicious meal in the beamed restaurant.*

Price Guide:
single £50-£65
double/twin £75-£110
four poster from £120

Awards/Recognition: 1 AA Rosette 2008-2009

Location: On The A684; Leyburn, 8 miles; Hawes, 9 miles; Harrogate, 42 miles

Attractions: Cauldron Falls at West Burton; Semerwater Lake; Bolton Castle; Fountains Abbey

A cosy, welcoming, 17th-century coaching inn on the edge of a pretty little village in the heart of the Yorkshire Dales, this has traditionally been an ideal base for walking, riding, touring and exploring ancient sites. But this is also a great place to escape to if you just need to get away for some peace and quiet. Just ten minutes' walk away is the spectacular Aysgarth Falls, carved out of the River Ure on its descent to mid Wensleydale; featured in the film Robin Hood, Prince of Thieves. Bedrooms, including a spacious family room, mix period charm with contemporary luxury that includes walk-in showers and under-floor heating. Enjoy drinks in the friendly bar, decorated with painted portraits of past and present locals, and dine in the wonderful restaurant where the wholesome menu presents traditional English dishes.

THE DEVONSHIRE FELL

BURNSALL, SKIPTON, NORTH YORKSHIRE BD23 6BT

Tel: 0845 365 2462 **International:** +44 (0)1756 718111 **Fax:** 01756 710564
Web: www.johansens.com/devonshirefell **E-mail:** res@devonshirehotels.co.uk

Our inspector loved: *The wonderful surprise as you step inside and see contemporary art. Choose from imaginatively designed menus and sleep in one of the startlingly decorated bedrooms.*

Price Guide:
single £110
double/twin £145–£192
suite £213

The Devonshire Fell is in a rare location where the views are simply stunning. Step inside to meet bold bright colours created by The Duchess of Devonshire. Large comfortable sofas, a wood burning stove and original contemporary art combine to create an inviting atmosphere. This is very much "city chic in the countryside" with impeccable standards throughout. Menus are sourced locally, wherever possible, and from the kitchen gardens at its sister hotel in Bolton Abbey. The 10 bedrooms and 2 family suites incorporate fresh and vivid colours, CD/DVD players and flat-screen TVs and of course breathtaking views. Guests are offered complimentary use of the spa and leisure facilities at The Devonshire Health Spa at nearby Bolton Abbey. The Dalzell Room is perfect for private events.

Location: On the B6160; A59, 6 miles; Skipton, 7 miles; Harrogate, 22 miles

Attractions: Bolton Abbey Estate; Yorkshire Dales; Malham Cove; Skipton Castle

DUNSLEY HALL

DUNSLEY, WHITBY, NORTH YORKSHIRE YO21 3TL
Tel: 0845 365 3276 **International:** +44 (0)1947 893437 **Fax:** 01947 893505
Web: www.johansens.com/dunsleyhall **E-mail:** reception@dunsleyhall.com

Our inspector loved: *The lounge with Inglenook fireplace and original stained-glass window depicting a seafaring scene.*

Price Guide:
single from £95
double/twin from £149
four poster from £180
deluxe from £198

Awards/Recognition: 1 AA Rosette 2007-2008

Location: A171, 2 miles; Whitby, 3 miles; Scarborough, 21 miles

Attractions: Whitby Abbey; Robin Hoods Bay; North Yorkshire Moors Steam Railway; Birthplace of Captain Cook

Dunsley Hall hotel stands in 4 acres of magnificent landscaped gardens in the North Yorkshire Moors National Park and has remained virtually unaltered since it was built at the turn of the 20th century. Some of the individually decorated bedrooms, 2 with four-poster beds, enjoy a fantastic view of the sea, just a few minutes walk away, and feature fine fabrics and furniture. All bedrooms are non-smoking. Mellow oak panelling, a handsome Inglenook carved fireplace and stained glass windows enhance the drawing room's relaxing and restful atmosphere. From the Oak Room, Terrace Suite or Pyman Bar, you can enjoy award-winning regional dishes and seafood specialities made from only the freshest of ingredients. There is also a cottage available by prior request.

159

MARMADUKES HOTEL

ST PETERS GROVE, BOOTHAM, YORK, NORTH YORKSHIRE YO30 6AQ
Tel: 0845 365 4852 **International:** +44 (0)1904 640101
Web: www.johansens.com/marmadukes **E-mail:** mail@marmadukeshotels.co.uk

Our inspector loved: The loft suite has a free-standing Victorian style bath for two, a wet room and barrel sauna with CD music system. Pure indulgence!

Price Guide:
single £65
double £140
suite £320

Awards/Recognition: 1 AA Rosette 2008-2009

Location: Town Centre, 0.3 miles; A19, 0.3 miles

Attractions: York Minster; Castle Howard; Jorvik Centre; North York Moors

Ideally located in the heart of historic York, in its own peaceful grounds and just a short stroll from York Minster and the ancient city walls. Originally a Victorian gentleman's residence, this unique, AA 4 Star boutique hotel combines classical style with modern elegance. The 19 rooms are individually decorated with carefully selected antiques and offset by stunning Italian fabrics. Bed frames have been handcrafted and handmade mattresses are covered in the crispest Egyptian cotton. For a truly romantic break, reserve the Loft Suite, luxurious and contemporary this suite features a private lounge with champagne table, dressing room and the stunning bathroom boasts a barrel sauna with CD music system and a double ended bath for two. Continue to indulge with a candle-lit dinner at The Chop Room, serving fine Yorkshire cuisine.

THE WORSLEY ARMS HOTEL

HOVINGHAM, NEAR YORK, NORTH YORKSHIRE YO62 4LA
Tel: 0845 365 2746 **International:** +44 (0)1653 628234 **Fax:** 01653 628130
Web: www.johansens.com/worsleyarms **E-mail:** enquiries@worsleyarms.co.uk

Our inspector loved: Relaxing in the cosiest corner of the lounge, by an open fire. A perfect place for an after dinner drink.

Price Guide:
single £85–£110
double/twin £115–£200

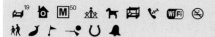

Awards/Recognition: 1 AA Rosette 2007-2008

Location: On the B1257; Malton, 8 miles; Helmsley, 8 miles; York, 30 miles

Attractions: Castle Howard; North York Moors; Yorkshire Dales; York Minster

The Worsley Arms is an attractive Georgian spa hotel in the heart of Hovingham, an unspoilt Yorkshire village dating back to Roman times. The hotel overlooks the village green and was built in 1841 by the baronet Sir William Worsley whose nearby family home, Hovingham Hall is the birthplace of the Duchess of Kent. Today the hotel is owned and run by Anthony and Sally Finn. Elegant furnishings and open fires create a welcoming atmosphere.The award-winning restaurant offers creatively prepared dishes, including game from the estate. Visit the wine cellar to choose your wine for dinner. The Cricketers bar provides a more informal setting to enjoy modern cooking at its best. The bedrooms vary in size some with views over the pretty village green.

THE DUSTY MILLER & COINERS RESTAURANT

BURNLEY ROAD, MYTHOLMROYD, HEBDEN BRIDGE, WEST YORKSHIRE HX7 5LH

Tel: 0845 365 3781 **International:** +44 (0)1422 885959

Web: www.johansens.com/dustymiller **E-mail:** thedustymiller@hotmail.co.uk

Our inspector loved: *Dining near the theatre kitchen with the opportunity to chat with the chef.*

Price Guide:
single £54-£69
double £69
family room £69-£100

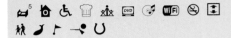

Location: On the A646; M62 Jct 24, 13 miles; Halifax, 7 miles; Leeds Bradford International Airport, 22 miles

Attractions: Bronte Parsonage Birth Place of Charlotte Brontë; Dean Clough Mills; Shibden Hall; Keighley & Worth Valley Railway

Located in the rural village of Mytholmroyd and nestled in the Calder Valley, the lively Dusty Miller & Coiners Restaurant is the perfect place to eat, drink and stay. A Grade II listed 250-year-old roadside inn which has been lovingly restored to provide contemporary surroundings and a welcoming atmosphere. There are 5 comfortable bedrooms, some with original fireplaces and stonework, and a snug lounge bar with log burner and soft leather sofas and chairs that will beckon you before dining in Coiners Restaurant. An enticing international menu is prepared under the direction of chef proprietor Philip Webster who uses fresh, locally sourced ingredients, some of which are available to buy. Enjoy narrow boat trips on the Rochdale canal, as well as fantastic cycling and walking along this stretch of the Pennine Way, just beneath Blackstone Edge where one of England's most dramatic Roman roads can be discovered amidst the heather.

HEY GREEN COUNTRY HOUSE HOTEL

WATERS ROAD, MARSDEN, WEST YORKSHIRE HD7 6NG
Tel: 0845 365 1846 **International:** +44 (0)1484 848000 **Fax:** 01484 847605
Web: www.johansens.com/heygreen **E-mail:** info@heygreen.com

***Our inspector loved:** The hotel's setting above 2 lakes surrounded by rhododendrons and ferns - a wonderful place to take a stroll.*

Price Guide:
single from £89
double from £119

Location: A62, 0.33 miles; Marsden, 1 mile; Oldham, 8 miles; Huddersfield, 10 miles

Attractions: Standedge Canal Tunnel; Start of Pennine Way; Last ot the Summer Wine Country; Bronte Country

For peace, tranquillity and the silence of still air, few can better this West Yorkshire hotel overlooking the Colne Valley surrounded by green pastures, dry-stone walls and little grey farms tucked into hillsides. Victorian, with parts dating from the 1700s, the imposing Hey Green stands in 15 acres of grounds encompassing 2 lakes that attract guests to stretch their legs and enjoy water-edge walks among shady trees and knee-high ferns. A warm, welcoming ambience pervades the house where the staff's concern for guest comfort is reminiscent of a private house rather than a busy hotel. The grand sweeping staircase leads up to the tastefully furnished bedrooms from where you can admire the views of the grounds. Room 11 is worth a special note due to its original 1890s four poster and bathroom with spa bath. The restaurant with its flagstone flooring and open fire is to be found in the oldest part of the building, here the menu emphasises the best of British cuisine.

THE SHIBDEN MILL INN

SHIBDEN MILL FOLD, SHIBDEN, HALIFAX, WEST YORKSHIRE HX3 7UL
Tel: 0845 365 4617 **International:** +44 (0)1422 365 840 **Fax:** 01422 362 971
Web: www.johansens.com/shibdenmill **E-mail:** enquiries@shibdenmillinn.com

Our inspector loved: *The individually-styled bedrooms with lovely personal touches such as "themed" books and retro "Bush" radios.*

Price Guide:
single £72-£95
double £90-£110
suite £135-£145

Awards/Recognition: 1 AA Rosette 2007-2008

Location: A58, 1 miles; M62, 6 miles; Halifax, 3 miles; Leeds, 11 miles; Leeds/Bradford Airport, 20 miles

Attractions: Shibden Hall and Park; Yorkshire Dales; Dean Clough Art Galleries; Piece Hall

With the gentle murmurings of Shibden Brook running past its door, this delightful 16th-century inn is a haven from the rush of everyday life. Just 3 miles to Halifax and 11 to Leeds, this is a great find for not only those on a break but a refreshing stop for the business traveller. The bar, with its low beams and open fires, serves an extensive range of beer including its own local brew. While the restaurant, where menus are inspired by local produce including fine Yorkshire cheese, features higher, equally impressive ceilings and a private dining room for small parties. Plenty of care and attention to detail has been paid to ensure your stay is memorable and the little touches and warm service are well worth the visit.

To us, no two hotels are the same

Insurance cover exclusive to Condé Nast Johansens recommended hotels

Tel: 0044 7768093718
Email: Johansens@jltgroup.com

Insurance | Experience | Excellence
Preferred insurance partner of Condé Nast Johansens

JARDINE LLOYD THOMPSON
Leisure

© Jmci | Dreamstime.com

Ireland

For further information on Ireland, please contact:

The Irish Tourist Board
(Bord Fáilte Eíreann)
Baggot Street Bridge
Dublin 2
Tel: +353 (0)1 602 4000
Internet: www.ireland.ie

Tourism Ireland
Tourism Centre
Suffolk Street
Dublin 2
Tel: 0800 039 7000
Internet: www.discoverireland.com

Northern Ireland Tourist Information
Belfast Welcome Centre
47 Donegall Place
Belfast, BT1 5AD
Tel: +44 (0)28 9024 6609
Internet: www.gotobelfast.com

or see **pages 206-208** for details of local historic houses, castles and gardens to visit during your stay.

For additional places to stay in Northern Ireland & Ireland, turn to **pages 204-205** where a listing of our Recommended Hotels & Spas Guide can be found.

The following Irish hotels and spas can be found in our Recommended Hotels & Spas guide 2009

More information on our portfolio of guides can be found on page 13.

a ANTRIM - BELFAST (NORTHERN IRELAND)

Ten Square
10 Donegall Square South, Belfast BT1 5JD
Tel: 028 90 241 001
Web: www.johansens.com/tensquare

b CARLOW - TULLOW

Mount Wolseley Hotel, Spa & Country Club
Tullow, Co Carlow, Ireland
Tel: 00 353 599 180100
Web: www.johansens.com/mountwolseley

c CORK - MALLOW

Longueville House & Presidents' Restaurant
Mallow, Co Cork, Ireland
Tel: 00 353 22 47156
Web: www.johansens.com/longuevillehouse

d DONEGAL - DONEGAL TOWN (LOUGH ESKE)

Harvey's Point
Lough Eske, Donegal Town, Co Donegal, Ireland
Tel: 00 353 74 972 2208
Web: www.johansens.com/harveyspoint

e DUBLIN - KILLINEY

Fitzpatrick Castle Hotel
Killiney, Co Dublin
Tel: 00 353 1 230 5400
Web: www.johansens.com/fitzpatrickcastle

f GALWAY - CLIFDEN (CONNEMARA)

Abbeyglen Castle
Sky Road, Clifden, Co Galway, Ireland
Tel: 00 353 95 21201
Web: www.johansens.com/abbeyglen

g GALWAY - CONNEMARA

Cashel House
Cashel, Connemara, Co Galway, Ireland
Tel: 00 353 95 31001
Web: www.johansens.com/cashelhouse

h GALWAY - RECESS

Ballynahinch Castle Hotel
Recess, Connemara, Galway, Ireland
Tel: 00 353 953 1006
Web: www.johansens.com/ballynahinch

i KERRY - KENMARE

Park Hotel Kenmare & Sámas
Kenmare, Co. Kerry, Ireland
Tel: 00 353 64 41200
Web: www.johansens.com/parkkenmare

j KERRY - KILLARNEY

The Brehon
Muckross Road, Killarney, Co. Kerry, Ireland
Tel: 00 353 64 30700
Web: www.johansens.com/thebrehon

k KERRY - KILLARNEY

Cahernane House Hotel
Muckross Road, Killarney, Co Kerry, Ireland
Tel: 00 353 64 31895
Web: www.johansens.com/cahernane

m KERRY - KILLARNEY

The Europe Hotel & Resort
Killarney, Co Kerry, Ireland
Tel: 00 353 64 71300
Web: www.johansens.com/europekerry

n KERRY - KILLARNEY

Hotel Dunloe Castle
Beaufort, Killarney, Co Kerry, Ireland
Tel: 00 353 64 44111
Web: www.johansens.com/dunloecastle

p MAYO - BALLINA

Mount Falcon Country House Hotel & Spa
Foxford Road, Ballina, Co Mayo, Ireland
Tel: 00 353 967 4472
Web: www.johansens.com/mountfalcon

q MAYO - CONG

Ashford Castle
Cong, Co Mayo, Ireland
Tel: 00 353 94 95 46003
Web: www.johansens.com/ashfordcastle

r MAYO - CASTLEBAR

The Harlequin
Lannagh Road, Castlebar, Co Mayo, Ireland
Tel: 00 353 949 286 200
Web: www.johansens.com/harlequin

s MAYO - WESTPORT

Knockranny House Hotel & Spa
Westport, Co Mayo, Ireland
Tel: 00 353 98 28600
Web: www.johansens.com/knockranny

t MONAGHAN - CARRICKMACROSS

Nuremore Hotel and Country Club
Carrickmacross, Co Monaghan, Ireland
Tel: 00 353 42 9661438
Web: www.johansens.com/nuremore

u TIPPERARY - THURLES

The Horse and Jockey Hotel
Thurles, Co Tipperary, Ireland
Tel: 00 353 504 44192
Web: www.johansens.com/horseandjockey

v WEXFORD - ARTHURSTOWN (NEAR WATERFORD)

Dunbrody Country House & Cookery School
Arthurstown, Co Wexford, Ireland
Tel: 00 353 51 389 600
Web: www.johansens.com/dunbrody

w WEXFORD - GOREY

Marlfield House
Courtown Road R742, Gorey, Co Wexford, Ireland
Tel: 00 353 53 94 21124
Web: www.johansens.com/marlfieldhouse

x WEXFORD - ROSSLARE

Kelly's Resort Hotel & Spa
Rosslare, Co Wexford, Ireland
Tel: 00 353 53 91 32114
Web: www.johansens.com/kellysresort

y WICKLOW - ENNISKERRY

The Ritz-Carlton, Powerscourt
Powerscourt Estate, Enniskerry, Co Wicklow
Tel: 00 353 1 274 8888
Web: www.johansens.com/ritzcarlton

For further information, hotel search, gift certificates, online bookshop and special offers visit:

www.johansens.com

ARD NA SIDHE

KILLARNEY, KILLORGLIN, CO KERRY, IRELAND
Tel: 00 353 66 976 9105 **Fax:** 00 353 66 976 9282
Web: www.johansens.com/ardnasidhe **E-mail:** reservations@ardnasidhe.com

Our inspector loved: *The peace and tranquility for those who want it and fishing rods, boats and croquet for those who don't .*

Price Guide: (euro, open 1st May – 15th October 2009)
single €150-€270
double €170-€300

Location: Killorglin, 4 miles; Killarney N22, 18 miles; Kerry Airport, 20 miles

Attractions: Dingle Bay; Gap of Dunloe; Ring of Kerry

Standing majestically above the iridescent waters of Caragh Lake is a Victorian mansion whose name romantically translates to "the hill of the fairies". It's the sheer tranquillity of the place that seems to get under your skin from the moment you step out of the car. There is an old world enchantment about the hotel with its classical style, antique furnishings and paintings. After a relaxed dinner adjourn to the terrace and night sky, or alternatively a large cosy sofa and a crackling peat fire. Botany enthusiasts will enjoy the award-winning gardens, which are a haven for ferns, hybrid rhododendrons, fuchias and Lavateras. Paths and cuttings wind their way through the grounds and on the lakeside you can take the rowing boat out to explore or to try a spot of fishing.

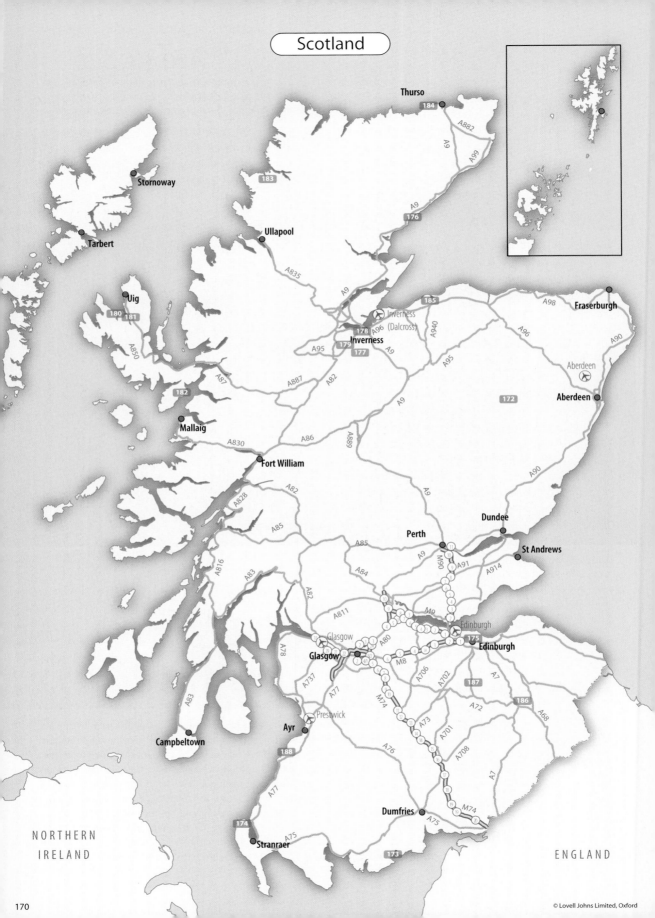

Scotland

© Ewan Chesser | Dreamstime.com

Scotland

For further information on Scotland, please contact:

Visit Scotland
Ocean Point 1,
94 Ocean Drive, Leith
Edinburgh EH6 6JH
Tel: +44 (0)131 472 2222 or +44 (0)1463 716 996
Internet: www.visitscotland.com

Greater Glasgow & Clyde Valley Tourist Board
110 George Square
Glasgow G2 1DY
Tel: +44 (0)141 204 4400
Internet: www.seeglasgow.com

Edinburgh & Lothians Tourist Board
Tel: +44 (0)845 2255 121
Internet: www.edinburgh.org

The Scottish Borders Tourist Board
Tel: 0870 608 0404
Internet: www.scot-borders.co.uk

or see **pages 206-208** for details of local historic houses, castles and gardens to visit during your stay.

For additional places to stay in Scotland, turn to **pages 204-205** where a listing of our Recommended Hotels & Spas Guide can be found.

DARROCH LEARG

BRAEMAR ROAD, BALLATER, ABERDEENSHIRE AB35 5UX
Tel: 0845 365 3263 **International:** +44 (0)13397 55443 **Fax:** 013397 55252
Web: www.johansens.com/darrochlearg **E-mail:** enquiries@darrochlearg.co.uk

Our inspector loved: The quite superb wine list.

Price Guide:
single £110–£140
double/twin £180–£270

Awards/Recognition: 3 AA Rosettes 2008-2009

Location: Ballater village, 10-min walk; Aberdeen, 42 miles

Attractions: Balmoral; River Dee at the doorstep; Stunning countryside; Castle and Whisky Trails

Situated in 4 acres of leafy grounds Darroch Learg is situated on the side of the hill which dominates Ballater. The hotel was built in 1888 as a fashionable country residence, with panoramic views over the golf course, River Dee and Balmoral Estate to the fine peaks of the Grampian Mountains. Bedrooms are comfortable and individually furnished. The reception rooms are similarly elegant and welcoming and log fires create a particularly cosy atmosphere on chilly nights. Excellent food for which the chef was awarded Hotel Chef of the Year in 2005 whilst the wine list has achieved 13th place in the Top 100 UK Restaurants Wine Lists guide. The views are stunning with a wonderful outlook south over the hills of Glen Muick.

BALCARY BAY HOTEL

AUCHENCAIRN, NR CASTLE DOUGLAS, DUMFRIES & GALLOWAY DG7 1QZ
Tel: 0845 365 3026 **International:** +44 (0)1556 640217/640311 **Fax:** 01556 640272
Web: www.johansens.com/balcarybay **E-mail:** reservations@balcary-bay-hotel.co.uk

Our inspector loved: *The beautiful bay on which it stands and its secluded location.*

Price Guide:
single £69
double/twin £124–£160

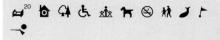

Awards/Recognition: Condé Nast Johansens Most Excellent Waterside Hotel Award 2008; 2 AA Rosettes 2006-2007

Location: Off the A711, 0.9 miles; Auchencairn, 2 miles; Castle Douglas, 9 miles

Attractions: Various Golf Courses; Galloway Wildlife Conservation Park; Threave Castle; Threave Estate and Gardens

At the end of a narrow lane, and enjoying a surprisingly warm, Gulf Stream climate, this traditional, secluded hideaway on the Solway Firth is still close to the bustling market town of Dumfries. You will have the reassuring intimacy of a family-run hotel, whilst enjoying all the ingredients for a peaceful, romantic visit. As you sit in the lounge overlooking the bay, only the call of sea birds and gently lapping waves compete for your attention. You should make the most of local delicacies such as lobster, prawns and salmon, and the great coastal walks that this corner of Scotland has to offer. Nearby are several excellent golf courses, salmon rivers and trout lochs, sailing, shooting, riding and bird-watching.

CORSEWALL LIGHTHOUSE HOTEL

CORSEWALL POINT, NEAR KIRKCOLM, STRANRAER, DG9 0QG
Tel: 0845 365 2859 **International:** +44 (0)1776 853220 **Fax:** 01776 854231
Web: www.johansens.com/lighthousehotel **E-mail:** info@lighthousehotel.co.uk

Our inspector loved: *The unique luxury hotel and the most spectacular coastline.*

Price Guide: (including breakfast and dinner)
double £150-£250
suite £210-£280

Awards/Recognition: 1 AA Rosette 2007-2008

Location: A718, 4 miles; Stranraer Ferry, 11 miles; Prestwick Airport, 60 miles

Attractions: Mull of Galloway Lighthouse; Culzean Castle; Logan Botanic Gardens

Perched high on a clifftop, just yards from a glazier-like face, Corsewall Lighthouse is either being dashed by high rising storm spray or smoothed by calmer summer waters at its rocky foot. This sparkling white lighthouse is a gorgeous little retreat that exudes the warmth, charm and romance of its early 19th-century origins with the comforts and style of a very unique hotel. It's a delightfully restored "A" listed national treasure that you will adore. Views are dazzling by day and star-scattered by night, taking in meadowland and a spectacular seascape brightened by several other working Scottish and Irish lighthouses whose knife-like beams warn of inshore dangers. Flexible accommodation includes three 2-bedroom suites, and the restaurant menu is inspired by seasonal offerings from both the sea and land.

THE HUDSON HOTEL

9 - 11 HOPE STREET, EDINBURGH EH2 4EL
Tel: 0845 365 4627 **International:** +44 (0)131 247 7000 **Fax:** 0131 247 7001
Web: www.johansens.com/hudsonedinburgh **E-mail:** hudsonhotel@festival-inns.co.uk

Our inspector loved: The 18th-century building with contemporary interior design.

Price Guide: (room only)
double £130-£160

Location: West End of Edinburgh, on-site; Haymarket Railway Station, 5-min walk; Edinburgh Airport, 20-min drive

Attractions: Edinburgh Castle; Royal Yacht Britannia; Royal Mile; George Street; EICC

The Hudson Hotel is a chic interpretation of Edinburgh's new cosmopolitan personality, with contemporary, cutting-edge design and state-of-the-art technology combined with many authentic 18th-century period features. The essence of this stylish boutique hotel is serenity within a vibrant city, reflected by a calming interior design. The colour schemes are rich and inviting, the furniture is gorgeous and every room has stunning modern art on its walls. And to top it all, there is a wonderful bar downstairs with friendly staff who serve delicious meals, and an exclusive discreet nightclub that is open to the wee hours of the morning that takes care not to disturb the rest of the hotel. You will love the central location just off popular Princes Street where there are plenty of shops, and the castle is within brisk walking distance. All in all, this is the perfect base from which to explore the delights of the city.

ROYAL MARINE HOTEL, RESTAURANT & SPA

GOLF ROAD, BRORA, SUTHERLAND KW9 6QS
Tel: 0845 365 2309 **International:** +44 (0)1408 621252 **Fax:** 01408 621181
Web: www.johansens.com/royalmarinebrora **E-mail:** info@royalmarinebrora.com

Our inspector loved: *The atmosphere of a bygone age and the newly styled bedrooms that feature every modern convenience.*

Price Guide:
single from £85
double £130-£190
suite £190

Location: Brora Town centre, 2-min walk; Inverness, 1-hour drive

Attractions: Brora and Royal Dornoch Golf Course; Fly fishing; Clynelish Distillery; Dunrobin Castle

Originally built as a private country house, the Royal Marine was designed by the renowned Scottish architect Sir Robert Lorimer in the early 1900s. The wonderful carved wooden fireplaces and arches, and the panelled walled snooker room, are complemented by the contemporary interior fabrics of rich blues, gold and taupe. A perfect retreat for all the family, with a large pool, spa facilities and its own beauty salon. Several championship links golf courses are on the doorstep including Royal Dornoch and Tain and the James Braid Brora Golf Course. Fly fishing on Loch Brora in one of the hotel's boats, mountain biking and hill walking can all be enjoyed here and it's well worth getting up extra early to experience the spectacular sunrises over the sea. The food is fabulous, with no less than 3 restaurants giving you a delicious choice of dining: light meals in the Garden Room, full flavored Scottish cuisine in the Bistro and an à la carte menu in Lorimers.

THE STEADINGS AT THE GROUSE & TROUT

FLICHITY, FARR, SOUTH LOCH NESS, INVERNESS IV2 6XD
Tel: 0845 365 2698 **International:** +44 (0)1808 521314 **Fax:** 01808 521741
Web: www.johansens.com/steadings **E-mail:** stay@steadingshotel.co.uk

Our inspector loved: *Very cosy and comfortable with stunning scenery of the highlands.*

Price Guide:
single £68–£78
double £95–£145

Location: On the B851 ; A9 to Fort Augustus Road, 7 miles; Inverness, 12 miles; Inverness Airport, 20 miles

Attractions: Loch Ness and Caledonian Canal;Cairngorm Mountains; Culloden Battlefield; Dolphins in Moray Firth

The wonderful panoramic scenery and wildlife to be seen from the conservatory of this rustic, unpretentious inn is second to none. Built in 1860, the property was originally outbuildings, thankfully salvaged from the Flichity Inn, destroyed in 1964. Jump on the whisky trail and explore the castles, lochs and glens of the hidden Highlands, while looking out for herds of deer, wild goats, grouse, and heron landing on the Flichity Loch - if you're really lucky you might even spot osprey whisking away a salmon, or a stoat playing with the resident hare family on the hotel's lawn. Enjoy a local beer in The Grouse & Trout Lounge Bar and delicious Scottish and international food alongside an excellent wine list and, of course, fine Scottish malt whiskies.

DUNAIN PARK HOTEL & RESTAURANT

LOCH NESS ROAD, INVERNESS IV3 8JN
Tel: 0845 365 3275 **International:** +44 (0)1463 230512 **Fax:** 01463 224532
Web: www.johansens.com/dunainpark **E-mail:** info@dunainparkhotel.co.uk

Our inspector loved: The seclusion of this fine Georgian country house refurbished in a stunning contemporary style.

Price Guide:
single from £145
double from £180
suite £250

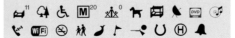

Built in the 18th century, this beautiful hotel is situated in 6 acres of the finest grounds and gardens to be found in Inverness. Classic contemporary, the rooms ooze style, epitomising the best of country house chic. The clever use of vibrant crimson, gold, bronze and rich chocolate emphasises the original features wonderfully. You needn't worry about the attention to detail, which is particularly visible in the large bedroom suites that boast 2 plasma TVs, DVD players and ipod docking stations alongside delectable toiletries and the best Egyptian linens. Executive Chef George Mackay and his team have developed an outstanding menu of seasonal dishes that feature the finest local produce and best described as modern Scottish with a twist. Close to the centre of Inverness, you benefit from all city facilities including theatre, Loch Ness and golf.

Location: Inverness, 2 miles; Invernesss Airport, 12 miles

Attractions: Loch Ness; Urquhart Castle; Culloden Battlefield; Dolphin watching in Moray Firth

LOCH NESS LODGE

BRACHLA, LOCH NESS-SIDE, INVERNESS IV3 8LA
Tel: 0845 365 4625 **International:** +44 (0)1456 459469 **Fax:** 01456 459439
Web: www.johansens.com/lochnesslodge **E-mail:** escape@loch-ness-lodge.com

Our inspector loved: *The gastronomic experience and views of Loch Ness.*

Price Guide:
single £120-£180
double £190-£280

Location: Inverness, 15-min drive; Inverness Airport, 40-min drive; Cairngorm National Park, 40-min drive, Isle of Skye, 1½ hours drive

Attractions: Cruise on Loch Ness to Urquhart Castle; Culloden Battlefield; Whisky Trail; Cawdor Castle

With views over the iconic Loch Ness, the Lodge cannot fail to impress in the location stakes, and does its utmost to ensure you have the perfect Highland experience on every level. The mix of traditional Scottish architecture and contemporary design works beautifully, and the superbly designed bedrooms embody sophisticated style with their goose down duvets, elegant fabrics and carefully chosen furnishings in natural hues and tones. Each is named after a Highland loch or glen and offers wonderful views. The Lodge is very passionate about the food it serves, and works closely with local artisan suppliers who share their "field to mouth" ethic. The icing on the cake is Escape, the Lodge's spa and therapy suite. This is the perfect location for an overnight escape or to exclusively hire for a house party, intimate wedding or corporate event.

GRESHORNISH HOUSE

EDINBANE, BY PORTREE, ISLE OF SKYE IV51 9PN
Tel: 0845 365 1798 **International:** +44 (0)1470 582266 **Fax:** 01470 582345
Web: www.johansens.com/greshornishhouse **E-mail:** info@greshornishhouse.com

Our inspector loved: The peace and tranquility in gorgeous surroundings with superb food.

Price Guide:
single £60–£165
double £120–£248
family £162.50–£240

Experience the open-door policy of this typical family run Skye manor house, very much in keeping with the island's hospitable traditions. Secluded in a beautiful lochside setting, the oldest part of the building dates back to the mid-18th century. The bedrooms are distinctive and comfortable - one allegedly haunted. However, there is nothing spooky in the candle-lit dining room, where an abundance of local seafood, game, Skye lamb, Scotch beef and cheeses are on offer. After dinner enjoy snooker and chess, or take a quiet moment by the drawing room fire to really appreciate a good malt whisky. The hotel is the perfect base for exploring the north end of Skye, or simply a place to relax and unwind whilst being looked after by a delightful team of people. Non-Smoking throughout the hotel.

Location: A850, 2.5 miles; Portree, 17 miles; Inverness Airport, 145 miles; Skye Bridge, 53 miles

Attractions: Dunvegan Castle; Talisker Distillery; Edinbane Pottery; Skyeskyns Tannery

SKEABOST COUNTRY HOUSE

SKEABOST BRIDGE, PORTREE IV51 9NP
Tel: 0845 365 4016 **International:** +44 (0)1470 532202 **Fax:** 01470 532761
Web: www.johansens.com/skeabost **E-mail:** reservations.skeabost@ohiml.com

Our inspector loved: *The stunning situation by the sea-fed loch and the well-tended grounds.*

Price Guide:
double £99-£198

Location: Off the A850; Skye Bridge, 43 miles; Inverness Airport, 135 miles

Attractions: Dunvegan Castle; Talisker Distillery; Skye Scenery; Boat Trips

Originally a hunting lodge, this beautiful country house is steeped in history and set in a magical position on the edge of Loch Snizort. Crackling open fires, rich colour schemes and period décor create a cosy ambience that you will find most welcoming after a day's exploring. Bedrooms are equally inviting, some with sumptuous four posters and breathtaking views. Fine dining in the stunning wood-panelled dining room is a delicious experience in local cuisine. A good menu is also served in the relaxed Conservatory Bistro, which has spectacular views over the loch. With the magnificent Highlands landscape as a backdrop, simply stepping into the garden is a delight, where you will find yourself surrounded by beautiful rhododendrons and azaleas. Consider late night golf on the hotels own 9-hole course in the light hours of summer.

TORAVAIG HOUSE

KNOCK BAY, SLEAT, ISLE OF SKYE IV44 8RE
Tel: 0845 365 2756 **International:** +44 (0)1471 833231 **Fax:** 01471 833231
Web: www.johansens.com/toravaig **E-mail:** info@skyehotel.co.uk

Our inspector loved: *The relaxed atmosphere, scenic location and contemporary dining - a perfect romantic retreat.*

Price Guide: (including dinner)
double £180–£250

Awards/Recognition: Condé Nast Johansens Most Excellent Service Award 2006; 2 AA Rosettes 2007-2008; Eat Scotland Silver Award 2008

Location: On A851; Broadford, 12 miles; Skye Bridge, 16.5 miles; Portree, 37 miles

Attractions: Talisker Distillery and Visitor Centre; Sea Trips; Dunvegan Castle; Portree

Owners Anne Gracie and Kenneth Gunn have turned Toravaig House into a luxurious, affordable hotel, somewhere you'll happily spend time and deservedly recognised by its many awards. Overlooking the Sound of Sleat, its comfortable bedrooms, all named after Hebridean Islands, have little Scottish touches, and the elegant Iona restaurant, serves first class food from fresh local produce. Of course the great outdoors has masses to offer here, with fantastic low-level walking and climbing in the Cuillin Mountains. Even better, Ken's affinity with the sea is illustrated by daily skippered charters on the hotel's yacht, "Solus na Mara," that take you around the south of Skye and the mainland. Skye's Sleat Peninsula, a hotbed of highland culture as well as being renowned for its musical events, holds a splendid Feis in mid-July.

RUDDYGLOW PARK

LOCH ASSYNT, BY LAIRG, SUTHERLAND IV27 4HB
Tel: 0845 365 2315 **International:** +44 (0)1571 822216 **Fax:** 01571 822216
Web: www.johansens.com/ruddyglowpark **E-mail:** info@ruddyglowpark.com

Our inspector loved: *The added extras and very relaxed atmosphere makes this an exceptionally pleasurable experience.*

Price Guide:
twin from £120
double from £120
suite from £140

Location: on A837; Lochinver, 6 miles; Inverness, 100 miles

Attractions: Stalking; Geopark; Eas-Coul-Aulin via Kylesku; Cape Wrath

This unique tranquil country house has a superb elevated position with spectacular views over acres of much loved and well tended woodland gardens, majestic mountains and Scottish lochs. Owner Patricia Filmer-Sankey, named the hotel after the 1920s National Hunt racehorse and winner of more than 27 races, "Ruddyglow," ridden by her father. Comfortable bedrooms feature Egyptian cotton bed linen, pure Hungarian goose down duvets, velvety bathrobes, jacuzzi baths and indulgent accessories. Mighty breakfasts are made from the best local organic ingredients and dinners are cooked by prior arrangement. An exceptional addition this year is a private secluded cabin that is not only environmentally and ecologically friendly but decidedly luxurious. The main room is large and airy with beautiful honey gold beams and the bathroom indulges with a two meter Villeroy & Boch bath fed with pure water from a natural spring. A place to relax the mind, body and soul.

FORSS HOUSE HOTEL

FORSS, NEAR THURSO, CAITHNESS KW14 7XY

Tel: 0845 365 1749 **International:** +44 (0)1847 861201 **Fax:** 01847 861301
Web: www.johansens.com/forsshousehotel **E-mail:** anne@forsshousehotel.co.uk

Our inspector loved: *Time stands still here. It is so peaceful and relaxing with such attentive staff.*

Price Guide:
single £95–£110
double/twin £125–£160
suite £230

If you love open spaces and the grand landscapes of the Scottish Highlands you will adore this 200-year-old house, carefully restored by the owners, who also refurbished Ackergill Tower. The bedrooms and master bedrooms have all been carefully decorated with luxurious soft furnishings and feature elegant, tiled bathrooms. Take breakfast in the light and airy conservatory, whilst the more classic dining-room is the perfect setting for intimate dinners. Each dish is prepared with a simplicity that retains the true flavours of the finest local ingredients, seasonal meat and fish sourced from surrounding estates, rivers and the coastline of Forss and are complemented by an extensive and inspiring wine collection. The house nestles in a tree-lined glen with its own swirling river for fishing.

Awards/Recognition: 1 AA Rosettes 2007-2008

Location: On the A836; A9, 4.6 miles; Thurso, 5 miles; Wick Airport, 27 miles

Attractions: John O'Groats; Castle of Mey; Old Pulteney Distillery; Orkney

KNOCKOMIE HOTEL

GRANTOWN ROAD, FORRES, MORAYSHIRE IV36 2SG
Tel: 0845 365 1963 **International:** +44 (0)1309 673146 **Fax:** 01309 673290
Web: www.johansens.com/knockomiehotel **E-mail:** stay@knockomie.co.uk

Our inspector loved: The newly refurbished dining room, done in contemporary style, with mirrors placed in the window shutters has a wonderful "wow" factor and floods the room with light.

Price Guide:
single £115
double/twin £170
four poster £210

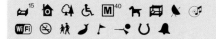

Awards/Recognition: Condé Nast Johansens / Taittinger Wine List Award 2006

Location: On A940; 1.6 miles south of Forres; Forres Railway Station, 1.5 miles; Inverness Airport, 20 miles

Attractions: Cawdor Castle; Brodie Castle; Malt Whisky Trail; Loch Ness

Defined by the Arts and Crafts movement, this elegant house was transformed in 1914 into what it is today. Paying guests are recorded as early as the 1840s, although its metamorphosis into a stylish hotel is somewhat more recent! Owners, Gavin and Penny Ellis have created a personal, intimate atmosphere, with just 15 bedrooms, and you can kick back and relax from the moment you arrive. This is Malt Whisky country, so do visit one of the local distilleries, and with Loch Ness to the west and Speyside to the east, you're surrounded by beautiful places. At the end of a full day's exploring or playing golf on one of a number of championship and challenging courses look forward to a drink in the delightful and well-stocked bar followed by carefully prepared menus balancing traditional Scottish ingredients with lighter dishes.

FAUHOPE COUNTRY HOUSE

GATTONSIDE, MELROSE, BORDERS TD6 9LU
Tel: 0845 365 4631 **International:** +44 (0)1896 823184
Web: www.johansens.com/fauhopehouse **E-mail:** info@fauhopehouse.com

Our inspector loved: *The hospitality that far exceeds your hopes.*

Price Guide:
double from £120

Location: Just off B6360; Melrose, 2.6 miles; A68, 2.2 miles; Edinburgh Airport, 45 miles

Attractions: Abbotsford, Home of Sir Walter Scott Melrose Abbey; Dryburgh Abbey; Floors Castle

This secluded country house is a wonderful example of Arts and Crafts architecture and, with its extensive grounds and beautiful river views, is truly inspirational. A relaxed and welcoming atmosphere is created by the wonderful warmth of the hospitality and combined with an air of elegance this is a very special place. Spacious bedrooms are beautifully styled with antiques and fine fabrics. Breakfasts are a feast with local produce and freshly picked berries when in season. In the afternoon, while away the hours in the beautiful drawing room and read a book, or if you prefer to do something a bit more energetic, the historic town of Melrose is just a short walk across the Georgian suspension footbridge over the Tweed. Here you will find a good selection of restaurants and pubs to choose from for your evening meal.

CASTLE VENLAW

EDINBURGH ROAD, PEEBLES EH45 8QG

Tel: 0845 365 3226 **International:** +44 (0)1721 720384 **Fax:** 01721 724066
Web: www.johansens.com/venlaw **E-mail:** stay@venlaw.co.uk

Our inspector loved: *The historic property nestled in 12 acres of woodlands.*

Price Guide:
double/twin £120–£180
four poster £167–£207
romantic suite from £257

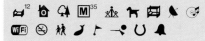

Awards/Recognition: Hotel Review Scotland Gold Plate Award 2008

Location: Just off the A703; Edinburgh, 40-min drive; Glasgow, 90-min drive

Attractions: Traquair House; Neidpath Castle; Dawyck and Kailzie Gardens; Edinburgh Castle

Built as a private residence in 1782 the Castle is a short distance from Edinburgh yet within the peaceful Borders countryside overlooking the royal and ancient town of Peebles. This acclaimed 4-star hotel maintains country house traditions and a relaxed informality, from the Library with its oak panelling and log fire, to the 12 bedrooms and suites - all named after Scotland's finest malt whiskies. Enjoy the recently added four-poster romantic suites as well as the spacious restaurant offering menus where delicious local produce such as Borders salmon, lamb and game are given an international flavour. Explore the countryside where historic ruins can be appreciated. Short breaks are available all year and the Castle is available for exclusive use for parties and weddings.

Culzean Castle – The Eisenhower Apartment

MAYBOLE, AYRSHIRE KA19 8LE
Tel: 0845 365 3257 **International:** +44 (0)1655 884455 **Fax:** 01655 884503
Web: www.johansens.com/culzeancastle **E-mail:** culzean@nts.org.uk

Our inspector loved: *The height of luxury with magnificent views.*

Price Guide:

(including breakfast and afternoon tea)
single from £140
double from £225

Take care when looking down! A 6 bedroom presidential apartment retained for General Eisenhower in his lifetime when the Castle was handed over to the National Trust for Scotland in 1945. Enter through the extremely impressive armoury at the front door and as you arrive on the top floor you'll know that you are entering a rather splendid home. "This is a place I can relax" said Eisenhower, and that sentiment is exemplified by the friendly staff looking after you. Whether you are travelling on your own, as a couple, or maybe wishing to book all the rooms for that special party, the Castle will make you feel most welcome. Excellent links courses in the area and you have access to the Castle and its 560-acre country park with its woodlands, deer park and Victorian Vinery during opening hours.

Location: Just off the A719; A77, 4 miles; Ayr, 12 miles; Prestwick Airport, 16 miles

Attractions: Alloway - Home of Robert Burns; The Bachelors' Club; Souter Johnnie's Cottage; Championship Golf Courses

Get your personalised red carpet experience with our **personal insurance approach**

Step this way for our Made-to-measure Personal Insurance Solutions

Very often personal insurance policies are not designed to your individual requirements; with JLT we are proud to be different.

As far as we're concerned, providing personal risk management and insurance solutions for some of the UK's most high profile, successful, affluent individuals demands a truly tailored service.

That's why we have a reputation for treating our clients like VIP's and why our highly personalised service is renowned for its 'red carpet' approach.

As one of our VIP Clients you could benefit from our highly personalised approach with all your insurance needs packaged into one policy: Home, Car, Breakdown Travel, Boat, Property Let and Holiday Home.

Take the first step towards a 'red carpet' service and a made-to-measure Personal Insurance Solution now.

To see how you could benefit from our service contact us today on:

0800 230 0833

if calling from outside the UK
Tel: +44(0)121 626 7855

Proud to be the recommended Personal Lines Insurance provider of Condé Nast Johansens

Jardine Lloyd Thompson Personal Risks. A division of Jardine Lloyd Thompson UK Limited. Lloyd's Broker.
Authorised and Regulated by the Financial Services Authority. A member of the Jardine Lloyd Thompson Group.
Registered Office: 6 Friars, London EC3N 2PH. Registered in England No 00338645. VAT No. 244 2321 96

JARDINE LLOYD THOMPSON
Personal Risks

3872_08/08

Wales

Holyhead

Llandudno

Caernarfon

*Snowdonia
National Park*

Wrexham

Dolgellau

Aberystwyth

Fishguard

Carmarthen

Pembroke

Brecon

Swansea

Abergavenny

Brecon Beacons National Park

Cardiff

Cardiff

ENGLAND

Wales

For further information on Wales, please contact:

Wales Tourist Board
PO Box 113, Bangor, LL54 4WW
Tel: 08708 300 306
Web: www.visitwales.com

North Wales Tourism
77 Conway Road, Colwyn Bay, Conway LL29 7LN
Tel: +44 (0)1492 531731
Web: www.nwt.co.uk

Mid Wales Tourism
The Station, Machynlleth, Powys SY20 8TG
Tel: (Freephone) 0800 273747
Web: www.visitmidwales.co.uk

South West Wales Tourism Partnership
The Coach House, Aberglasney Gardens, Llangathen,
Carmarthenshire SA32 8QH
Tel: +44 (0)1558 669091
Web: www.swwtp.co.uk

or see **pages 206-208** for details of local historic houses, castles and gardens to visit during your stay.

For additional places to stay in Wales, turn to **pages 204-205** where a listing of our Recommended Hotels & Spas Guide can be found.

TY MAWR COUNTRY HOTEL

BRECHFA, CARMARTHENSHIRE SA32 7RA
Tel: 0845 365 2781 **International:** +44 (0)1267 202332
Web: www.johansens.com/tymawr **E-mail:** info@wales-country-hotel.co.uk

Our inspector loved: *The quality of the locally sourced produce that gives an excellent menu a unique sense of place.*

Price Guide:
single £70-£90
double £98-£118

Nestling in the Brechfa Forest within the heart of the lush, rolling Carmarthenshire countryside, Ty Mawr Country Hotel is the perfect "escape from it all" retreat. And despite its easy accessibility from the M4, this former 15th-century farmhouse retains an atmosphere of idyllic remoteness. Refreshingly simple in style and décor - preferring an understated but cosy approach - Ty Mawr is not without sophistication demonstrated by its meticulously sourced menu of local produce. The restaurant's menu includes the very best the region has to offer: Welsh black beef, Welsh lamb and locally caught fish and shellfish, as well as vegetables from its own kitchen garden. The 5 bedrooms are comfortable and well equipped with antique pine furniture.

Awards/Recognition: Condé Nast Johansens Most Excellent Value for Money Award 2007

Location: Carmarthen, 20-min drive; Cardiff, 75-min drive; M4, 30-min drive; Llandeilo, 20-min drive

Attractions: National Botanical Gardens of Wales; Aberglasney House and Gardens; Newton House and Dinefwr Park; Dylan Thomas' Boathouse at Laugharne

Tan-Y-Foel Country House

CAPEL GARMON, NR BETWS-Y-COED, CONWY LL26 0RE
Tel: 0845 365 2387 **International:** +44 (0)1690 710507 **Fax:** 01690 710681
Web: www.johansens.com/tanyfoel **E-mail:** enquiries@tyfhotel.co.uk

***Our inspector loved:** The calm serenity of this amazing location. Breathtaking views.*

Price Guide: (including dinner)
double (single occupancy) from £160
double from £248

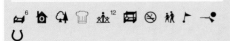

Awards/Recognition: 3 AA Rosettes 2008-2009; Condé Nast Johansens Most Excellent Country House Award 2006

Location: A470, 2 miles; A55, 16 miles; A5, 4 miles; Betws-y-Coed, 3.1 miles

Attractions: Snowdonia National Park; Narrow Gauge and Mountain Railways; Conwy Castle; Anglesey

An oasis of calm and tranquility, this Welsh stone house is a unique blend of country elegance and contemporary bijou. On arrival you're immediately struck by the serenity of this spectacular location, offering fabulous views of the lush Conwy Valley and rugged Snowdonia mountains. Bedrooms are strikingly furnished and individually styled - the attention to detail is impressive. Taking advantage of the rich and fertile surroundings, owner Janet, a member of "The Master Chefs of Great Britain", sources the best local produce - fresh fish, Welsh black beef and organically grown vegetables for her creative menus, and daughter Kelly complements both parents with her own skills. Deservedly a past Conde Nast Johansens and Welsh Tourish Board award winner and more recently the AA Guest Accommodation of The Year 2008-2009 For Wales,. A no smoking policy prevails.

PENTRE MAWR COUNTRY HOUSE

LLANDYRNOG, DENBIGH, NORTH WALES LL16 4LA
Tel: 0845 365 4051 **International:** +44 (0)1824 790732
Web: www.johansens.com/pentremawr **E-mail:** info@pentremawrcountryhouse.co.uk

Our inspector loved: *This uniqueness of this experience. Southern Africa meets North Wales in this fabulous country retreat.*

Price Guide: (per person)
£47.50-£75
dinner £30

This hotel is simply unique both in style and character. Nestled in the lush and rolling Denbighshire countryside, Pentre Mawr manages to be both classical and adventurous. A true Welsh country house with well appointed bedrooms, large cosy drawing room and both a formal dining room and conservatory overlooking the pool. The menu is a delightful adventure, with carefully sourced local meats and cheeses combining with exquisite homemade breads and ice creams. Influenced by a love of the outdoors and with their vast shared knowledge of the hospitality industry, owners Bre and Graham Carrington-Sykes have set up luxurious canvas safari lodges that bring guests closer to nature without ever compromising on comfort. All have stunning broad wooden verandas finished with hot tubs. It is rare these days to find something truly original, but you'll find something special here in the heart of beautiful North Wales.

Location: Ruthin, 7 miles; Chester, 29 miles; Manchester Airport, 59 miles; A55 Expressway, 6 miles

Attractions: Offa's Dyke Path National Trail; Snowdonia National park; Historic Chester

Porth Tocyn Country House Hotel

ABERSOCH, PWLLHELI, GWYNEDD LL53 7BU
Tel: 0845 365 2136 **International:** +44 (0)1758 713303 **Fax:** 01758 713538
Web: www.johansens.com/porthtocyn **E-mail:** bookings@porthtocyn.fsnet.co.uk

Our inspector loved: The quirky, lovable character of this absolute gem of a seaside retreat. A testament that style always wins out over fashion.

Price Guide: (including continental breakfast)
single £65–£90
double/twin £90–£170

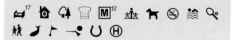

Awards/Recognition: Condé Nast Johansens Most Excellent Value Award 2008; 2 AA Rosettes 2008-2009

Location: A499, 3 miles; A479, 9 miles; Chester, 100 miles; Shrewsbury, 104 miles

Attractions: Snowdonia National Park; Portmeirion; Lloyd George Museum; Heritage Coast Line

From the moment you walk into Porth Tocyn you will feel relaxed, comfortable and at home which is why so many guests return again and again. Intimate sitting rooms overflow with country antiques and the softest of enveloping armchairs. The lawned gardens extend towards Cardigan Bay and the mountains of Snowdonia, plus you are close to the glorious beaches of the Lleyn Peninsula. Superbly located for some of the best walking and golf around, this delightful hotel has been owned by one family for 3 generations. Its continuity is to be treasured. Most bedrooms have sea views and some are ideal for families, and for that extra sense of privacy there is a gorgeous 2-bedroom self-contained cottage within the grounds. Memorable dinners are served in the award-winning restaurant and summer lunches on the terrace or poolside.

BAE ABERMAW

PANORAMA HILL, BARMOUTH, GWYNEDD LL42 1DQ
Tel: 0845 365 3023 **International:** +44 (0)1341 280550 **Fax:** 01341 280346
Web: www.johansens.com/baeabermaw **E-mail:** enquiries@baeabermaw.com

Our inspector loved: The chic and contemporary feel of this fabulously appointed property – standing just a pebbles throw from Barmouth estuary, harbour and beach. Deliciously creative restaurant menu.

Price Guide:
single £86–£110
double/twin £126–£158

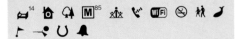

Awards/Recognition: 1 AA Rosette 2008-2009

Location: A496, 0.25 miles; A470, 8 miles; Birmingham Airport, 108 miles; Manchester Airport, 110 miles

Attractions: Mawddach Estuary; Snowdonia National Park; Royal St Davids Golf Course; Portmeirion

First time visitors to this hillside hotel overlooking the lovely Mawddach Estuary and backed by Snowdonia National Park are in for a surprise as it's owners David and Suzi Reeve have created a truly impressive retreat. The hotel offers the best of everything and sets itself above the label of "seaside hotel". Cool neutral colours - white, cream, flax, beige - stripped floorboards and streamlined sofas suggest a minimalist feel, whilst natural stone and wood is prominent in the excellent restaurant. The cuisine has some modern and exciting interpretations of classic British dishes with a French influence. Local produce is much in use, particularly Welsh black beef, marsh lamb and sole, plus a choice of vegetarian options. The hotel also serves Sunday lunch and classic afternoon teas. Bedrooms are stylishly decorated and feature deep baths and luxurious toiletries.

LLWYNDU FARMHOUSE

LLANABER, NR BARMOUTH, GWYNEDD LL42 1RR
Tel: 0845 365 3721 **International:** +44 (0)1341 280144 **Fax:** 01341 281236
Web: www.johansens.com/llwyndu **E-mail:** intouch@llwyndu-farmhouse.co.uk

Our inspector loved: Its dramatic coastal location. A very warm welcome.

Price Guide:
double £88–£98

Location: A 496, 0.25 miles; A 470, 12 miles; A487, 14 miles

Attractions: Harlech Castle; Little Railways; Portmeirion; Snowdonia National Park Scenery

If you are look for something historic and unspoilt this should be on your list. Overlooking a secluded bay this grade II listed farmhouse has been lovingly restored by owners Peter and Paula Thompson. Full of character and charm, many quirky original features have been kept including the inglenook fireplaces, stone staircase and even a sink fitted onto a door. Two of the three bedrooms have four posters and whilst all have up to date comforts they exude the personality of a welcoming 16th century home. In the evenings you can dine by candle light in the cosy and warm restaurant, perfect for an intimate evening or gathering of friends. Dishes are imaginatively prepared by Peter who uses fresh Welsh ingredients with flair. You shouldn't leave without trying a national favourite - Welsh rarebit with laver bread.

THE BELL AT SKENFRITH

SKENFRITH, MONMOUTHSHIRE NP7 8UH
Tel: 0845 365 2403 **International:** +44 (0)1600 750235 **Fax:** 01600 750525
Web: www.johansens.com/bellskenfrith **E-mail:** enquiries@skenfrith.co.uk

Our inspector loved: The beautiful Heckham Peckham bedroom!

Price Guide:
single £75–£120 (not available at weekends)
double/twin £110–£170
four-poster £195–£220

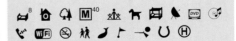

Awards/Recognition: 2 AA Rosettes 2008-2009; Condé Nast Johansens Most Excellent Traditional Inn 2007

Location: Off the B4521; A466, 3.4 miles; A49, 7.2 miles; Monmouth, 8 miles

Attractions: Llanthony Priory, Abergavenny; Tintern Abbey; Monmouth; Ross-on-Wye

A beautifully renovated 17th-century coaching inn surrounded by unspoilt Monmouthshire countryside and overlooking historic castle ruins. It's a dream come true if you're looking for a quiet retreat to escape to, with its roaring log fires, flagstone floors, stunning oak beams and deep sofas. Bedrooms are homely with pure wool Welsh blankets, finest linen and views of the Welsh hills or River Monnow. In the evenings you'll be happy to sip a glass of wine or real ale before tucking into an organically produced dinner created by the award winning kitchen. Wanting to grow many of their own ingredients this year they have successfully developed a Kitchen Garden which now helps flavour the imaginative menus.

THE CROWN AT WHITEBROOK

WHITEBROOK, MONMOUTHSHIRE NP25 4TX
Tel: 0845 365 2439 **International:** +44 (0)1600 860254 **Fax:** 01600 860607
Web: www.johansens.com/crownatwhitebrook **E-mail:** info@crownatwhitebrook.co.uk

Our inspector loved: *The fabulous food at this little gem, tucked away in a gorgeous spot.*

Price Guide:
single £90
double £100–£120

Awards/Recognition: 1 Star Michelin 2008; 2 AA Rosettes 2008-2009; AA Wine Award, Wales 2008

Location: A466, 2 miles; B4293, 3 miles; Monmouth, 5 miles

Attractions: Monmouth; Wye Valley; Tintern Abbey; Chepstow Racecourse

Visitors to The Crown tend to come away waxing lyrical about its romantic setting, great rooms and fabulous food; and we would have to agree! Dubbed Wales' first "restaurant with rooms" and with a growing reputation, Head Chef James Sommerin ensures the food takes centre stage, creating modern Michelin Star menus with classic French style. You won't feel overawed in the restaurant here however, as the atmosphere is unpretentious and intimate, with friendly, attentive service. All 8 bedrooms have been lovingly refurbished and look across rolling countryside. Impressive facilities such as flat-screen TVs, Internet and "comfort cool" heating systems are the icing on the cake. Outside the surrounding designated area of outstanding natural beauty is bound to entice you to explore. Wake up each morning to a sumptuous Welsh breakfast!

PENALLY ABBEY

PENALLY, TENBY, PEMBROKESHIRE SA70 7PY
Tel: 0845 365 2103 **International:** +44 (0)1834 843033 **Fax:** 01834 844714
Web: www.johansens.com/penallyabbey **E-mail:** penally.abbey@btinternet.com

Our inspector loved: *The air of relaxation. Gorgeous gothic door frames.*

Price Guide:
Single £140
Double/twin £150–£192
Suite £246

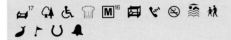

Awards/Recognition: 1 AA Rosette 2007–2008

Location: A4139, 0.5 mile; M4, 38 miles; Swansea, 48 miles; Bristol, 124 miles

Attractions: Caldey Island; Pembroke Castle; Tenby; National Botanical Gardens Aberglasney

Built on the site of an ancient monastery and perched majestically on high, Penally Abby Hotel offers breathtaking views of the Pembrokeshire Coastline. You're struck immediately by the gothic charm and grandness of this country house, in particular the thick stone walls, intricately decorated windows and antique furniture. The gardens, which sweep round the hotel on two sides, are charming and deceptively large. The candle lit restaurant's beautiful hand carved fireplace and crystal chandelier create an intimate, romantic air. The hotel comprises of three separate limestone buildings: St Deiniol's Lodge, the Coach House and Abbey House, all are of a high standard, but different in style and décor. The bedrooms in Abbey House are particularly stunning. A number of famous faces (see the discreet picture of Mick Jagger at reception) have passed though Penally's doors, and it's easy to see how they where charmed by this escape.

WOLFSCASTLE COUNTRY HOTEL & RESTAURANT

WOLF'S CASTLE, HAVERFORDWEST, PEMBROKESHIRE SA62 5LZ
Tel: 0845 365 2817 **International:** +44 (0)1437 741225 **Fax:** 01437 741383
Web: www.johansens.com/wolfscastle **E-mail:** enquiries@wolfscastle.com

Our inspector loved: *The genuine and heart warming welcome.*

Price Guide:
single £70-£90
double/twin £100-£135

Awards/Recognition: 1 AA Rosette 2008-2009

Location: Just off the A40; Fishguard, 7 miles; Haverfordwest, 7 miles; Cardiff, 100 miles

Attractions: Pembrokeshire Coast National Park; St Davids Cathedral and Bishops Palace; Skomer and Ramsey Island

Situated in the glorious Pembrokeshire countryside, this former vicarage has a very warm and welcoming atmosphere. Andrew Stirling the owner/manager of 29 years, is supported by a close network of staff, several of whom have been at Wolfscastle for many years. The charming non-smoking bedrooms, including 4 luxurious Executive Suites, combine elegant period décor with contemporary facilities. Try the excellent restaurant where you can taste delicious menus based on fresh local produce. After a day walking the coastal paths, enjoy the log fire in the bar. Both dining areas offer an à la carte and bar menu. The main function room is ideal for conferences and social events and opens onto a magnificent patio/garden area. For smaller parties choose the Barclay Suite, named after the retired pianist.

EGERTON GREY

PORTHKERRY, NR CARDIFF, VALE OF GLAMORGAN CF62 3BZ
Tel: 0845 365 3281 **International:** +44 (0)1446 711666 **Fax:** 01446 711690
Web: www.johansens.com/egertongrey **E-mail:** info@egertongrey.co.uk

Our inspector loved: A true traditional country house with many historic features and lots of antiques, set in a beautiful secluded valley.

Price Guide:
single £90–£120
double/twin £130–£150

Location: A4226, 2 miles; M4 jct 33, 11 miles; Cardiff, 12 miles

Attractions: Wales Millennium Centre and Cardiff Bay attractions/events,;Wales Millenium Stadium; St Fagans Museum; Glamorgan Heritage Coast

Originally a distinguished country house dating from the 19th century, this intimate luxury hotel offers a high level of comfort. Nestling in seven acres of wooded valley the hotel enjoys views of Porthkerry Park and the coast. All nine bedrooms have been beautifully restored and well decorated but are also equipped with modern features. The Edwardian drawing room features intricate plaster mouldings, cosy sofas, chandeliers and an open fireplace. The library may be used for private dining and overlooks the garden. Two bedrooms offer original Edwardian baths and some have four poster beds. The restaurant, formerly a billiard room, impresses with deep Cuban mahogany panelling and offers the best of Welsh cooking, traditional recipes and well presented dishes. Often used for royal visits, what makes Egerton Grey very special is the thoughtful and attentive customer service from the owners Richard Morgan Price and Huw Thomas and their staff.

Divine Bathing Products in 300ml Dispenser Sizes

Exclusively from Pacific Direct. Condé Nast Johansens Preferred Partner for 10 Years

PENHALIGON'S LONDON **Elemis** FLORIS LONDON NP NATURAL PRODUCTS Nina Campbell BRONNLEY Salvatore Ferragamo THE WHITE COMPANY LONDON

Create a luxurious and intimate environment with captivating retail toiletries in 300ml dispenser sizes. Standard sizes will fit your current bracket or the new chrome Tamper Proof (single or double) bracket.

Pacific Direct

Email: sales@pacificdirect.co.uk
Tel: +44 (0)1234 347 140

www.pacificdirect.co.uk

Hotels, Great Britain & Ireland

All the properties listed below can be found in our Recommended Hotels & Spas, Great Britain & Ireland 2009 Guide.
More information on our portfolio of guides can be found on page 13.

Channel Islands

The Atlantic Hotel and Ocean Restaurant	Channel Islands	0845 365 2395
The Club Hotel & Spa, Bohemia Restaurant	Channel Islands	0845 365 2419
Fermain Valley Hotel	Channel Islands	0845 365 3950
Longueville Manor	Channel Islands	0845 365 2038
The Old Government House Hotel	Channel Islands	0845 365 3927
The Royal Yacht Hotel	Channel Islands	0845 365 3873

England

The Bath Priory Hotel, Restaurant & Spa	B & NE Somerset	0845 365 2397
Dukes Hotel	B & NE Somerset	0845 365 3274
Homewood Park	B & NE Somerset	0845 365 1875
Hunstrete House	B & NE Somerset	0845 365 1906
The Park	B & NE Somerset	0845 365 2619
The Royal Crescent Hotel	B & NE Somerset	0845 365 2679
Luton Hoo Hotel, Golf & Spa	Bedfordshire	0845 365 3458

Cliveden & The Pavilion Spa	**Berkshire**	**0845 365 3236**
Donnington Valley Hotel and Spa	Berkshire	0845 365 3267
Fredrick's – Hotel Restaurant Spa	Berkshire	0845 365 1758
The French Horn	Berkshire	0845 365 2496
Harte & Garter Hotel & Spa	Berkshire	0845 365 3813
The Vineyard At Stockcross	Berkshire	0845 365 2716
Danesfield House Hotel and Spa	Buckinghamshire	0845 365 3261
Hartwell House Hotel, Restaurant & Spa	Buckinghamshire	0845 365 1824
Stoke Park	Buckinghamshire	0845 365 2374
Stoke Place	Buckinghamshire	0845 365 2843
Green Bough Hotel	Cheshire	0845 365 1796
Rowton Hall Hotel, Health Club & Spa	Cheshire	0845 365 2308
Budock Vean - The Hotel on the River	Cornwall	0845 365 3212
Fowey Hall & Aquae Sulis Retreat	Cornwall	0845 365 1754
The Garrack Hotel & Restaurant	Cornwall	0845 365 2497
Hell Bay	Cornwall	0845 365 1837
The Lugger Hotel	Cornwall	0845 365 2584
Meudon Hotel	Cornwall	0845 365 2059
The Nare Hotel	Cornwall	0845 365 2603
The Polurrian Hotel	Cornwall	0845 365 2849
St Michael's Hotel & Spa	Cornwall	0845 365 2358
Talland Bay Hotel	Cornwall	0845 365 2386
Armathwaite Hall Country House	Cumbria	0845 365 3617
Dale Head Hall Lakeside Hotel	Cumbria	0845 365 3258
Holbeck Ghyll Country House Hotel	Cumbria	0845 365 1872
The Inn on the Lake	Cumbria	0845 365 2548
Lakeside Hotel on Lake Windermere	Cumbria	0845 365 1978
Linthwaite House Hotel	Cumbria	0845 365 2031
The Lodore Falls Hotel	Cumbria	0845 365 2581
Lovelady Shield Country House Hotel	Cumbria	0845 365 2042

Netherwood Hotel	Cumbria	0845 365 2082
Rothay Manor	Cumbria	0845 365 2307
The Samling	Cumbria	0845 365 4035
Sharrow Bay Country House Hotel	Cumbria	0845 365 2346
Tufton Arms Hotel	Cumbria	0845 365 2766
Callow Hall	Derbyshire	0845 365 3221
Cathedral Quarter Hotel	Derbyshire	0845 365 3917
The Izaak Walton Hotel	Derbyshire	0845 365 2561
Riber Hall	Derbyshire	0845 365 2149
Risley Hall Hotel and Spa	Derbyshire	0845 365 3795
The Arundell Arms	Devon	0845 365 2394
Buckland-Tout-Saints	Devon	0845 365 3211
Combe House	Devon	0845 365 3241
Gidleigh Park	Devon	0845 365 1759
Hotel Riviera	Devon	0845 365 1904
Ilsington Country House Hotel	Devon	0845 365 1925
Langdon Court & Restaurant	Devon	0845 365 1985
Lewtrenchard Manor	Devon	0845 365 2018
Northcote Manor Country House Hotel	Devon	0845 365 2087
Orestone Manor	Devon	0845 365 2095
Soar Mill Cove Hotel	Devon	0845 365 2349
The Tides Reach Hotel	Devon	0845 365 2713
Watersmeet Hotel	Devon	0845 365 2793
The Woolacombe Bay Hotel	Devon	0845 365 2819
Moonfleet Manor	Dorset	0845 365 2074
The Priory Hotel	Dorset	0845 365 2651
Stock Hill Country House Hotel	Dorset	0845 365 2371
Summer Lodge Country House Hotel	Dorset	0845 365 2381
Seaham Hall Hotel & Serenity Spa	Durham	0845 365 4036
Maison Talbooth	Essex	0845 365 4612
Burleigh Court	Gloucestershire	0845 365 3217
Calcot Manor Hotel & Spa	Gloucestershire	0845 365 3220
Charingworth Manor	Gloucestershire	0845 365 3298
Corse Lawn House Hotel	Gloucestershire	0845 365 3249
The Greenway	Gloucestershire	0845 365 2514
Lower Slaughter Manor	Gloucestershire	0845 365 2047
Stonehouse Court Hotel	Gloucestershire	0845 365 2378
Washbourne Court	Gloucestershire	0845 365 2791
Thornbury Castle	S Gloucestershire	0845 365 2749
Chewton Glen	Hampshire	0845 365 3233
Chilworth Manor	Hampshire	0845 365 3234
Esseborne Manor	Hampshire	0845 365 3284
New Park Manor and Bath House Spa	Hampshire	0845 365 2084
Oakley Hall	Hampshire	0845 365 4628
Tylney Hall	Hampshire	0845 365 2782
Westover Hall	Hampshire	0845 365 3425
Castle House	Herefordshire	0845 365 3225
Down Hall Country House Hotel	Hertfordshire	0845 365 3271
Great Hallingbury Manor Hotel	Hertfordshire	0845 365 4629
St Michael's Manor	Hertfordshire	0845 365 2359
Eastwell Manor	Kent	0845 365 3279
The Gibbon Bridge Hotel	Lancashire	0845 365 2501
Stapleford Park Country House	Leicestershire	0845 365 2367
The George Of Stamford	Lincolnshire	0845 365 3295
41	London	0845 365 3601
51 Buckingham Gate	London	0845 365 2653
Beaufort House	London	0845 365 3029
The Capital Hotel & Restaurant	London	0845 365 2413
The Egerton House Hotel	London	0845 365 2483
Jumeirah Carlton Tower	London	0845 365 1932
Jumeirah Lowndes Hotel	London	0845 365 1934
Kensington House Hotel	London	0845 365 1936
The Mandeville Hotel	London	0845 365 2589
The Mayflower Hotel	London	0845 365 2591
Milestone Hotel	London	0845 365 2594
The New Linden Hotel	London	0845 365 3915
No.11 London	London	0845 365 3926
The Parkcity Hotel	London	0845 365 4031
Sofitel London St James	London	0845 365 2351

Hotels, Great Britain & Ireland

All the properties listed below can be found in our Recommended Hotels & Spas, Great Britain & Ireland 2009 Guide.
More information on our portfolio of guides can be found on page 13.

Twenty Nevern Square	London	0845 365 2769
Westbury Hotel	London	0845 365 4028
The Wyndham Grand London Chelsea Harbour	London	0845 365 3786
Congham Hall	Norfolk	0845 365 3244
The Hoste Arms	Norfolk	0845 365 2536
Rushton Hall Hotel & Spa	Northamptonshire	0845 365 2316
Whittlebury Hall	Northamptonshire	0845 365 2804
Hart's Hotel	Nottinghamshire	0845 365 3826
Lace Market Hotel	Nottinghamshire	0845 365 1973
Ye Olde Bell Hotel & Restaurant	Nottinghamshire	0845 365 3457
Le Manoir Aux Quat' Saisons	Oxfordshire	0845 365 2014
Old Bank Hotel	Oxfordshire	0845 365 4608
The Old Parsonage Hotel	Oxfordshire	0845 365 4607
The Springs Hotel & Golf Club	Oxfordshire	0845 365 2697
Hambleton Hall	Rutland	0845 365 1809
The Castle at Taunton	Somerset	0845 365 2415
Charlton House Hotel	Somerset	0845 365 2876
Mount Somerset Country House Hotel	Somerset	0845 365 2076
Ston Easton Park	Somerset	0845 365 2376
Hoar Cross Hall Spa Resort	Staffordshire	0845 365 1864
Bedford Lodge Hotel	Suffolk	0845 365 3785
The Dower House Apartments	Suffolk	0845 365 4037
Hintlesham Hall	Suffolk	0845 365 1857
The Ickworth Hotel & Aquae Sulis Retreat	Suffolk	0845 365 2539
Kesgrave Hall	Suffolk	0845 365 4613
Seckford Hall	Suffolk	0845 365 2319
Great Fosters	Surrey	0845 365 1793
Lythe Hill Hotel & Spa	Surrey	0845 365 2052
The Richmond Gate Hotel and Restaurant	Surrey	0845 365 2674
Ashdown Park Hotel and Country Club	East Sussex	0845 365 2896
Dale Hill	East Sussex	0845 365 3259
Deans Place Hotel	East Sussex	0845 365 3264
The Grand Hotel	East Sussex	0845 365 2504
Horsted Place Country House Hotel	East Sussex	0845 365 1893
Lansdowne Place, Boutique Hotel & Spa	East Sussex	0845 365 1987
Newick Park	East Sussex	0845 365 2085
Pelham House	East Sussex	0845 365 2098
The PowderMills	East Sussex	0845 365 2648
Royal York Hotel	East Sussex	0845 365 4619
Amberley Castle	West Sussex	0845 365 3612
Bailiffscourt Hotel & Spa	West Sussex	0845 365 3025
The Goodwood Park Hotel	West Sussex	0845 365 4632
Ockenden Manor	West Sussex	0845 365 2093
The Spread Eagle Hotel & Spa	West Sussex	0845 365 2695
The Vermont Hotel	Tyne & Wear	0845 365 2714
Ardencote Manor Hotel	Warwickshire	0845 365 3615
Mallory Court	Warwickshire	0845 365 2053
Nailcote Hall	Warwickshire	0845 365 2078
Wroxall Abbey Estate	Warwickshire	0845 365 2835
Bishopstrow House & Spa	Wiltshire	0845 365 3038
Howard's House	Wiltshire	0845 365 1905
Lucknam Park, Bath	Wiltshire	0845 365 2048
The Pear Tree At Purton	Wiltshire	0845 365 2635
Whatley Manor	Wiltshire	0845 365 2801
Woolley Grange	Wiltshire	0845 365 2831
Brockencote Hall	Worcestershire	0845 365 3204
Buckland Manor	Worcestershire	0845 365 3210
The Cottage in the Wood	Worcestershire	0845 365 2431
The Elms Hotel & Aquae Sulis Spa	Worcestershire	0845 365 2485
The Evesham Hotel	Worcestershire	0845 365 2487
Black Swan Hotel	North Yorkshire	0845 365 3792
Burythorpe House	North Yorkshire	0845 365 3709
The Devonshire Arms Country House	North Yorkshire	0845 365 2461
The Grange Hotel	North Yorkshire	0845 365 2507
Judges Country House Hotel	North Yorkshire	0845 365 1928
Middlethorpe Hall Hotel, Restaurant & Spa	North Yorkshire	0845 365 2061
The Pheasant	North Yorkshire	0845 365 2641
Simonstone Hall	North Yorkshire	0845 365 2348

Ireland

Mount Wolseley Hotel	Carlow	00 353 599 180100
Longueville House	Cork	00 353 22 47156
Harvey's Point	Donegal	00 353 74 972 2208
Fitzpatrick Castle Hotel	Dublin	00 353 1 230 5400
Abbeyglen Castle	Galway	00 353 95 21201
Ballynahinch Castle Hotel	Galway	00 353 953 1006
Cashel House	Galway	00 353 95 31001
The Brehon	Kerry	00 353 64 30700
Cahernane House Hotel	Kerry	00 353 64 31895
The Europe Hotel & Resort	Kerry	00 353 64 71300
Hotel Dunloe Castle	Kerry	00 353 64 44111
Park Hotel Kenmare & Sámas	Kerry	00 353 64 41200
Ashford Castle	Mayo	00 353 94 95 46003
The Harlequin	Mayo	00 353 949 286 200
Knockranny House Hotel & Spa	Mayo	00 353 98 28600
Mount Falcon Country House Hotel & Spa	Mayo	00 353 967 4472
Nuremore Hotel and Country Club	Monaghan	00 353 42 9661438
The Horse and Jockey Hotel	Tipperary	00 353 504 44192
Dunbrody Country House	Wexford	00 353 51 389 600
Kelly's Resort Hotel & Spa	Wexford	00 353 53 91 32114
Marlfield House	Wexford	00 353 53 94 21124
The Ritz-Carlton, Powerscourt	Wicklow	00 353 1 274 8888

N Ireland

Ten Square	Antrim	0845 365 4032

Scotland

Craigellachie Hotel of Speyside	Aberdeenshire	0845 365 3874
Ardanaiseig	Argyll & Bute	0845 365 3614
Stonefield Castle	Argyll & Bute	0845 365 4605
Auchen Castle	Dumfries & Galloway	0845 365 4015
Kirroughtree House	Dumfries & Galloway	0845 365 1962
Old Course Hotel Golf Resort & Spa	Fife	0845 365 4018
Mar Hall Hotel & Spa	Glasgow	0845 365 2054
Bunchrew House Hotel	Highland	0845 365 3214
Cuillin Hills Hotel	Highland	0845 365 3255
Inverlochy Castle	Highland	0845 365 1926
Rocpool Reserve	Highland	0845 365 2304
Royal Highland Hotel	Highland	0845 365 4621
The Torridon	Highland	0845 365 2037
Tulloch Castle Hotel	Highland	0845 365 4021
Dalhousie Castle and Spa	Midlothian	0845 365 3260
Glenskirlie House & Castle	Stirling	0845 365 4017

Wales

Miskin Manor Country House Hotel	Cardiff	0845 365 2069
Falcondale Mansion Hotel	Ceredigion	0845 365 3287
Ynyshir Hall	Ceredigion	0845 365 3426
Bodysgallen Hall & Spa	Conwy	0845 365 3039
St Tudno Hotel & Restaurant	Conwy	0845 365 2361
Palé Hall	Gwynedd	0845 365 2096
Penmaenuchaf Hall	Gwynedd	0845 365 2104
Celtic Manor Resort	Newport	0845 365 3297
Lamphey Court Hotel & Spa	Pembrokeshire	0845 365 1982
St Brides Spa Hotel	Pembrokeshire	0845 365 3925
Warpool Court Hotel	Pembrokeshire	0845 365 2786
The Lake Country House and Spa	Powys	0845 365 2571
Lake Vyrnwy Hotel	Powys	0845 365 1976
Llangoed Hall	Powys	0845 365 2034
Holm House	Vale of Glamorgan	0845 365 2869

Historic Houses, Castles & Gardens

We are pleased to feature over 150 places to visit during your stay at a Condé Nast Johansens Recommendation. More information about these attractions, including opening times and entry fees, can be found on www.johansens.com

England

Bath & North East Somerset

Cothay Manor and Gardens – Greenham, Wellington, Bath & North East Somerset TA21 0JR. Tel: 01823 672283
Great House Farm – Wells Rd, Theale, Wedmore, Bath & North East Somerset BS28 4SJ. Tel: 01934 713133
Maunsel House – North Newton, Nr Bridgwater, Bath & North East Somerset TA7 0BU. Tel: 01278 661076
Orchard Wyndham – Williton, Taunton, Bath & North East Somerset TA4 4HH. Tel: 01984 632309

Bedfordshire

Woburn Abbey – Woburn, Bedfordshire MK17 9WA. Tel: 01525 290666
Moggerhanger Park – Park Road, Moggerhanger, Bedfordshire MK44 3RW. Tel: 01767 641007

Berkshire

Eton College – The Visits Office, Windsor, Berkshire SL4 6DW. Tel: 01753 671177

Buckinghamshire

Nether Winchendon House – Nr Aylesbury, Buckinghamshire HP18 0DY. Tel: 01844 290199
Waddesdon Manor – Waddesdon, Nr Aylesbury, Buckinghamshire HP18 0JH. Tel: 01296 653211

Cambridgeshire

Mannington Hall – King's Parade, Cambridge, Cambridgeshire CB2 1ST. Tel: 01223 331212
The Manor – Hemingford Grey, Huntingdon, Cambridgeshire PE28 9BN. Tel: 01480 463134

Cheshire

Dorfold Hall – Nantwich, Cheshire CW5 8LD. Tel: 01270 625245
Holmston Hall Barn – Little Budworth, Tarporley, Cheshire CW6 9AW. Tel: 01829 760366
Ness Botanic Gardens – Ness, Neston, South Wirral, Cheshire CH64 4AY. Tel: 0151 353 0123
Rode Hall and Gardens – Scholar Green, Cheshire ST7 3QP. Tel: 01270 882961

Cornwall

Mount Edgcumbe House & Country Park – Cremyll, Cornwall PL10 1HZ. Tel: 01752 822236

Cumbria

Holker Hall and Gardens – Cark-in-Cartmel, nr Grange-over-Sands, Cumbria LA11 7PL. Tel: 01539 558328
Isel Hall – Cockermouth, Cumbria CA13 0QG. Tel: 01900 821778

Derbyshire

Haddon Hall – Bakewell, Derbyshire DE45 1LA. Tel: 01629 812855
Melbourne Hall & Gardens – Melbourne, Derbyshire DE73 8EN. Tel: 01332 862502
Renishaw Hall Gardens – Nr Sheffield, Derbyshire S21 3WB. Tel: 01246 432310

Devon

Anderton House – Goodleigh, Devon EX32 7NR. Tel: 01628 825920
Bowringsleigh – Kingsbridge, Devon TQ7 3LL. Tel: 01548 852014
Downes – Crediton, Devon EX17 3PL. Tel: 01392 439046

Dorset

Clavell Tower – Kimmeridge, Nr Wareham, Dorset. Tel: 01628 825920
Lulworth Castle & Park – East Lulworth, Wareham, Dorset BH20 5QS. Tel: 0845 450 1054

Mapperton Gardens – Mapperton, Beaminster, Dorset DT8 3NR. Tel: 01308 862645
Minterne Gardens – Minterne Magna, Nr Dorchester, Dorset DT2 7AU. Tel: 01300 341370
Moignes Court – Owermoigne, Dorchester, Dorset DT2 8HY. Tel: 01305 853300
Sherborne Castle – New Road, Sherborne, Dorset DT9 5NR. Tel: 01935 813182

Durham

Raby Castle – Staindrop, Darlington, Durham DL2 3AH. Tel: 01833 660 202

Essex

Hedingham Castle – Bayley Street, Castle Hedingham, Nr Halstead, Essex CO9 3DJ. Tel: 01787 460261
Ingatestone – Hall Lane, Ingatestone, Essex CM4 9NR. Tel: 01277 353010

Gloucestershire

Cheltenham Art Gallery & Museum – Clarence Street, Cheltenham, Gloucestershire GL50 3JT. Tel: 01242 237431
Hardwicke court – Nr Gloucester, Gloucestershire GL2 4RS. Tel: 01452 720212
Old Campden House – Chipping Campden, Gloucestershire GL55 6LR. Tel: 01628 825920
Owlpen Manor – Owlpen, Nr Uley, Gloucestershire GL11 5BZ. Tel: 01453 860261
Sezincote House & Garden – Moreton-in-Marsh, Gloucestershire GL56 9AW. Tel: 01386 700444
Sudeley castle – Winchcombe, Gloucestershire GL54 5JP. Tel: 01242 602308

Hampshire

Beaulieu – Beaulieu Enterprises Ltd, John Montagu Bldg, Hampshire SO42 7ZN. Tel: 01590 612345
Buckler's Hard – Beaulieu, Brockenhurst, Hampshire SO42 7XB. Tel: 01590 614641
Gilbert White's House & The Oates M – Selborne, Nr. Alton, Hampshire GU34 3JH. Tel: 01420 511275
Greywell Hill House – Greywell, Hook, Hampshire RG29 1DG

Hertfordshire

Ashridge – Berkhamsted, Hertfordshire HP4 1NS. Tel: 01442 841027
Hatfield House – Hatfield, Hertfordshire AL9 5NQ. Tel: 01707 287010
Knebworth House – Knebworth, Hertfordshire SG3 6PY. Tel: 01462 812661

Kent

Belmont House – Belmont Park, Throwley, Faversham, Kent ME13 0HH. Tel: 01795 890202
Bromley Museum – The Priory, Church Hill, Orpington, Kent BR6 0HH. Tel: 01689 873826
Finchcocks, Living Museum of Music – Goudhurst, Kent TN17 1HH. Tel: 01580 211702
The Grange – Ramsgate, Kent. Tel: 01628 825925
Groombridge Place Gardens & Enchanted Forest – Groombridge, Tunbridge Wells, Kent TN3 9QG. Tel: 01892 861444
Marle Place Gardens – Marle Place Road, Brenchley, Kent TN12 7HS. Tel: 01892 722304
Mount Ephraim Gardens – Hernhill, Nr Faversham, Kent ME13 9TX. Tel: 01227 751496
The New College of Cobham – Cobhambury Road, Cobham, Nr Gravesend, Kent DA12 3BG. Tel: 01474 812503
Rochester Castle – The Lodge, Rochester-upon-Medway, Medway, Kent ME1 1SX. Tel: 01634 402276
Upnor Castle – Upnor, Kent ME2 4XG. Tel: 01634 718742

Lancashire

Townhead House – Slaidburn, via Clitheroe, Lancashire BBY 3AG. Tel: 01772 421566

London

Burgh House – New End Square, Hampstead, London NW3 1LT. Tel: 020 7431 0144

Historic Houses, Castles & Gardens

We are pleased to feature over 150 places to visit during your stay at a Condé Nast Johansens Recommendation.
More information about these attractions, including opening times and entry fees, can be found on www.johansens.com

Pitzhanger Manor House – Walpole Park, Mattock Lane, Ealing,
London W5 5EQ. Tel: 020 8567 1227
Royal Institution Michael Faraday Museum – 21 Albemarle Street,
London W1S 4BS. Tel: 020 7409 2992
Spencer House – 27 St. Jame's Place, London SW1A 1NR. Tel: 020 7514 1958
St Paul's Cathedral – The Chapter House, St Paul's Churchyard,
London EC4M 8AD. Tel: 020 7246 8350
Syon park – Syon Park, Brentford, London TW8 8JF. Tel: 020 8560 0881

Norfolk

Mannington Estate – Mannington Hall, Norfolk NR11 7BB. Tel: 01263 584175
Mannington Hall – Saxthorpe, Norfolk NR11 7BB. Tel: 01263 584175
Stody Lodge Gardens – Melton Constable , Norfolk NR24 2EW.
Tel: 01263 860572
Walsingham Abbey Grounds – Little Walsingham, Norfolk NR22 6BP.
Tel: 01328 820259

Northamptonshire

Coton Manor Garden – Nr Guilsborough, Northamptonshire NN6 8RQ.
Tel: 01604 740219
Haddonstone Show Gardens – The Forge House, Church Lane, East Haddon,
Northamptonshire NN6 8DB. Tel: 01604 770711

Northumberland

Alnwick Castle – Alnwick, Northumberland NE66 1NQ. Tel: 01665 510777
Chipchase Castle & Gardens – Wark on Tyne, Hexham,
Northumberland NE48 3NT. Tel: 01434 230203

Oxfordshire

Kingston Bagpuize House – Abingdon, Oxfordshire OX13 5AX.
Tel: 01865 820259
Mapledurham House – Nr Reading, Oxfordshire RG4 7TR. Tel: 01189 723350
Stonor Park – Nr Henley-on-Thames, Oxfordshire RG9 6HF. Tel: 01491 638587
Sulgrave Manor – Manor Road, Sulgrave, Banbury, Oxfordshire OX17 2SD.
Tel: 01295 760205
Wallingford Castle Gardens – Castle Street, Wallingford, Oxfordshire OX10 0AL.
Tel: 01491 835373

Shropshire

Hawkstone Park & Follies – Weston-under-Redcastle, Nr Shrewsbury,
Shropshire SY4 5UY. Tel: 01939 200 611
Shrewsbury castle – Castle Street, Shrewsbury, Shropshire SY1 2AT.
Tel: 01743 358516
Shrewsbury Museum & Art Gallery – Barker Street, Shrewsbury,
Shropshire SY1 1QH. Tel: 01743 361196

Somerset

East Lambrook Manor Gardens – East Lambrook, South Petherton,
Somerset TA13 5HH
Hestercombe Gardens – Cheddon Fitzpaine, Taunton, Somerset TA2 8LG.
Tel: 01823 413923
Milton Lodge Gardens – Old Bristol Road, Wells, Somerset BA5 3AQ.
Tel: 01749 672168
Robin Hood's Hut – Halswell, Goathurst, Somerset. Tel: 01628 825925

Staffordshire

Izaak Walton's Cottage – Worston Lane, Shallowford, Staffordshire ST15 0PA.
Tel: 01785 760278
Stafford Castle & Visitor Centre – Newport Road, Stafford,
Staffordshire ST16 1DJ. Tel: 01785 257698
The Ancient High House – Greengate Street, Stafford, Staffordshire ST16 2JA.
Tel: 01785 619131
Whitmore Hall – Whitmore, Nr Newcastle-under-Lyme, Staffordshire ST5 5HW.
Tel: 01782 680478

Suffolk

Freston Tower – Near Ipswich, Suffolk. Tel: 01628 825920

Kentwell Hall – Long Melford, Sudbury, Suffolk CO10 9BA. Tel: 01787 310207
Newbourne Hall – Newbourne, Nr Woodbridge, Suffolk IP12 4NP.
Tel: 01473 736764
Otley Hall – Hall Lane, Otley, Nr Ipswich, Suffolk IP6 9PA. Tel: 01473 890264

Surrey

Claremont – Claremont Drive, Esher, Surrey KT10 9LY. Tel: 01372 473623
Guildford House Gallery – 155 High Street, Guildford, Surrey GU1 3AJ.
Tel: 01483 444740
Loseley Park – Guildford, Surrey GU3 1HS. Tel: 01483 304 440

East Sussex

Anne of Cleves House and Museum – 52 Southover High Street, Lewes,
East Sussex BN7 1JA. Tel: 01273 474610
Bentley Wildfowl & Motor Museum – Halland, Nr. Lewes, East Sussex BN8 5AF.
Tel: 01825 840573
Charleston – Firle, Nr Lewes, East Sussex BN8 6LL. Tel: 01323 811626
Gardens and Grounds of Herstmonceux Castle – Hailsham,
East Sussex BN27 1RN. Tel: 01323 833816
Michelham Priory – Upper Dicker, Hailsham, East Sussex BN27 3QS.
Tel: 01323 844224
Pashley Manor Gardens – Ticehurst, East Sussex TN5 7HE. Tel: 01580 200888
Wilmington Priory – Wilmington, Nr Eastbourne, East Sussex BN26 5SW.
Tel: 01628 825920

West Sussex

Borde Hill – Balcombe Road, Haywards Heath, West Sussex RH16 1XP.
Tel: 01444 450326
Denmans Garden – Denmans Lane, Fontwell, West Sussex BN18 0SU.
Tel: 01243 542808
Fishbourne Roman Palace – Salthill Road, Fishbourne, Chichester,
West Sussex PO19 3QR. Tel: 01243 785859
High Beeches Gardens – Handcross, West Sussex RH17 6HQ. Tel: 01444 400589
Leonardslee Lakes and Gardens – Lower Beeding, West Sussex RH13 6PP.
Tel: 01403 891212
Lewes Castle and Barbican House Museum – Barbican House, 169 High Street,
Lewes, West Sussex BN7 1YE. Tel: 01273 486290
Marlipins Museum – High Street, Shoreham-by-Sea, West Sussex BN43 5DA.
Tel: 01273 462994
Parham House & Gardens – Parham Park, Nr Pulborough,
West Sussex RH20 4HS. Tel: 01903 742021
The Priest's House – North Lane, West Hoathly, West Sussex RH19 4PP.
Tel: 01342 810479
West Dean Gardens – The Edward James Foundation, Estate Office West Dean,
Chichester, West Sussex PO18 0QZ. Tel: 01243 818210
Worthing Museum & Art Gallery – Chapel Road, Worthing,
West Sussex BN11 1HP. Tel: 01903 221448

Warwickshire

Arbury Hall – Nuneaton, Warwickshire CV10 7PT. Tel: 02476 382804
Shakespeare Houses – The Shakespeare Centre, Henley Street,
Stratford-upon-Avon, Warwickshire CV37 6QW. Tel: 01789 204016

West Midlands

The Barber Institute of Fine Arts – University of Birmingham, Edgbaston,
Birmingham, West Midlands B15 2TS. Tel: 0121 414 7333
The Birmingham Botanical Gardens & Glasshouses – Westbourne Road,
Edgbaston, Birmingham, West Midlands B15 3TR. Tel: 0121 454 1860

Worcestershire

Harvington Hall – Harvington, Kidderminster, Worcestershire DY10 4LR.
Tel: 01562 777846
Little Malvern Court – Nr Malvern, Worcestershire WR14 4JN.
Tel: 01684 892988

North Yorkshire

Allerton castle – Allerton Castle, Allerton Park, North Yorkshire HG5 0SE.
Tel: 01423 331123

Historic Houses, Castles & Gardens

We are pleased to feature over 150 places to visit during your stay at a Condé Nast Johansens Recommendation.
More information about these attractions, including opening times and entry fees, can be found on www.johansens.com

Duncombe Park – Helmsley, Ryedale, York, North Yorkshire YO62 5EB.
Tel: 01439 770213
Forbidden Corner – Tupgill Park Estate, Coverham, Nr Middleham,
North Yorkshire DL8 4TJ. Tel: 01969 640638
Fountains Abbey and Studley Royal Water Garden – Ripon , Nr Harrogate,
North Yorkshire HG4 3DY. Tel: 01765 608888
Newburgh Priory – Coxwold, York, North Yorkshire YO61 4AS.
Tel: 01347 868 435
Skipton Castle – Skipton, North Yorkshire BD23 1AW. Tel: 01756 792442

West Yorkshire

Bramham Park – The Estate Office, Bramham Park, Wetherby, West Yorkshire
LS23 6ND. Tel: 01937 846000
Ledston Hall – Hall Lane, Ledston, Castleford, West Yorkshire WF10 2BB.
Tel: 01423 523 423

N Ireland

Down

North Down Museum – Town Hall, Bangor, Down BT20 4BTN.
Tel: 02891 271200
Seaforde Gardens – Seaforde, Downpatrick, Down BT30 8PG.
Tel: 02844 811225

Ireland

Cork

Blarney Castle, House and Garden – Blarney, Cork. Tel: 00 353 21 4385252

Offaly

Birr Castle Demesne – Birr Co.Offaly, Offaly. Tel: 00 353 5791 20336

Wexford

Kilmokea Country Manor and Gardens – Great Island, Campile, Wexford.
Tel: 00 353 51 388109

Wicklow

Mount Usher Gardens – Ashford, Wicklow. Tel: 00 353 40440205

Scotland

Ayrshire

Kelburn Castle and Country Centre – Kelburn, Fairlie (Nr Largs),
Ayrshire KA29 0BE. Tel: 01475 568685

Borders

Floors Castle – Kelso, Borders TD5 7SF. Tel: 01573 223333

Dumfries & Galloway

Ardwell Gardens – Ardwell House, Ardwell, Stranraer,
Dumfries & Galloway DG9 9LY. Tel: 01776 860227
Castle Kennedy Gardens – The Estates Office, Rephad, Stranraer,
Dumfries & Galloway DG9 8BX. Tel: 01776 702024
Drumlanrig Castle, Gardens & Country Park – Thornhill, Dumfriesshire,
Dumfries & Galloway DG3 4AQ. Tel: 01848 331555
Gilnockie Tower – 7 Riverside Park, , Canonbie , Dumfriesshire,
Dumfries & Galloway DG14 0UG. Tel: 01387 371876
Glenmalloch Lodge – Newton Stewart, Dumfries & Galloway. Tel: 01628 825920

Highland

Armadale Castle Gardens & Museum of the Isles – Armadale, Sleat,
Isle of Skye, Highland IV45 8RS. Tel: 01471 844305

Inveraray castle – Cherry Park, Inveraray, Highland PA32 8XF. Tel: 01499 302203
Mount Stuart – Isle of Bute, Highland PA20 9LR. Tel: 01700 503877
Scone Palace – Scone, Perth, Perthshire, Highland PH2 6BD. Tel: 01738 552300

North Ayrshire

Auchinleck House – Ochiltree, North Ayrshire. Tel: 01628 825920

Scottish Borders

Bowhill House & Country Park – Bowhill, Selkirk, Scottish Borders TD7 5ET.
Tel: 01750 22204
Manderston – Duns, Berwickshire, Scottish Borders TD11 3PP.
Tel: 01361 883 450
Paxton House & Country Park – Paxton, Nr Berwick upon Tweed,
Scottish Borders TD15 1SZ. Tel: 01289 386291
Traquair House – Innerleithen, Peebles, Scottish Borders EH44 6PW.
Tel: 01896 830 323

West Lothian

Newliston – South Queensferry, West Lothian, West Lothian EH30 9SL.
Tel: 0131 333 3231
Hopetoun House – South Queensferry, West Lothian, West Lothian EH30 9SL.
Tel: 0131 331 2451

Wales

Conwy

Bodnant Garden – Tal Y Cafn, Conwy LL28 5RE. Tel: 01492 650460

Denbighshire

Dolbelydr – Trefnant, Denbighshire. Tel: 01628 825920
Flintshire

Golden Grove – Llanasa, Nr Holywell, Flintshire CH8 9NA. Tel: 01745 854452

Gwynedd

Oriel Plas Glyn-Y-Weddw Art Gallery – Llanbedrog, Pwllheli,
Gwynedd LL53 7TT. Tel: 01758 740 763
Plas Brondanw Gardens – Llanfrothen, Nr Penrhyndeudraeth,
Gwynedd LL48 6ET. Tel: 01743 241181
Portmeirion Village & Gardens – Portmeirion Village, Portmeirion,
Gwynedd LL48 6ET. Tel: (01766) 770228

Monmouthshire

Llanvihangel Court – Nr Abergavenny, Monmouthshire NP7 8DH.
Tel: 01873 890 217
Usk Castle – Castle House, Monmouth Rd, Usk, Monmouthshire NP15 1SD.
Tel: 01291 672563

Pembrokeshire

St David's Cathedral – The Deanery, The Close, St Davids,
Pembrokeshire SA62 6RH. Tel: 01437 720 199

France

Château de Chenonceau – 37150 Chenonceaux, Loire Valley 37150.
Tel: 00 33 2 47 23 90 07
Château de Goulaine – 44115 Haute-Goulaine, Pays-de-Loire Loire-Atlantique.
Tel: 00 33 2 40 54 91 42

The Netherlands

Het Loo Palace National Museum – Koninklijk Park 1, NL–7315 JA Apeldoorn,.
Tel: 00 31 55 577 2400

Hotels, Europe & The Mediterranean

All the properties listed below can be found in our Recommended Hotels & Spas, Europe & The Mediterranean 2009 Guide.
More information on our portfolio of guides can be found on page 13.

Andorra

Hotel Grau Roig	Grau Roig	+376 75 55 56
Sport Hotel Hermitage & Spa	Soldeu	+376 87 06 70

Austria

Palais Coburg Residenz	Vienna	+43 1 518 180

Belgium

Grand Hotel Damier	Kortrijk	+32 56 22 15 47
Hostellerie Trôs~Marets	Malmédy	+32 80 33 79 17
Hostellerie Ter Driezen	Turnhout	+32 14 41 87 57

Czech Republic

Aria Hotel Prague	Prague	+420 225 334 111
Bellagio Hotel Prague	Prague	+420 221 778 999
Golden Well Hotel	Prague	+420 257 011 213
MaMaison Pachtuv Palace	Prague	+420 234 705 111
MaMaison Riverside Hotel	Prague	+420 225 994 611
Hotel Nautilus	Tábor	+420 380 900 900

Estonia

Ammende Villa	Pärnu	+372 44 73 888

France

Domaine de la Grange de Condé	Alsace~Lorraine	+33 3 87 79 30 50
Hostellerie les Bas Rupts Le Chalet Fleuri	Alsace~Lorraine	+33 3 29 63 09 25
Hôtel à la Cour d'Alsace	Alsace~Lorraine	+33 3 88 95 07 00
Hôtel Les Têtes	Alsace~Lorraine	+33 3 89 24 43 43
Romantik Hôtel le Maréchal	Alsace~Lorraine	+33 3 89 41 60 32
Château de Bonaban	Brittany	+33 2 99 58 24 50
Domaine de Rochevilaine	Brittany	+33 2 97 41 61 61
Hôtel l'Agapa & Spa	Brittany	+33 2 96 49 01 10
Ti al Lannec	Brittany	+33 2 96 15 01 01
Château Hôtel André Ziltener	Burgundy - Franche~Comte	+33 3 80 62 41 62
Abbaye de la Bussière	Burgundy - Franche~Comté	+33 3 80 49 02 29
Château de Vault de Lugny	Burgundy - Franche~Comté	+33 3 86 34 07 86
Hostellerie des Monts de Vaux	Burgundy - Franche~Comté	+33 3 84 37 12 50
Château d'Etoges	Champagne~Ardennes	+33 3 26 59 30 08
Château de Fère	Champagne~Ardennes	+33 3 23 82 21 13
Domaine du Château de Barive	Champagne~Ardennes	+33 3 23 22 15 15
Château Eza	Côte d'Azur	+33 4 93 41 12 24
Hôtel La Pérouse	Côte d'Azur	+ 33 4 93 62 34 63
La Ferme d'Augustin	Côte d'Azur	+33 4 94 55 97 00
La Villa Mauresque	Côte d'Azur	+33 494 83 02 42
Le Bailli de Suffren	Côte d'Azur	+33 4 98 04 47 00
Le Moulin de Mougins	Côte d'Azur	+33 4 93 75 78 24
Château de la Barre	Loire Valley	+33 2 43 35 00 17
Château de Pray	Loire Valley	+33 247 57 23 67
Château de Verrières	Loire Valley	+33 2 41 38 05 15
Château des Briottières	Loire Valley	+33 2 41 42 00 02
Hostellerie des Hauts de Sainte~Maure	Loire Valley	+33 2 47 65 50 65
Le Manoir les Minimes	Loire Valley	+33 2 47 30 40 40

Le Manoir Saint Thomas	Loire Valley	+33 2 47 23 21 82
Château de Floure	Midi~Pyrénées	+33 4 68 79 11 29
Hôtel Lous Grits	Midi~Pyrénées	+33 5 62 28 37 10

Château la Chenevière	**Normandy**	**+33 2 31 51 25 25**
Château les Bruyères	Normandy	+33 2 31 32 22 45
Manoir de la Poterie, Spa "Les Thermes"	Normandy	+33 2 31 88 10 40
Manoir de Mathan	Normandy	+33 2 31 22 21 73
Carlton Hôtel	North - Picardy	+33 3 20 13 33 13
Château de Cocove	North - Picardy	+33 3 21 82 68 29
Château de Courcelles	North - Picardy	+33 3 23 74 13 53
Hospes Lancaster	Paris	+33 1 40 76 40 76
Hôtel Balzac	Paris	+33 1 44 35 18 00
Hôtel de Sers	Paris	+33 1 53 23 75 75
Hôtel des Académies et des Arts	Paris	+33 1 43 26 66 44
Hôtel du Petit Moulin	Paris	+33 1 42 74 10 10
Hôtel Duc de Saint~Simon	Paris	+33 1 44 39 20 20
Hôtel Duret	Paris	+33 1 45 00 42 60
Hôtel le Tourville	Paris	+33 1 47 05 62 62
Hôtel San Régis	Paris	+33 1 44 95 16 16
La Trémoille	Paris	+33 1 56 52 14 00
Le Bellechasse	Paris	+33 1 45 50 22 31
Le Sainte~Beuve	Paris	+33 1 45 48 20 07
Château de l'Yeuse	Poitou~Charentes	+33 5 45 36 82 60
Hôtel "Résidence de France"	Poitou~Charentes	+33 5 46 28 06 00
Château de Massillan	Provence	+33 4 90 40 64 51
Château de Montcaud	Provence	+33 4 66 89 60 60
Domaine le Hameau des Baux	Provence	+33 4 90 54 10 30
L'Estelle en Camargue	Provence	+33 4 90 97 89 01
La Bastide Rose	Provence	+ 33 4 90 02 14 33
Le Mas de la Rose	Provence	+33 4 90 73 08 91
Le Spinaker	Provence	+33 4 66 53 36 37
Manoir de la Roseraie	Provence	+33 4 75 46 58 15
Chalet Hôtel Kaya	Rhône~Alpes	+33 4 79 41 42 00
Chalet Hôtel La Marmotte	Rhône~Alpes	+33 4 50 75 80 33
Château de Bagnols	Rhône~Alpes	+33 4 74 71 40 00
Château de Coudrée	Rhône~Alpes	+33 4 50 72 62 33
Hôtel Helvie	Rhône~Alpes	+33 4 75 94 65 85
Le Beau Rivage	Rhône~Alpes	+33 4 74 56 82 82
Le Fer à Cheval	Rhône~Alpes	+33 4 50 21 30 39
Château de Sanse	South West	+33 5 57 56 41 10
Château les Merles	South West	+33 5 53 63 13 42
Hôtel du Palais	South West	+33 5 59 41 64 00
Le Relais du Château Franc Mayne	South West	+33 5 57 24 62 61

Great Britain

Ashdown Park Hotel	England	+44 1342 824 988
The French Horn	England	+44 1189 692 204
The Grand Hotel	England	+44 1323 412345
Jumeirah Carlton Tower	England	+44 20 7235 1234
Jumeirah Lowndes Hotel	England	+44 20 7823 1234

Hotels, Europe & The Mediterranean

All the properties listed below can be found in our Recommended Hotels & Spas, Europe & The Mediterranean 2009 Guide. More information on our portfolio of guides can be found on page 13.

Luton Hoo Hotel, Golf & Spa	England	+44 1582 734437
The Mayflower Hotel	England	+44 20 7370 0991
The New Linden Hotel	England	+44 20 7221 4321
Twenty Nevern Square	England	+44 20 7565 9555
Tylney Hall	England	+44 1256 764881

Greece

O&B Athens Boutique Hotel	Athens	+30 21033 12940
Argentikon Luxury Suites	Chios	+30 22710 33111
OUT OF THE BLUE,		
Capsis Elite Resort	Crete	+30 21061 49563
Paradise Island Villas	Crete	+30 28970 22893

Pleiades Luxurious Villas	**Crete**	**+30 28410 90450**
St Nicolas Bay Resort Hotel & Villas	Crete	+30 28410 25041
Villas Hotel Domes of Elounda	Crete	+30 28410 41924
Pavezzo Country Retreat	Lefkada	+30 26450 71782
Apanema	Mykonos	+30 22890 28590
Mykonos Theoxenia Hotel	Mykonos	+30 22890 22230
Tharroe of Mykonos	Mykonos	+30 22890 27370
Petra Hotel	Patmos Island	+30 22470 34020
Canaves Oia	Santorini	+30 22860 71453
Ikies Traditional Houses	Santorini	+30 22860 71311

Hungary

Allegro Hotel - Tihany Centrum	Tihany - Lake Balaton	+36 87 448 456

Italy

Furore Inn Resort & Spa	Campania	+39 089 830 4711
Hotel Villa Maria	Campania	+39 089 857255
Hotel Posta (Historical Residence)	Emilia Romagna	+39 05 22 43 29 44
Hotel Villa Roncuzzi	Emilia Romagna	+39 0544 534776
Palazzo Dalla Rosa Prati	Emilia Romagna	+39 0521 386 429
Torre di San Martino -		
Historical Residence	Emilia Romagna	+39 0523 972002
Buonanotte Garibaldi	Lazio	+39 06 58 330 733
Casa Howard Guest Houses -		
Rome & Florence	Lazio	+39 06 69924555
Casa Montani -		
Luxury Town House	Lazio	+39 06 3260 0421
Hotel dei Borgognoni	Lazio	+39 06 6994 1505
Hotel dei Consoli	Lazio	+39 0668 892 972
Hotel Fenix	Lazio	+39 06 8540 741
La Posta Vecchia	Lazio	+39 0699 49501
Villa La Cerretana	Lazio	+39 0761 1762565
Villa Spalletti Trivelli	Lazio	+39 06 48907934

Abbadia San Giorgio -		
Historical Residence	Liguria	+39 0185 491119
Grand Hotel Diana Majestic	Liguria	+39 0183 402 727
Grand Hotel Miramare	Liguria	+39 0185 287013
Hotel Punta Est	Liguria	+39 019 600611
Hotel San Giorgio - Portofino House	Liguria	+39 0185 26991
Hotel Vis à Vis	Liguria	+39 0185 42661
Bagni di Bormio Spa Resort	Lombardy	+39 0342 910131
Grand Hotel Gardone Riviera	Lombardy	+39 0365 20261
Hotel Bellerive	Lombardy	+39 0365 520 410
Hotel de la Ville	Lombardy	+39 039 39421
Hotel Parco San Marco		
Beach Resort, Golf & SPA	Lombardy	+39 0344 629111
L'Albereta	Lombardy	+39 030 7760 550
Petit Palais Maison de Charme	Lombardy	+39 02 584 891
THE PLACE -		
Luxury serviced apartments	Lombardy	+39 02 76026633
Albergo L'Ostelliere	Piemonte	+39 0143 607 801
Cascina Langa	Piemonte	+39 0173 630289
Foresteria dei Poderi Einaudi	Piemonte	+39 0173 70414
Hotel Cristallo	Piemonte	+39 0163 922 822
Hotel Pironi	Piemonte	+39 0323 70624
Hotel Principi di Piemonte	Piemonte	+39 011 55151
Relais San Maurizio	Piemonte	+39 0141 841900
Villa dal Pozzo d'Annone	Piemonte	+39 0322 7255
Villa e Palazzo Aminta	Piemonte	+39 0323 933 818
Borgobianco Resort & SPA	Puglia	+39 080 8870001
Country House Cefalicchio	Puglia	+39 0883 642123
Hotel Titano	San Marino Republic	+378 0549 991007
Grand Hotel in Porto Cervo	Sardinia	+39 0789 91533
Petra Segreta Resort & SPA	Sardinia	+39 0789 183 1365
Villa Las Tronas	Sardinia	+39 079 981 818
Baia Taormina		
Grand Palace Hotels & Spa	Sicily	+39 0942 756292
Grand Hotel Arciduca	Sicily	+39 090 9812136
Grand Hotel Atlantis Bay	Sicily	+39 0942 618011
Grand Hotel Mazzarò Sea Palace	Sicily	+39 0942 612111
Hotel Signum	Sicily	+39 090 9844222
Hotel Villa Carlotta	Sicily	+39 0942 626058
Hotel Villa Ducale	Sicily	+39 0942 28153
Locanda Don Serafino	Sicily	+39 0932 220065
Palazzo Failla Hotel	Sicily	+39 0932 941059
Poggio del Sole Resort	Sicily	+39 0932 666 452
Alpenpalace Deluxe Hotel		
& Spa Resort	Trentino - Alto Adige / Dolomites	+39 0474 670230
Castel Fragsburg	Trentino - Alto Adige / Dolomites	+39 0473 244071
Du Lac et Du Parc Grand Resort	Trentino - Alto Adige / Dolomites	+39 0464 566600
GranPanorama Hotel Miramonti	Trentino - Alto Adige / Dolomites	+39 0473 27 93 35
Hotel Gardena Grödnerhof	Trentino - Alto Adige / Dolomites	+39 0471 796 315
Romantik Hotel Cappella	Trentino - Alto Adige / Dolomites	+39 0471 836183
Romantik Hotel		
Post Cavallino Bianco	Trentino - Alto Adige / Dolomites	+39 0471 613113
Albergo Pietrasanta -		
Palazzo Barsanti Bonetti	Tuscany	+39 0584 793 727
Borgo La Bagnaia Resort,		
Spa and Events Venue	Tuscany	+39 0577 813000
Borgo San Felice	Tuscany	+39 0577 3964
Casa Howard Guest Houses -		
Rome and Florence	Tuscany	+39 066 992 4555
Castello Banfi - Il Borgo	Tuscany	+39 0577 877 700
Country House Casa Cornacchi	Tuscany	+39 055 998229
Hotel Byron	Tuscany	+39 0584 787 052

Hotels, Europe & The Mediterranean

All the properties listed below can be found in our Recommended Hotels & Spas, Europe & The Mediterranean 2009 Guide. More information on our portfolio of guides can be found on page 13.

Hotel Plaza e de Russie ....Tuscany ....+39 0584 44449
Hotel Villa Ottone ....Tuscany ....+39 0565 933 042
Il Pellicano Hotel ....Tuscany ....+39 0564 858111
L'Andana ....Tuscany ....+39 0564 944 800
Lucignanello Bandini
    (Borgo Storico) ....Tuscany ....+39 0577 803 068
Marignolle Relais & Charme ....Tuscany ....+39 055 228 6910
Monsignor Della Casa
    Country Resort ....Tuscany ....+39 055 840 821
Palazzo Magnani Feroni -
    all-suites florence ....Tuscany ....+39 055 2399544
Petriolo Spa & Resort ....Tuscany ....+39 0564 9091
Relais la Suvera (Dimora Storica) ...Tuscany ....+39 0577 960 300
Relais Piazza Signoria ....Tuscany ....+39 055 3987239
Relais Poggio ai Santi ....Tuscany ....+39 0565 798032
Relais Santa Croce ....Tuscany ....+39 055 234 2230
Relais Villa Antea ....Tuscany ....+39 055 484106
Relais Villa Belpoggio
    (Historical House) ....Tuscany ....+39 055 9694411
Residenza del Moro ....Tuscany ....+39 055 290884
Tombolo Talasso Resort ....Tuscany ....+39 0565 74530
Villa le Piazzole ....Tuscany ....+39 055 223520
Villa Poggiano ....Tuscany ....+39 0578 758292
Abbazia San Faustino -
    Luxury Country House ....Umbria ....+39 339 720 1717
Castello di Petroia ....Umbria ....+39 075 92 02 87
I Casali di Monticchio ....Umbria ....+39 0763 62 83 65
L'Antico Forziere ....Umbria ....+39 075 972 4314
Le Torri di Bagnara (Mediaeval
    Historical Residences) ....Umbria ....+39 075 579 2001
Romantik Hotel le Silve
    di Armenzano ....Umbria ....+39 075 801 9000
Hotel Jolanda Sport ....Valle d'Aosta ....+39 0125 366 140
Mont Blanc Hotel Village ....Valle d'Aosta ....+39 0165 864 111
Albergo Quattro Fontane -
    Residenza d'Epoca ....Veneto ....+39 041 526 0227
Ca Maria Adele ....Veneto ....+39 041 52 03 078
Ca' Nigra Lagoon Resort ....Veneto ....+39 041 2750047
Ca' Sagredo Hotel ....Veneto ....+39 041 2413111
Charming House DD724 ....Veneto ....+39 041 277 0262
Color Hotel ....Veneto ....+39 045 621 0857
Hotel Flora.......................................Veneto ....+39 041 52 05 844
Hotel Giorgione ....Veneto ....+39 041 522 5810
Hotel Sant' Elena Venezia ....Veneto ....+39 041 27 17 811
Locanda San Verolo ....Veneto ....+39 045 720 09 30
Locanda San Vigilio..........................Veneto ....+39 045 725 66 88
Londra Palace ....Veneto ....+39 041 5200533
Methis Hotel ....Veneto ....+39 049 872 5555
Novecento Boutique Hotel ....Veneto ....+39 041 24 13 765
Park Hotel Brasilia ....Veneto ....+39 0421 380851
Relais Duca di Dolle.........................Veneto ....+39 0438 975 809
Relais la Magioca ....Veneto ....+39 045 600 0167

Latvia

TB Palace Hotel & Spa ....Jürmala..........................+371 6 7147094
Hotel Bergs......................................Riga ....+371 6777 0900

Luxembourg

Hotel Saint~Nicolas & Spa ....Remich ....+35 226 663

The Netherlands

Ambassade Hotel.............................Amsterdam ....+31 20 5550 222
Auberge de Campveerse Toren ......Veere ....+31 0118 501 291

Poland

MaMaison Le Régina Hotel ....Warsaw ....+48 22531 6000

Portugal

Convento de São Paulo.....................Alentejo ....+351 266 989 160
Convento do Espinheiro,
    Heritage Hotel & Spa ....Alentejo ....+351 266 788 200

Quinta da Malhadinha Nova ....Alentejo ....+351 284 965 432
As Cascatas Hotel Apartamentos ......Algarve ....+351 289 304 900
Casa da Moura..................................Algarve ....+351 282 770730
Hilton Vilamoura As Cascatas
    Golf Resort & Spa........................Algarve ....+351 289 304 000
Hotel Quinta do Lago........................Algarve ....+351 289 350 350
Quinta Jacintina -
    my secret garden hotel ....Algarve ....+351 289 350 090
Ria Park Hotel & Spa ....Algarve ....+351 289 359 800
Tivoli Marina Vilamoura ....Algarve ....+351 289 303 303
As Janelas Verdes.............................Lisbon & Tagus Valley ......+351 21 39 68 143
Heritage Av Liberdade......................Lisbon & Tagus Valley.......+351 213 404 040
Hotel Albatroz ....Lisbon & Tagus Valley.......+351 21 484 73 80
Hotel Britania ....Lisbon & Tagus Valley.......+351 21 31 55 016
Hotel Cascais Mirage ....Lisbon & Tagus Valley.......+351 210 060 600
Lisboa Plaza Hotel ....Lisbon & Tagus Valley.......+351 213 218 218
Palacio Estoril, Hotel & Golf ....Lisbon & Tagus Valley.......+351 21 464 80 00
Solar do Castelo ....Lisbon & Tagus Valley.......+351 218 806 050
Tivoli Lisboa ....Lisbon & Tagus Valley......+ 351 21 319 89 00
The Westin CampoReal
    Golf Resort & Spa........................Lisbon & Tagus Valley.......+351 261 960 900
CS Madeira Atlantic
    Resort & Sea Spa ....Madeira ....+351 291 717 600
Quinta da Bela Vista ....Madeira ....+351 291 706 400
Quinta das Vistas Palace Gardens......Madeira ....+351 291 750 000
Quinta do Monte ....Madeira ....+351 291 780 100
CS Vintage House Hotel ....Oporto & Northern
                                                        Portugal.........................+351 254 730 230
Quinta de San José ....Oporto & Northern
                                                        Portugal.........................+351 254 422017

Russia

MaMaison Pokrovka Suite Hotel ....Moscow ....+7 495 229 5757

Slovenia

Hotel Golf Bled ....Bled ....+386 4579 1700

Spain

Barceló la Bobadilla.........................Andalucía ....+34 958 32 18 61

Hotels, Europe & The Mediterranean

All the properties listed below can be found in our Recommended Hotels & Spas, Europe & The Mediterranean 2009 Guide. More information on our portfolio of guides can be found on page 13.

Casa de los Bates	Andalucía	+34 958 349 495
Casa No 7	Andalucía	+34 954 221 581
Casa Romana Hotel Boutique	Andalucía	+34 954 915 170
Casa Viña de Alcantara	Andalucía	+34 956 393 010
El Ladrón de Agua	Andalucía	+34 958 21 50 40
El Molino de Santillán	Andalucía	+34 952 40 09 49
Fairplay Golf Hotel & Spa	Andalucía	+34 956 429100
Gran Hotel Elba Estepona & Thalasso Spa	Andalucía	+34 952 809 200
Hacienda Benazuza el Bulli Hotel	Andalucía	+34 955 70 33 44
Hacienda La Boticaria	Andalucía	+34 955 69 88 20
Hacienda La Colorá	Andalucía	+34 957 336077
Hospes las Casas del Rey de Baeza	Andalucía	+34 954 561 496
Hospes Palacio de los Patos	Andalucía	+34 958 535 790
Hospes Palacio del Bailío	Andalucía	+34 957 498 993
Hotel Casa Morisca	Andalucía	+34 958 221 100
Hotel Incosol	Andalucía	+34 952 860909
Hotel La Fuente del Sol	Andalucía	+34 951 70 07 70
Hotel Palacio de Los Granados	Andalucía	+34 955 905 344
Hotel Palacio de Santa Inés	Andalucía	+34 958 22 23 62
Mikasa Suites & Spa	Andalucía	+34 950 138 073
Palacio de los Navas	Andalucía	+34 958 21 57 60
Posada de Palacio	Andalucía	+34 956 36 4840
Santa Isabel la Real	Andalucía	+34 958 294 658
V...	Andalucía	+34 956 451 757
Hotel La Cepada	Asturias	+34 985 84 94 45
Palacio de Cutre	Asturias	+34 985 70 80 72
Atzaró Agroturismo	Balearic Islands	+34 971 33 88 38
Blau Porto Petro Beach Resort & Spa	Balearic Islands	+34 971 648 282
Can Lluc	Balearic Islands	+34 971 198 673
Cas Gasi	Balearic Islands	+34 971 197 700
Hospes Maricel	Balearic Islands	+34 971 707 744
Hotel Aimia	Balearic Islands	+34 971 631 200
Hotel Cala Sant Vicenç	Balearic Islands	+34 971 53 02 50
Hotel La Moraleja	Balearic Islands	+34 971 534 010
Hotel Mirador de Dalt Vila	Balearic Islands	+34 971 30 30 45
Hotel Tres	Balearic Islands	+34 971 717 333
Palacio Ca Sa Galesa	Balearic Islands	+34 971 715 400

Read's Hotel & Vespasian Spa	**Balearic Islands**	**+34 971 14 02 61**
Son Brull Hotel & Spa	Balearic Islands	+34 971 53 53 53
Son Granot	Balearic Islands	+34 971 355 555
Valldemossa Hotel & Restaurant	Balearic Islands	+34 971 61 26 26
Abama	Canary Islands	+34 902 105 600
Gran Melía Salinas	Canary Islands	+34 928 59 00 40
Princesa Yaiza Suite Hotel Resort	Canary Islands	+34 928 519 222
La Casona de Cosgaya	Cantabria	+34 942 733 077
Posada Los Nogales	Cantabria	+34 942 589 222
Hotel Rector	Castilla y León	+34 923 21 84 82
Posada de la Casa del Abad de Ampudia	Castilla y León	+34 979 768 008
Finca Canturias	Castilla~La Mancha	+34 925 59 41 08
Hotel Palacio de la Serna	Castilla~La Mancha	+34 926 84 2208
Valdepalacios Hotel	Castilla~La Mancha	+34 925 457 534

Abac Barcelona	Cataluña	+34 93 319 6600
Can Bonastre Wine Resort	Cataluña	+34 93 772 87 67
Dolce Sitges Hotel	Cataluña	+34 938 109 000
Hospes Villa Paulita	Cataluña	+34 972 884 662
Hotel Barcelona Catedral	Cataluña	+34 93 304 22 55
Hotel Casa Fuster	Cataluña	+34 93 255 30 00
Hotel Claris	Cataluña	+34 93 487 62 62
Hotel Cram	Cataluña	+34 93 216 77 00
Hotel Duquesa de Cardona	Cataluña	+34 93 268 90 90
Hotel Gran Derby	Cataluña	+34 93 445 2544
Hotel Granados 83	Cataluña	+34 93 492 96 70
Hotel Omm	Cataluña	+34 93 445 40 00
Hotel Rigat Park & Spa Beach Hotel	Cataluña	+34 972 36 52 00
Hotel Santa Marta	Cataluña	+34 972 364 904
Mas Passamaner	Cataluña	+34 977 766 333
Romantic Villa - Hotel Vistabella	Cataluña	+34 972 25 62 00
San Sebastian Playa Hotel	Cataluña	+34 93 894 86 76
Casa Palacio Conde de la Corte	Extremadura	+34 924 563 311
Gran Hotel Atlantis Bahía Real	Fuerteventura	+34 928 53 64 44
Augusta Spa Resort	Galicia	+34 986 72 78 78
AC Hotel Santo Mauro	Madrid	+34 91 319 69 00
Antiguo Convento	Madrid	+34 91 632 22 20
Gran Meliá Fénix	Madrid	+34 91 431 67 00
Hospes Madrid	Madrid	+34 914 322 911
Hotel Orfila	Madrid	+34 91 702 77 70
Hotel Urban	Madrid	+34 91 787 77 70
Hotel Villa Real	Madrid	+34 914 20 37 67
Hotel Etxegana	País Vasco	+34 946 338 448
Hotel Pampinot	País Vasco	+34 943 640 600
Hospes Amérigo	Valencia	+34 965 14 65 70
Hospes Palau de la Mar	Valencia	+34 96 316 2884
Hotel Ferrero	Valencia	+34 962 35 51 75
Hotel Mont Sant	Valencia	+34 962 27 50 81
Hotel Neptuno	Valencia	+34 963 567 777
Hotel Sidi Saler & Spa	Valencia	+34 961 61 04 11
Hotel Sidi San Juan & Spa	Valencia	+34 96 516 13 00
Hotel Termas Marinas el Palasiet	Valencia	+34 964 300 250
La Madrugada	Valencia	+34 965 733 156
Mas de Canicattí	Valencia	+34 96 165 05 34
Villa Marisol	Valencia	+34 96 587 57 00

Switzerland

Park Hotel Weggis	Weggis	+41 41 392 05 05
Hotel Caprice	Wengen	+41 33 856 06 06

Turkey

The Marmara Antalya	Antalya	+90 242 249 36 00
Tuvana Residence	Antalya	+90 242 247 60 15
Sungate Port Royal	Antalya - Kemer	+90 242 824 00 00
Ada Hotel	Bodrum	+90 252 377 59 15
Divan Bodrum Palmira	Bodrum	+90 252 377 5601
Kempinski Hotel Barbaros Bay	Bodrum	+90 252 311 0303
The Marmara Bodrum	Bodrum	+90 252 313 8130
Oyster Residence	Fethiye - Ölüdeniz	+90 252 617 0765
A'jia Hotel	Istanbul	+90 216 413 9300
Bosphorus Palace Hotel	Istanbul	+90 216 422 00 03
The Marmara Istanbul	Istanbul	+90 212 251 4696
The Marmara Pera	Istanbul	+90 212 251 4646
Sirkeci Konak	Istanbul	+90 212 528 4344
Sumahan On The Water	Istanbul	+90 216 422 8000
Villa Mahal	Kalkan	+90 242 844 32 68
Golden Key Bördübet	Marmaris	+90 252 436 92 30
Richmond Nua Wellness - Spa	Sapanca - Sakarya	+90 264 582 2100
Cappadocia Cave Resorts & Spa	Uchisar-Cappadocia	+90 384 219 3194
Sacred House	Ürgüp	+90 384 341 7102

Hotels - The Americas

Properties listed below can be found in our Recommended Hotels, Inns, Resorts & Spas - The Americas, Atlantic, Caribbean & Pacific 2009 Guide. More information on our portfolio of guides can be found on page 13

Recommendations in Canada

CANADA - BRITISH COLUMBIA (VANCOUVER)

Wedgewood Hotel & Spa

845 Hornby Street, Vancouver,
British Columbia V6Z 1V1

Tel: +1 604 689 7777
Web: www.johansens.com/wedgewoodbc

CANADA - BRITISH COLUMBIA (MALAHAT)

The Aerie Resort & Spa

P.O. Box 108, 600 Ebedora Lane, Malahat, Victoria,
British Columbia V0R 2L0

Tel: +1 250 743 7115
Web: www.johansens.com/aeriebc

CANADA - BRITISH COLUMBIA (VICTORIA)

Brentwood Bay Lodge & Spa

849 Verdier Avenue, Victoria,
British Columbia V8M 1C5

Tel: +1 250 544 2079
Web: www.johansens.com/brentwood

CANADA - BRITISH COLUMBIA (SALT SPRING ISLAND)

Hastings House Country Estate

160 Upper Ganges Road, Salt Spring Island,
British Columbia V8K 2S2

Tel: +1 250 537 2362
Web: www.johansens.com/hastingshouse

CANADA - BRITISH COLUMBIA (VICTORIA)

Fairholme Manor

638 Rockland Place, Victoria, British Columbia V8S 3R2

Tel: +1 250 598 3240
Web: www.johansens.com/fairholme

CANADA - BRITISH COLUMBIA (SOOKE)

Sooke Harbour House

1528 Whiffen Spit Road, Sooke,
British Columbia V9Z 0T4

Tel: +1 250 642 3421
Web: www.johansens.com/sookeharbour

CANADA - BRITISH COLUMBIA (VICTORIA)

Villa Marco Polo Inn

1524 Shasta Place, Victoria, British Columbia V8S 1X9

Tel: +1 250 370 1524
Web: www.johansens.com/villamarcopolo

CANADA - BRITISH COLUMBIA (TOFINO)

Clayoquot Wilderness Resort

Bedwell River Outpost, Box 130, Tofino,
British Columbia V0R 2Z0

Tel: +1 250 726 8235
Web: www.johansens.com/clayoquot

CANADA - BRITISH COLUMBIA (WHISTLER)

Adara Hotel

4122 Village Green, Whistler, British Columbia V0N 1B4

Tel: +1 604 905 4009
Web: www.johansens.com/adara

CANADA - BRITISH COLUMBIA (TOFINO)

Wickaninnish Inn

Osprey Lane at Chesterman Beach, Tofino,
British Columbia V0R 2Z0

Tel: +1 250 725 3100
Web: www.johansens.com/wickaninnish

CANADA - NOVA SCOTIA (EAST KEMPTVILLE)

Trout Point Lodge of Nova Scotia

189 Trout Point Road, Off the East Branch Road and
Highway 203, East Kemptville, Nova Scotia B0W 1Y0

Tel: +1 902 761 2142
Web: www.johansens.com/troutpoint

CANADA - BRITISH COLUMBIA (VANCOUVER)

Pan Pacific Vancouver

300-999 Canada Place, Vancouver, British Columbia
V6C 3B5

Tel: +1 604 662 8111
Web: www.johansens.com/panpacific

CANADA - NOVA SCOTIA (WALLACE)

Fox Harb'r

1337 Fox Harbour Road, Wallace, Nova Scotia B0K 1Y0

Tel: +1 902 257 1801
Web: www.johansens.com/foxharbr

CANADA - BRITISH COLUMBIA (VANCOUVER)

The Sutton Place Hotel Vancouver

845 Burrard Street, Vancouver,
British Columbia V6Z 2K6

Tel: +1 604 682 5511
Web: www.johansens.com/suttonplacebc

CANADA - ONTARIO (MCKELLAR)

Inn at Manitou

81 Inn Road, McKellar, Ontario P0G 1C0

Tel: +1 705 389 2171
Web: www.johansens.com/manitou

Hotels - The Americas

Properties listed below can be found in our Recommended Hotels, Inns, Resorts & Spas - The Americas, Atlantic, Caribbean & Pacific 2009 Guide. More information on our portfolio of guides can be found on page 13

CANADA - ONTARIO (NIAGARA-ON-THE-LAKE)

The Charles Inn

209 Queen Street, Box 642, Niagara-on-the-Lake, Ontario L0S 1J0

Tel: +1 905 468 4588

Web: www.johansens.com/charlesinnca

CANADA - ONTARIO (NIAGARA-ON-THE-LAKE)

Harbour House

85 Melville Street, Box 760, Niagara-on-the-Lake, Ontario

Tel: +1 905 468 4683

Web: www.johansens.com/harbourhouseca

CANADA - ONTARIO (NIAGARA-ON-THE-LAKE)

Riverbend Inn & Vineyard

16104 Niagara River Parkway, Niagara-on-the-Lake, Ontario L0S 1J0

Tel: +1 905 468 8866

Web: www.johansens.com/riverbend

CANADA - ONTARIO (NIAGARA-ON-THE-LAKE)

Shaw Club Hotel & Spa

P.O. Box 642, 92 Picton Street, Niagara-on-the-Lake, Ontario L0S 1J0

Tel: +1 905 468 5711

Web: www.johansens.com/shawclub

CANADA - ONTARIO (TORONTO)

Windsor Arms

18 St. Thomas Street, Toronto, Ontario M5S 3E7

Tel: +1 416 971 9666

Web: www.johansens.com/windsorarms

CANADA - QUÉBEC (LA MALBAIE)

La Pinsonnière

124 Saint-Raphaël, Cap-à-l'Aigle, La Malbaie, Québec G5A 1X9

Tel: +1 418 665 4431

Web: www.johansens.com/lapinsonniere

CANADA - QUÉBEC (MONT-TREMBLANT)

Hôtel Quintessence

3004 chemin de la chapelle, Mont-Tremblant, Québec J8E 1E1

Tel: +1 819 425 3400

Web: www.johansens.com/quintessence

CANADA - QUÉBEC (MONTRÉAL)

Auberge du Vieux-Port

97 de la Commune Est, Montréal, Québec H2Y 1J1

Tel: +1 514 876 0081

Web: www.johansens.com/aubergeduvieuxport

CANADA - QUÉBEC (MONTRÉAL)

Hôtel Nelligan

106 rue Saint-Paul Ouest, Montréal, Québec H2Y 1Z3

Tel: +1 514 788 2040

Web: www.johansens.com/nelligan

CANADA - QUÉBEC (MONTRÉAL)

Le Place d'Armes Hôtel & Suites

55 rue Saint-Jacques Ouest, Montréal, Québec H2Y 3X2

Tel: +1 514 842 1887

Web: www.johansens.com/hotelplacedarmes

CANADA - QUÉBEC (NORTH HATLEY)

Manoir Hovey

575 Hovey Road, North Hatley, Québec J0B 2CO

Tel: +1 819 842 2421

Web: www.johansens.com/manoirhovey

Recommendations in Mexico

MEXICO - BAJA CALIFORNIA SUR (CABO SAN LUCAS)

Esperanza, an Auberge Resort

Km. 7 Carretera Transpeninsular, Punta Ballena, Cabo San Lucas, Baja California Sur 23410

Tel: +52 624 145 6400

Web: www.johansens.com/esperanza

MEXICO - BAJA CALIFORNIA SUR (LOS CABOS)

Marquis Los Cabos Beach Resort & Spa

Lote 74, Km. 21.5 Carretera Transpeninsular, Fraccionamiento Cabo Real, Los Cabos, Baja California Sur 23400

Tel: +52 624 144 2000

Web: www.johansens.com/marquisloscabos

MEXICO - BAJA CALIFORNIA SUR (SAN JOSÉ DEL CABO)

Casa del Mar Suites Golf & Spa Resort

KM 19.5 Carretera Transpeninsular, San José del Cabo, Baja California Sur 23400

Tel: +52 624 145 7700

Web: www.johansens.com/casadelmar

MEXICO - BAJA CALIFORNIA SUR (SAN JOSÉ DEL CABO)

Casa Natalia

Blvd. Mijares 4, San José Del Cabo, Baja California Sur 23400

Tel: +52 624 146 7100

Web: www.johansens.com/casanatalia

Hotels - The Americas

Properties listed below can be found in our Recommended Hotels, Inns, Resorts & Spas - The Americas, Atlantic, Caribbean & Pacific 2009 Guide. More information on our portfolio of guides can be found on page 13

MEXICO - BAJA CALIFORNIA SUR (SAN JOSÉ DEL CABO)

Las Ventanas al Paraíso, A Rosewood Resort

KM 19.5 Carretera Transpeninsular, San José del Cabo, Baja California Sur 23400

Tel: +52 624 144 2800

Web: www.johansens.com/lasventanas

MEXICO - JALISCO (GUADALAJARA)

Clarum 101

Parque Juan Diego 101, Col. Chapalita, C.P. 45050, Guadalajara, Jalisco

Tel: +52 33 1201 7507

Web: www.johansens.com/clarum101

MEXICO - DISTRITO FEDERAL (MEXICO CITY)

Hotel Boutique Casa Vieja Mexico

Eugenio Sue 45 (Colonia Polanco), Mexico Distrito Federal 11560

Tel: +52 55 52 82 0067

Web: www.johansens.com/casavieja

MEXICO - JALISCO (PUERTO VALLARTA)

Casa Velas Hotel Boutique

Pelicanos 311, Fracc. Marina Vallarta, Puerto Vallarta, Jalisco 48354

Tel: +52 322 226 6688

Web: www.johansens.com/casavelas

MEXICO - GUANAJUATO (GUANAJUATO)

Quinta Las Acacias

Paseo de la Presa 168, Guanajuato, Guanajuato 36000

Tel: +52 473 731 1517

Web: www.johansens.com/acacias

MEXICO - MICHOACÁN (MORELIA)

Cantera Diez

Calle Benito Juárez 63, Centro, Morelia, Michoacán

Tel: +52 443 312 54 19

Web: www.johansens.com/canteradiez

MEXICO - GUERRERO (IXTAPA - ZIHUATANEJO)

Loma Del Mar

Fragatas Lote F17 Sec. Hotelera II, Ixtapa - Zihuatanejo, Guerrero 40884

Tel: +52 755 555 04 60

Web: www.johansens.com/lomadelmar

MEXICO - MICHOACÁN (MORELIA)

Hotel Virrey de Mendoza

Av. Madero Pte. 310, Centro Histórico, Morelia, Michoacán 58000

Tel: +52 44 33 12 06 33

Web: www.johansens.com/hvirrey

MEXICO - JALISCO (COSTALEGRE)

El Tamarindo Beach & Golf Resort

Km 7.5 Highway 200, Carretera Barra de Navidad - Puerto Vallarta, Cihuatlan, Jalisco 48970

Tel: +52 315 351 5031

Web: www.johansens.com/eltamarindo

MEXICO - MORELOS (CUERNAVACA)

Las Mañanitas

Ricardo Linares 107 Col Centro, Cuernavaca, Morelos 62000

Tel: +52 777 362 0023

Web: www.johansens.com/mananitas

MEXICO - JALISCO (COSTALEGRE - COSTA CAREYES)

El Careyes Beach Resort

Km 53.5, Carretera Barra de Navidad-Puerto Vallarta, Costa Careyes, Jalisco 48970

Tel: +52 315 351 0000

Web: www.johansens.com/elcareyes

MEXICO - MICHOACÁN (MORELIA)

Villa Montaña Hotel & Spa

Patzimba 201, Vista Bella, Morelia, Michoacán 58090

Tel: +52 443 314 02 31

Web: www.johansens.com/montana

MEXICO - JALISCO (COSTALEGRE - PUERTO VALLARTA)

Hotelito Desconocido

Playon de Mismaloya S/N,Municipio de Tomatlán, La Cruz de Loreto, Jalisco 48460

Tel: +52 322 281 4010

Web: www.johansens.com/hotelito

MEXICO - NAYARIT (NUEVO VALLARTA)

Grand Velas All Suites & Spa Resort

Av. Cocoteros 98 Sur, Nuevo Vallarta, Riviera Nayarit 63735

Tel: +52 322 226 8000

Web: www.johansens.com/grandvelas

MEXICO - JALISCO (COSTALEGRE - PUERTO VALLARTA)

Las Alamandas Resort

Carretera Barra de Navidad - Puerto Vallarta km 83.5, Col. Quemaro, Jalisco 48850

Tel: +52 322 285 5500

Web: www.johansens.com/alamandas

MEXICO - OAXACA (OAXACA)

Casa Cid de Leon

Av. Morelos 602, Centro, Oaxaca, Oaxaca 68000

Tel: +52 951 51 47013/60414

Web: www.johansens.com/leon

Hotels - The Americas

Properties listed below can be found in our Recommended Hotels, Inns, Resorts & Spas - The Americas, Atlantic, Caribbean & Pacific 2009 Guide. More information on our portfolio of guides can be found on page 13

MEXICO - OAXACA (OAXACA)

Casa Oaxaca

Calle García Vigil 407, Centro, Oaxaca, Oaxaca 68000

Tel: +52 951 514 4173
Web: www.johansens.com/oaxaca

U.S.A. - ARIZONA (GREER)

Hidden Meadow Ranch

620 Country Road 1325, Greer, Arizona 85927

Tel: +1 928 333 1000
Web: www.johansens.com/hiddenmeadow

MEXICO - OAXACA (OAXACA)

La Casona de Tita

García Vigil 805, Centro, C.P. 68000 Oaxaca, Oaxaca

Tel: +52 951 5 16 1400
Web: www.johansens.com/lacasonadetita

U.S.A. - ARIZONA (PARADISE VALLEY / SCOTTSDALE)

Sanctuary on Camelback Mountain

5700 East McDonald Drive, Scottsdale, Arizona 85253

Tel: +1 480 948 2100
Web: www.johansens.com/sanctuarycamelback

MEXICO - QUINTANA ROO (PLAYA DEL CARMEN)

Grand Velas All Suites & Spa Resort, Riviera Maya

Carretera Cancún-Tulum Km. 62, Playa del Carmen, Municipio del Solidaridad, Quintana Roo 77710

Tel: +52 984 109 5600
Web: www.johansens.com/rivieramaya

U.S.A. - ARIZONA (SEDONA)

Sedona Rouge Hotel & Spa

2250 West Highway 89A, Sedona, Arizona 86336

Tel: +1 928 203 4111
Web: www.johansens.com/sedonarouge

MEXICO - QUINTANA ROO (PUERTO MORELOS)

Ceiba del Mar Spa Resort

Costera Norte Lte. 1, S.M. 10, MZ. 26, Puerto Morelos, Quintana Roo 77580

Tel: +52 998 872 8060
Web: www.johansens.com/ceibademar

U.S.A. - ARIZONA (TUBAC)

Tubac Golf Resort & Spa

One Otero Road, Tubac, Arizona 85646

Tel: +1 520 398 2211
Web: www.johansens.com/tubac

MEXICO - QUINTANA ROO (TULUM)

Casa Nalum

Sian Ka'an Biosphere Reserve, Quintana Roo

Tel: +52 19991 639 510
Web: www.johansens.com/casanalum

U.S.A. - ARIZONA (TUCSON)

Arizona Inn

2200 East Elm Street, Tucson, Arizona 85719

Tel: +1 520 325 1541
Web: www.johansens.com/arizonainn

MEXICO - YUCATÁN (MÉRIDA)

Hacienda Xcanatún - Casa de Piedra

Calle 20 S/N, Comisaría Xcanatún, Km. 12 Carretera Mérida - Progreso, Mérida, Yucatán 9730

Tel: +52 999 941 0273
Web: www.johansens.com/xcanatun

U.S.A. - ARIZONA (TUCSON)

Tanque Verde Ranch

14301 East Speedway Boulevard, Tucson, Arizona 85748

Tel: +1 520 296 6275
Web: www.johansens.com/tanqueverde

U.S.A. - ARIZONA (WICKENBURG)

Rancho de los Caballeros

1551 South Vulture Mine Road, Wickenburg, Arizona 85390

Tel: +1 928 684 5484
Web: www.johansens.com/caballeros

Recommendations in U.S.A

U.S.A. - ALABAMA (PISGAH)

Lodge on Gorham's Bluff

101 Gorham Drive, Pisgah, Alabama 35765

Tel: +1 256 451 8439
Web: www.johansens.com/gorhamsbluff

U.S.A. - CALIFORNIA (BIG SUR)

Post Ranch Inn

Highway 1, P.O. Box 219, Big Sur, California 93920

Tel: +1 831 667 2200
Web: www.johansens.com/postranchinn

Hotels - The Americas

Properties listed below can be found in our Recommended Hotels, Inns, Resorts & Spas - The Americas, Atlantic, Caribbean & Pacific 2009 Guide.
More information on our portfolio of guides can be found on page 13

U.S.A. - CALIFORNIA (BIG SUR)

Ventana Inn and Spa

Highway 1, Big Sur, California 93920

Tel: +1 831 667 2331

Web: www.johansens.com/ventanainn

U.S.A. - CALIFORNIA (HEALDSBURG)

Hotel Healdsburg

25 Matheson Street, Healdsburg, California 95448

Tel: +1 707 431 2800

Web: www.johansens.com/healdsburg

U.S.A. - CALIFORNIA (CALISTOGA)

Calistoga Ranch

580 Lommel Road, Calistoga, California 94515

Tel: +1 707 254 2800

Web: www.johansens.com/calistogaranch

U.S.A. - CALIFORNIA (HEALDSBURG)

Les Mars

27 North, Healdsburg, California 95448

Tel: +1 707 433 4211

Web: www.johansens.com/lesmarshotel

U.S.A. - CALIFORNIA (CALISTOGA)

Solage Calistoga

755 Silverado Trail, Calistoga, California 94515

Tel: +1 707 226 0800

Web: www.johansens.com/solagecalistoga

U.S.A. - CALIFORNIA (LA JOLLA)

Estancia La Jolla Hotel & Spa

9700 North Torrey Pines Road, La Jolla, California 92037

Tel: +1 858 550 1000

Web: www.johansens.com/estancialajolla

U.S.A. - CALIFORNIA (CARMEL VALLEY)

Bernardus Lodge

415 Carmel Valley Road, Carmel Valley, California 93924

Tel: +1 831 658 3400

Web: www.johansens.com/bernardus

U.S.A. - CALIFORNIA (LITTLE RIVER)

Stevenswood Spa Resort

8211 North Highway 1, Little River, California 95456

Tel: +1 707 937 2810

Web: www.johansens.com/stevenswood

U.S.A. - CALIFORNIA (CARMEL-BY-THE-SEA)

L'Auberge Carmel

Monte Verde at Seventh, Carmel-by-the-Sea, California 93921

Tel: +1 831 624 8578

Web: www.johansens.com/laubergecarmel

U.S.A. - CALIFORNIA (LOS ANGELES)

Hotel Bel-Air

701 Stone Canyon Road, Los Angeles, California 90077

Tel: +1 310 472 1211

Web: www.johansens.com/belair

U.S.A. - CALIFORNIA (CARMEL-BY-THE-SEA)

Tradewinds Carmel

Mission Street at Third Avenue, Carmel-by-the-Sea, California 93921

Tel: +1 831 624 2776

Web: www.johansens.com/tradewinds

U.S.A. - CALIFORNIA (MALIBU)

Malibu Beach Inn

22878 Pacific Highway, Malibu, California 90265

Tel: +1 310 456 6444

Web: www.johansens.com/malibubeach

U.S.A. - CALIFORNIA (EUREKA)

The Carter House Inns

301 L Street, Eureka, California 95501

Tel: +1 707 444 8062

Web: www.johansens.com/carterhouse

U.S.A. - CALIFORNIA (MENDOCINO)

The Stanford Inn By The Sea

Coast Highway One & Comptche-Ukiah Road, Mendocino, California 95460

Tel: +1 707 937 5615

Web: www.johansens.com/stanfordinn

U.S.A. - CALIFORNIA (HEALDSBURG)

The Grape Leaf Inn

539 Johnson Street, Healdsburg, California 95448

Tel: +1 707 433 8140

Web: www.johansens.com/grapeleaf

U.S.A. - CALIFORNIA (MILL VALLEY)

Mill Valley Inn

165 Throckmorton Avenue, Mill Valley, California 94941

Tel: +1 415 389 6608

Web: www.johansens.com/millvalleyinn

Hotels - The Americas

Properties listed below can be found in our Recommended Hotels, Inns, Resorts & Spas - The Americas, Atlantic, Caribbean & Pacific 2009 Guide. More information on our portfolio of guides can be found on page 13

U.S.A. - CALIFORNIA (MONTEREY)

Old Monterey Inn

500 Martin Street, Monterey, California 93940

Tel: +1 831 375 8284
Web: www.johansens.com/oldmontereyinn

U.S.A. - CALIFORNIA (SANTA BARBARA)

Harbor View Inn

28 West Cabrillo Boulevard, Santa Barbara, California 93101

Tel: +1 805 963 0780
Web: www.johansens.com/harborview

U.S.A. - CALIFORNIA (NAPA)

1801 First Inn

1801 First Street, Napa, California 94559

Tel: +1 707 224 3739
Web: www.johansens.com/1801inn

U.S.A. - CALIFORNIA (SHELL BEACH)

Dolphin Bay Resort & Spa

2727 Shell Beach Road, Shell Beach, California 93449

Tel: +1 805 773 4300
Web: www.johansens.com/thedolphinbay

U.S.A. - CALIFORNIA (NAPA)

Milliken Creek Inn & Spa

1815 Silverado Trail, Napa, California 94558

Tel: +1 707 255 1197
Web: www.johansens.com/milliken

U.S.A. - CALIFORNIA (ST. HELENA)

The Inn at Southbridge

1020 Main Street, St. Helena, California 94574

Tel: +1 707 967 9400
Web: www.johansens.com/southbridge

U.S.A. - CALIFORNIA (NEWPORT BEACH)

Balboa Bay Club & Resort

1221 West Coast Highway, Newport Beach, California 92663

Tel: +1 949 645 5000
Web: www.johansens.com/balboabayclub

U.S.A. - CALIFORNIA (ST. HELENA)

Meadowood Napa Valley

900 Meadowood Lane, St. Helena, California 94574

Tel: +1 707 963 3646
Web: www.johansens.com/meadowood

U.S.A. - CALIFORNIA (OAKHURST)

Château du Sureau & Spa

48688 Victoria Lane, Oakhurst, California 93644

Tel: +1 559 683 6860
Web: www.johansens.com/chateausureau

U.S.A. - COLORADO (DENVER)

Castle Marne Bed & Breakfast Inn

1572 Race Street, Denver, Colorado 80206

Tel: +1 303 331 0621
Web: www.johansens.com/castlemarne

U.S.A. - CALIFORNIA (RANCHO SANTA FE)

The Inn at Rancho Santa Fe

5951 Linea del Cielo, Rancho Santa Fe, California 92067

Tel: +1 858 756 1131
Web: www.johansens.com/ranchosantafe

U.S.A. - COLORADO (DENVER)

Hotel Monaco

1717 Champa Street at 17th, Denver, Colorado 80202

Tel: +1 303 296 1717
Web: www.johansens.com/monaco

U.S.A. - CALIFORNIA (SAN DIEGO)

Tower23 Hotel

4551 Ocean Blvd., San Diego, California 92109

Tel: +1 858 270 2323
Web: www.johansens.com/tower23

U.S.A. - COLORADO (ESTES PARK)

Taharaa Mountain Lodge

3110 So. St. Vrain, Estes Park, Colorado 80517

Tel: +1 970 577 0098
Web: www.johansens.com/taharaa

U.S.A. - CALIFORNIA (SAN FRANCISCO BAY AREA)

Inn Above Tide

30 El Portal, Sausalito, California 94965

Tel: +1 415 332 9535
Web: www.johansens.com/innabovetide

U.S.A. - COLORADO (MANITOU SPRINGS)

The Cliff House at Pikes Peak

306 Cañon Avenue, Manitou Springs, Colorado 80829

Tel: +1 719 685 3000
Web: www.johansens.com/thecliffhouse

Properties listed below can be found in our Recommended Hotels, Inns, Resorts & Spas - The Americas, Atlantic, Caribbean & Pacific 2009 Guide.
More information on our portfolio of guides can be found on page 13

U.S.A. - COLORADO (MONTROSE)

Elk Mountain Resort

97 Elk Walk, Montrose, Colorado 81401

Tel: +1 970 252 4900

Web: www.johansens.com/elkmountain

U.S.A. - DELAWARE (REHOBOTH BEACH)

Boardwalk Plaza Hotel

Olive Avenue & The Boardwalk, Rehoboth Beach, Delaware 19971

Tel: +1 302 227 7169

Web: www.johansens.com/boardwalkplaza

U.S.A. - COLORADO (STEAMBOAT SPRINGS)

Vista Verde Guest Ranch

P.O. Box 770465, Steamboat Springs, Colorado 80477

Tel: +1 970 879 3858

Web: www.johansens.com/vistaverderanch

U.S.A. - DELAWARE (REHOBOTH BEACH)

Hotel Rehoboth

247 Rehoboth Avenue, Rehoboth Beach, Delaware 19971

Tel: +1 302 227 4300

Web: www.johansens.com/hotelrehoboth

U.S.A. - COLORADO (TELLURIDE)

**Fairmont Heritage Place,
Franz Klammer Lodge**

567 Mountain Village Boulevard, Telluride, Colorado 81435

Tel: +1 970 728 4239

Web: www.johansens.com/fairmont

U.S.A. - DELAWARE (WILMINGTON)

Inn at Montchanin Village

Route 100 & Kirk Road, Montchanin, Wilmington, Delaware 19710

Tel: +1 302 888 2133

Web: www.johansens.com/montchanin

U.S.A. - COLORADO (TELLURIDE)

The Hotel Telluride

199 North Cornet Street, Telluride, Colorado 81435

Tel: +1 970 369 1188

Web: www.johansens.com/telluride

U.S.A. - DISTRICT OF COLUMBIA (WASHINGTON)

The Hay-Adams

Sixteenth & H. Streets N.W., Washington D.C., District of Columbia 20006

Tel: +1 202 638 6600

Web: www.johansens.com/hayadams

U.S.A. - COLORADO (VAIL)

Vail Mountain Lodge & Spa

352 East Meadow Drive, Vail, Colorado 81657

Tel: +1 970 476 0700

Web: www.johansens.com/vailmountain

U.S.A. - FLORIDA (FISHER ISLAND)

Fisher Island Hotel & Resort

One Fisher Island Drive, Fisher Island, Florida 33109

Tel: +1 305 535 6000

Web: www.johansens.com/fisherisland

U.S.A. - CONNECTICUT (GREENWICH)

Delamar Greenwich Harbor

500 Steamboat Road, Greenwich, Connecticut 06830

Tel: +1 203 661 9800

Web: www.johansens.com/delamar

U.S.A. - FLORIDA (FORT MYERS)

Sanibel Harbour Resort and Spa

17260 Harbor Pointe Drive, Fort Myers, Florida 33908

Tel: +1 239 466 4000

Web: www.johansens.com/sanibelresort

U.S.A. - CONNECTICUT (WESTPORT)

The Inn at National Hall

2 Post Road West, Westport, Connecticut 06880

Tel: +1 203 221 1351

Web: www.johansens.com/nationalhall

U.S.A. - FLORIDA (JUPITER BEACH)

Jupiter Beach Resort & Spa

5 North A1A, Jupiter, Florida 33477-5190

Tel: +1 561 746 2511

Web: www.johansens.com/jupiterbeachresort

U.S.A. - DELAWARE (REHOBOTH BEACH)

The Bellmoor

Six Christian Street, Rehoboth Beach, Delaware 19971

Tel: +1 302 227 5800

Web: www.johansens.com/thebellmoor

U.S.A. - FLORIDA (KEY WEST)

The Gardens Hotel

526 Angela Street, Key West, Florida 33040

Tel: +1 305 294 2661

Web: www.johansens.com/gardenshotel

Hotels - The Americas

Properties listed below can be found in our Recommended Hotels, Inns, Resorts & Spas - The Americas, Atlantic, Caribbean & Pacific 2009 Guide. More information on our portfolio of guides can be found on page 13

U.S.A. - FLORIDA (KEY WEST)

Ocean Key Resort & Spa

Zero Duval Street, Key West, Florida 33040

Tel: +1 305 296 7701
Web: www.johansens.com/oceankey

U.S.A. - FLORIDA (SANTA ROSA BEACH)

WaterColor Inn & Resort

34 Goldenrod Circle, Santa Rosa Beach, Florida 32459

Tel: +1 850 534 5000
Web: www.johansens.com/watercolor

U.S.A. - FLORIDA (KEY WEST)

Sunset Key Guest Cottages

245 Front Street, Key West, Florida 33040

Tel: +1 305 292 5300
Web: www.johansens.com/sunsetkey

U.S.A. - FLORIDA (ST. PETE BEACH)

Don CeSar Beach Resort, A Loews Hotel

3400 Gulf Boulevard, St. Pete Beach, Florida 33706

Tel: +1 727 360 1881
Web: www.johansens.com/doncesar

U.S.A. - FLORIDA (MIAMI)

Grove Isle Hotel & Spa

Four Grove Isle Drive, Coconut Grove, Florida 33133

Tel: +1 305 858 8300
Web: www.johansens.com/groveisle

U.S.A. - GEORGIA (ADAIRSVILLE)

Barnsley Gardens Resort

597 Barnsley Gardens Road, Adairsville, Georgia 30103

Tel: +1 770 773 7480
Web: www.johansens.com/barnsleygardens

U.S.A. - FLORIDA (MIAMI BEACH)

Casa Tua

1700 James Avenue, Miami Beach, Florida 33139

Tel: +1 305 673 0973
Web: www.johansens.com/casatua

U.S.A. - GEORGIA (ATLANTA)

TWELVE Hotel Atlantic Station

361 17th Street, Atlanta, Georgia 30363

Tel: + 1 404 961 1212
Web: www.johansens.com/twelvehotelsas

U.S.A. - FLORIDA (MIAMI BEACH)

Hotel Victor

1144 Ocean Drive, Miami Beach, Florida 33139

Tel: +1 305 428 1234
Web: www.johansens.com/hotelvictor

U.S.A. - GEORGIA (ATLANTA)

TWELVE Hotel Centennial Park

817 West Peachtree Street, Atlanta, Georgia 30308

Tel: +1 404 418 1212
Web: www.johansens.com/twelvehotelscp

U.S.A. - FLORIDA (MIAMI BEACH)

The Setai Hotel & Resort

2001 Collins Avenue, Miami Beach, Florida 33139

Tel: +1 305 520 6000
Web: www.johansens.com/setai

U.S.A. - GEORGIA (CUMBERLAND ISLAND)

Greyfield Inn

Cumberland Island, Georgia

Tel: +1 904 261 6408
Web: www.johansens.com/greyfieldinn

U.S.A. - FLORIDA (NAPLES)

LaPlaya Beach & Golf Resort

9891 Gulf Shore Drive, Naples, Florida 34108

Tel: +1 239 597 3123
Web: www.johansens.com/laplaya

U.S.A. - GEORGIA (MADISON)

The James Madison Inn

260 West Washington Street, Madison, Georgia 30650

Tel: +1 706 342 7040
Web: www.johansens.com/jamesmadison

U.S.A. - FLORIDA (PALM BEACH)

The Brazilian Court

301 Australian Avenue, Palm Beach, Florida 33480

Tel: +1 561 655 7740
Web: www.johansens.com/braziliancourt

U.S.A. - GEORGIA (SAVANNAH)

The Presidents' Quarters Inn

225 East President Street, Savannah, Georgia 31401-3806

Tel: +1 912 233 1600
Web: www.johansens.com/presidentsquarters

Properties listed below can be found in our Recommended Hotels, Inns, Resorts & Spas - The Americas, Atlantic, Caribbean & Pacific 2009 Guide. More information on our portfolio of guides can be found on page 13

U.S.A. - IDAHO (KETCHUM)

Knob Hill Inn

960 North Main Street, P.O. Box 800, Ketchum, Idaho 83340

Tel: +1 208 726 8010
Web: www.johansens.com/knobhillinn

U.S.A. - MARYLAND (ANNAPOLIS)

The Annapolis Inn

144 Prince George Street, Annapolis, Maryland 21401-1723

Tel: +1 410 295 5200
Web: www.johansens.com/annapolisinn

U.S.A. - ILLINOIS (CHICAGO)

Hotel Sax Chicago

333 North Dearborn Street, Chicago, Illinois 60654

Tel: +1 312 245 0333
Web: www.johansens.com/hotelsax

U.S.A. - MARYLAND (FROSTBURG)

Savage River Lodge

1600 Mt. Aetna Road, Frostburg, Maryland 21532

Tel: +1 301 689 3200
Web: www.johansens.com/savageriver

U.S.A. - ILLINOIS (CHICAGO)

The Talbott Hotel

20 E. Delaware Place, Chicago, Illinois 60611

Tel: +1 312 944 4970
Web: www.johansens.com/talbotthotel

U.S.A. - MASSACHUSETTS (BOSTON)

Boston Harbor Hotel

70 Rowes Wharf, Boston, Massachusetts 2110

Tel: +1 617 439 7000
Web: www.johansens.com/bhh

U.S.A. - KANSAS (LAWRENCE)

The Eldridge Hotel

701 Massachusetts, Lawrence, Kansas 66044

Tel: +1 785 749 5011
Web: www.johansens.com/eldridge

U.S.A. - MASSACHUSETTS (BOSTON)

Fifteen Beacon

15 Beacon Street, Boston, Massachusetts 2108

Tel: +1 617 670 1500
Web: www.johansens.com/xvbeacon

U.S.A. - LOUISIANA (NEW ORLEANS)

Soniat House

1133 Chartres Street, New Orleans, Louisiana 70116

Tel: +1 504 522 0570
Web: www.johansens.com/soniathouse

U.S.A. - MASSACHUSETTS (BOSTON)

The Liberty Hotel

215 Charles Street, Boston, Massachusetts 02114

Tel: +1 617 224 4000
Web: www.johansens.com/liberty

U.S.A. - MAINE (GREENVILLE)

The Lodge At Moosehead Lake

368 Lily Bay Road, P.O. Box 1167, Greenville, Maine 04441

Tel: +1 207 695 4400
Web: www.johansens.com/lodgeatmooseheadlake

U.S.A. - MASSACHUSETTS (CAPE COD)

Wequassett Resort and Golf Club

On Pleasant Bay, Chatham, Massachusetts 02633

Tel: +1 508 432 5400
Web: www.johansens.com/wequassett

U.S.A. - MAINE (KENNEBUNKPORT)

The White Barn Inn

37 Beach Avenue, Kennebunkport, Maine 04043

Tel: +1 207 967 2321
Web: www.johansens.com/whitebarninn

U.S.A. - MASSACHUSETTS (IPSWICH)

The Inn at Castle Hill

280 Argilla Road, Ipswich, Massachusetts 01938

Tel: +1 978 412 2555
Web: www.johansens.com/castlehill

U.S.A. - MAINE (PORTLAND)

Portland Harbor Hotel

468 Fore Street, Portland, Maine 04101

Tel: +1 207 775 9090
Web: www.johansens.com/portlandharbor

U.S.A. - MASSACHUSETTS (LENOX)

Blantyre

16 Blantyre Road, P.O. Box 995, Lenox, Massachusetts 01240

Tel: +1 413 637 3556
Web: www.johansens.com/blantyre

Hotels - The Americas

Properties listed below can be found in our Recommended Hotels, Inns, Resorts & Spas - The Americas, Atlantic, Caribbean & Pacific 2009 Guide. More information on our portfolio of guides can be found on page 13

U.S.A. - MASSACHUSETTS (LENOX)

Cranwell Resort, Spa & Golf Club

55 Lee Road, Route 20, Lenox, Massachusetts 01240

Tel: +1 413 637 1364
Web: www.johansens.com/cranwell

U.S.A. - NEW HAMPSHIRE (WHITEFIELD / WHITE MOUNTAINS)

Mountain View Grand Resort & Spa

101 Mountain View Road, Whitefield,
New Hampshire 03598

Tel: +1 603 837 2100
Web: www.johansens.com/mountainview

U.S.A. - MASSACHUSETTS (MARTHA'S VINEYARD)

The Charlotte Inn

27 South Summer Street, Edgartown,
Massachusetts 02539

Tel: +1 508 627 4151
Web: www.johansens.com/charlotte

U.S.A. - NEW MEXICO (ESPAÑOLA)

Rancho de San Juan

P.O. Box 4140, Highway 285, Española,
New Mexico 87533

Tel: +1 505 753 6818
Web: www.johansens.com/ranchosanjuan

U.S.A. - MICHIGAN (ROCHESTER)

Royal Park Hotel

600 E. University Drive, Rochester, Michigan 48307

Tel: +1 248 652 2600
Web: www.johansens.com/royalparkmi

U.S.A. - NEW MEXICO (SANTA FE)

Encantado, an Auberge Resort

198 State Road 592, Santa Fe, New Mexico 87506

Tel: +1 505 988 9955
Web: www.johansens.com/encantado

U.S.A. - MISSISSIPPI (JACKSON)

Fairview Inn & Restaurant

734 Fairview Street, Jackson, Mississippi 39202

Tel: +1 601 948 3429
Web: www.johansens.com/fairviewinn

U.S.A. - NEW MEXICO (TAOS)

El Monte Sagrado Living Resort & Spa

317 Kit Carson Road, Taos, New Mexico 87571

Tel: +1 575 758 3502
Web: www.johansens.com/elmontesagrado

U.S.A. - MISSISSIPPI (NATCHEZ)

Monmouth Plantation

36 Melrose Avenue, Natchez, Mississippi 39120

Tel: +1 601 442 5852
Web: www.johansens.com/monmouthplantation

U.S.A. - NEW YORK (BUFFALO)

The Mansion on Delaware Avenue

414 Delaware Avenue, Buffalo, New York 14202

Tel: +1 716 886 3300
Web: www.johansens.com/mansionondelaware

U.S.A. - MISSISSIPPI (NESBIT)

Bonne Terre Country Inn

4715 Church Road West, Nesbit, Mississippi 38651

Tel: +1 662 781 5100
Web: www.johansens.com/bonneterre

U.S.A. - NEW YORK (HUNTINGTON)

OHEKA CASTLE Hotel & Estate

135 West Gate Drive, Huntington, New York 11743

Tel: +1 631 659 1400
Web: www.johansens.com/oheka

U.S.A. - MISSOURI (KANSAS CITY)

The Raphael Hotel

325 Ward Parkway, Kansas City, Missouri 64112

Tel: +1 816 756 3800
Web: www.johansens.com/raphael

U.S.A. - NEW YORK (LEWISTON)

Barton Hill Hotel & Spa

100 Center Street, Lewiston, New York 14092

Tel: +1 716 754 9070
Web: www.johansens.com/bartonhillhotel

U.S.A. - MONTANA (DARBY)

Triple Creek Ranch

5551 West Fork Road, Darby, Montana 59829

Tel: +1 406 821 4600
Web: www.johansens.com/triplecreek

U.S.A. - NEW YORK (NEW YORK CITY)

Hôtel Plaza Athénée

37 East 64th Street, New York City, New York 10065

Tel: +1 212 734 9100
Web: www.johansens.com/athenee

Hotels - The Americas

Properties listed below can be found in our Recommended Hotels, Inns, Resorts & Spas - The Americas, Atlantic, Caribbean & Pacific 2009 Guide. More information on our portfolio of guides can be found on page 13

U.S.A. - NEW YORK (NEW YORK CITY)

The Inn at Irving Place

56 Irving Place, New York, New York City 10003

Tel: +1 212 533 4600
Web: www.johansens.com/irving

U.S.A. - NEW YORK (TARRYTOWN)

Castle On The Hudson

400 Benedict Avenue, Tarrytown, New York 10591

Tel: +1 914 631 1980
Web: www.johansens.com/hudson

U.S.A. - NEW YORK (VERONA)

The Lodge at Turning Stone

5218 Patrick Road, Verona, New York 13478

Tel: +1 315 361 8525
Web: www.johansens.com/turningstone

U.S.A. - NEW YORK/LONG ISLAND (EAST HAMPTON)

The Baker House 1650

181 Main Street, East Hampton, New York 11937

Tel: +1 631 324 4081
Web: www.johansens.com/bakerhouse

U.S.A. - NEW YORK/LONG ISLAND (EAST HAMPTON)

The Mill House Inn

31 North Main Street, East Hampton, New York 11937

Tel: +1 631 324 9766
Web: www.johansens.com/millhouse

U.S.A. - NEW YORK/LONG ISLAND (SOUTHAMPTON)

1708 House

126 Main Street, Southampton, New York 11968

Tel: +1 631 287 1708
Web: www.johansens.com/1708house

U.S.A. - NORTH CAROLINA (ASHEVILLE)

Haywood Park Hotel

One Battery Park Avenue, Asheville,
North Carolina 28801

Tel: +1 828 252 2522
Web: www.johansens.com/haywoodpark

U.S.A. - NORTH CAROLINA (ASHEVILLE)

Inn on Biltmore Estate

One Antler Hill Road, Asheville, North Carolina 28803

Tel: +1 828 225 1600
Web: www.johansens.com/biltmore

U.S.A. - NORTH CAROLINA (CHAPEL HILL)

The Franklin Hotel

311 West Franklin Street, Chapel Hill,
North Carolina 27516

Tel: +1 919 442 9000
Web: www.johansens.com/franklinhotelnc

U.S.A. - NORTH CAROLINA (CHARLOTTE)

Ballantyne Resort

10000 Ballantyne Commons Parkway, Charlotte,
North Carolina 28277

Tel: +1 704 248 4000
Web: www.johansens.com/ballantyneresort

U.S.A. - NORTH CAROLINA (CHIMNEY ROCK)

The Esmeralda

910 Main Street, Chimney Rock, North Carolina 28720

Tel: +1 828 625 2999
Web: www.johansens.com/esmeralda

U.S.A. - NORTH CAROLINA (DUCK)

The Sanderling Resort & Spa

1461 Duck Road, Duck, North Carolina 27949

Tel: +1 252 261 4111
Web: www.johansens.com/sanderling

U.S.A. - NORTH CAROLINA (HIGHLANDS)

Inn at Half Mile Farm

P.O. Box 2769, 214 Half Mile Drive, Highlands,
North Carolina 28741

Tel: +1 828 526 8170
Web: www.johansens.com/halfmilefarm

U.S.A. - NORTH CAROLINA (HIGHLANDS)

Old Edwards Inn and Spa

445 Main Street, Highlands, North Carolina 28741

Tel: +1 828 526 8008
Web: www.johansens.com/oldedwards

U.S.A. - NORTH CAROLINA (SOUTHERN PINES)

The Jefferson Inn

150 West New Hampshire Avenue, Southern Pines,
North Carolina 28387

Tel: +1 910 692 9911
Web: www.johansens.com/jeffersoninn

U.S.A. - OKLAHOMA (OKLAHOMA CITY)

Colcord Hotel

15 North Robinson, Oklahoma City, Oklahoma 73102

Tel: +1 405 601 4300
Web: www.johansens.com/colcord

Hotels - The Americas

Properties listed below can be found in our Recommended Hotels, Inns, Resorts & Spas - The Americas, Atlantic, Caribbean & Pacific 2009 Guide. More information on our portfolio of guides can be found on page 13

U.S.A. - OKLAHOMA (TULSA)

Hotel Ambassador

1324 South Main Street, Tulsa, Oklahoma 74119

Tel: +1 918 587 8200
Web: www.johansens.com/ambassador

U.S.A. - RHODE ISLAND (PROVIDENCE)

Hotel Providence

311 Westminster Street, Providence,
Rhode Island 02903

Tel: +1 401 861 8000
Web: www.johansens.com/providence

U.S.A. - OREGON (ASHLAND)

The Winchester Inn & Restaurant

35 South Second Street, Ashland, Oregon 97520

Tel: +1 541 488 1113
Web: www.johansens.com/winchester

U.S.A. - SOUTH CAROLINA (BLUFFTON)

The Inn at Palmetto Bluff

476 Mount Pelia Road, Bluffton, South Carolina 29910

Tel: +1 843 706 6500
Web: www.johansens.com/palmettobluff

U.S.A. - OREGON (PORTLAND)

The Heathman Hotel

1001 S.W. Broadway, Portland, Oregon 97205

Tel: +1 503 241 4100
Web: www.johansens.com/heathman

U.S.A. - SOUTH CAROLINA (CHARLESTON)

The Boardwalk Inn at Wild Dunes Resort

5757 Palm Boulevard, Isle of Palms, South Carolina
29451

Tel: +1 843 886 6000
Web: www.johansens.com/boardwalk

U.S.A. - PENNSYLVANIA (NEW HOPE)

The Inn at Bowman's Hill

518 Lurgan Road, New Hope, Pennsylvania 18938

Tel: +1 215 862 8090
Web: www.johansens.com/bowmanshill

U.S.A. - SOUTH CAROLINA (CHARLESTON)

Charleston Harbor Resort & Marina

20 Patriots Point Road, Charleston,
South Carolina 29464

Tel: +1 843 856 0028
Web: www.johansens.com/charlestonharbor

U.S.A. - PENNSYLVANIA (PHILADELPHIA)

Rittenhouse 1715, A Boutique Hotel

1715 Rittenhouse Square, Philadelphia,
Pennsylvania 19103

Tel: +1 215 546 6500
Web: www.johansens.com/rittenhouse

U.S.A. - SOUTH CAROLINA (KIAWAH ISLAND)

The Sanctuary at Kiawah Island Golf Resort

One Sanctuary Beach Drive, Kiawah Island,
South Carolina 29455

Tel: +1 843 768 6000
Web: www.johansens.com/sanctuary

U.S.A. - PENNSYLVANIA (SKYTOP)

Skytop Lodge

One Skytop, Skytop, Pennsylvania 18357

Tel: +1 570 595 7401
Web: www.johansens.com/skytop

U.S.A. - SOUTH CAROLINA (TRAVELERS REST)

La Bastide

10 Road Of Vines, Travelers Rest, South Carolina 29690

Tel: +1 864 836 8463
Web: www.johansens.com/labastide

U.S.A. - RHODE ISLAND (NEWPORT)

Chanler at Cliff Walk

117 Memorial Boulevard, Newport, Rhode Island 02840

Tel: +1 401 847 1300
Web: www.johansens.com/chanler

U.S.A. - TENNESSEE (MEMPHIS)

The River Inn of Harbor Town

50 Harbor Town Square, Memphis, Tennessee 38103

Tel: +1 901 260 3333
Web: www.johansens.com/riverinnmemphis

U.S.A. - RHODE ISLAND (NEWPORT)

La Farge Perry House

24 Kay Street, Newport, Rhode Island 02840

Tel: +1 401 847 2223
Web: www.johansens.com/lafargeperry

U.S.A. - TENNESSEE (NASHVILLE)

The Hermitage Hotel

231 Sixth Avenue North, Nashville, Tennessee 37219

Tel: +1 615 244 3121
Web: www.johansens.com/hermitagetn

Hotels - The Americas

Properties listed below can be found in our Recommended Hotels, Inns, Resorts & Spas - The Americas, Atlantic, Caribbean & Pacific 2009 Guide. More information on our portfolio of guides can be found on page 13

U.S.A. - TEXAS (AUSTIN)

Mansion at Judges' Hill

1900 Rio Grande, Austin, Texas 78705

Tel: +1 512 495 1800
Web: www.johansens.com/judgeshill

U.S.A. - TEXAS (DALLAS)

The Joule

1530 Main Street, Dallas, Texas 75201

Tel: +1 214 748 1300
Web: www.johansens.com/thejoule

U.S.A. - TEXAS (GRANBURY)

The Inn on Lake Granbury

205 West Doyle Street, Granbury, Texas 76048

Tel: +1 817 573 0046
Web: www.johansens.com/lakegranbury

U.S.A. - TEXAS (HOUSTON)

Hotel Granduca

1080 Uptown Park Boulevard, Houston, Texas 77056

Tel: +1 713 418 1000
Web: www.johansens.com/granduca

U.S.A. - TEXAS (WASHINGTON)

Inn at Dos Brisas

10,000 Champions Drive, Washington, Texas 77880

Tel: +1 979 277 7750
Web: www.johansens.com/dosbrisas

U.S.A. - UTAH (MOAB)

Sorrel River Ranch Resort & Spa

Mile 17 Scenic Byway 128, H.C. 64 BOX 4002, Moab, Utah 84532

Tel: +1 435 259 4642
Web: www.johansens.com/sorrelriver

U.S.A. - UTAH (PARK CITY)

The Sky Lodge

201 Heber Avenue at Main Street, P.O. Box 683300, Park City, Utah 84068

Tel: +1 435 658 2500
Web: www.johansens.com/skylodge

U.S.A. - VERMONT (LUDLOW/OKEMO)

Castle Hill Resort & Spa

Jct. Routes 103 and 131, Cavendish, Vermont 05142

Tel: +1 802 226 7361
Web: www.johansens.com/castlehillvt

U.S.A. - VERMONT (MANCHESTER VILLAGE)

Equinox Resort & Spa

3567 Main Street, Manchester, Vermont 05254

Tel: +1 802 362 4700
Web: www.johansens.com/equinoxresort

U.S.A. - VERMONT (WARREN)

The Pitcher Inn

275 Main Street, P.O. Box 347, Warren, Vermont 05674

Tel: +1 802 496 6350
Web: www.johansens.com/pitcherinn

U.S.A. - VIRGINIA (GLOUCESTER)

The Inn at Warner Hall

4750 Warner Hall Road, Gloucester, Virginia 23061

Tel: +1 804 695 9565
Web: www.johansens.com/warnerhall

U.S.A. - VIRGINIA (IRVINGTON)

Hope and Glory Inn

65 Tavern Road, Irvington, Virginia 22480

Tel: +1 804 438 6053
Web: www.johansens.com/hopeandglory

U.S.A. - VIRGINIA (MIDDLEBURG)

The Goodstone Inn & Estate

36205 Snake Hill Road, Middleburg, Virginia 20117

Tel: +1 540 687 4645
Web: www.johansens.com/goodstoneinn

U.S.A. - VIRGINIA (RICHMOND)

The Jefferson

101 W. Franklin Street, Richmond, Virginia 23220

Tel: +1 804 788 8000
Web: www.johansens.com/jeffersonva

U.S.A. - VIRGINIA (STAUNTON)

Frederick House

28 North New Street, Staunton, Virginia 24401

Tel: +1 540 885 4220
Web: www.johansens.com/frederickhouse

U.S.A. - VIRGINIA (WILLIAMSBURG)

Wedmore Place

5810 Wessex Hundred, Williamsburg, Virginia 23185

Tel: +1 757 941 0310
Web: www.johansens.com/wedmoreplace

Hotels - The Americas

Properties listed below can be found in our Recommended Hotels, Inns, Resorts & Spas - The Americas, Atlantic, Caribbean & Pacific 2009 Guide. More information on our portfolio of guides can be found on page 13

U.S.A. - WASHINGTON (BELLEVUE)

The Bellevue Club Hotel

11200 S.E. 6th Street, Bellevue, Washington 98004

Tel: +1 425 455 1616
Web: www.johansens.com/bellevue

U.S.A. - WISCONSIN (WAUKESHA)

The Clarke Hotel

314 West Main Street, Waukesha, Wisconsin 53186

Tel: +1 262 549 3800
Web: www.johansens.com/clarkehotel

U.S.A. - WASHINGTON (BELLINGHAM)

The Chrysalis Inn and Spa

804 10th Street, Bellingham, Washington 98225

Tel: +1 360 756 1005
Web: www.johansens.com/chrysalis

Recommendations in Central America

U.S.A. - WASHINGTON (KIRKLAND)

The Heathman Hotel

220 Kirkland Avenue, Kirkland, Washington 98033

Tel: +1 425 284 5800
Web: www.johansens.com/heathmanwa

BELIZE - AMBERGRIS CAYE

Matachica Beach Resort

5 miles North of San Pedro, Ambergris Caye

Tel: +501 220 5010/11
Web: www.johansens.com/matachica

U.S.A. - WASHINGTON (SEATTLE)

Hotel Ändra

2000 Fourth Avenue, Seattle, Washington 98121

Tel: +1 206 448 8600
Web: www.johansens.com/hotelandra

BELIZE - AMBERGRIS CAYE (SAN PEDRO)

Victoria House

P.O. Box 22, San Pedro, Ambergris Caye

Tel: +501 226 2067
Web: www.johansens.com/victoriahouse

U.S.A. - WASHINGTON (SEATTLE)

Inn at the Market

86 Pine Street, Seattle, Washington 98101

Tel: +1 206 443 3600
Web: www.johansens.com/innatthemarket

BELIZE - CAYO (SAN IGNACIO)

The Lodge at Chaa Creek

P.O. Box 53, San Ignacio, Cayo

Tel: +501 824 2037
Web: www.johansens.com/chaacreek

U.S.A. - WASHINGTON (SPOKANE)

The Davenport Hotel and Tower

10 South Post Street, Spokane, Washington 99201

Tel: +1 509 455 8888
Web: www.johansens.com/davenport

BELIZE - ORANGE WALK DISTRICT (GALLON JUG)

Chan Chich Lodge

Gallon Jug, Orange Walk District

Tel: +501 223 4419
Web: www.johansens.com/chanchich

U.S.A. - WASHINGTON (WINTHROP)

Sun Mountain Lodge

P.O. Box 1,000, Winthrop, Washington 98862

Tel: +1 509 996 2211
Web: www.johansens.com/sunmountain

COSTA RICA - ALAJUELA (BAJOS DEL TORO)

El Silencio Lodge & Spa

Bajos del Toro, Alajuela

Tel: +506 2291 3044
Web: www.johansens.com/elsilencio

U.S.A. - WASHINGTON (WOODINVILLE)

The Herbfarm

14590 North East 145th Street, Woodinville, Washington 98072

Tel: +1 425 485 5300
Web: www.johansens.com/herbfarm

COSTA RICA - ALAJUELA (LA FORTUNA DE SAN CARLOS)

Tabacón Grand Spa Thermal Resort

La Fortuna de San Carlos, Arenal

Tel: +506 2519 1999
Web: www.johansens.com/tabacon

Properties listed below can be found in our Recommended Hotels, Inns, Resorts & Spas - The Americas, Atlantic, Caribbean & Pacific 2009 Guide. More information on our portfolio of guides can be found on page 13

COSTA RICA - GUANACASTE (ISLITA)

Hotel Punta Islita

Guanacaste

Tel: +506 2231 6122
Web: www.johansens.com/hotelpuntaislita

COSTA RICA - GUANACASTE (PLAYA CONCHAL)

Paradisus Playa Conchal

Bahía Brasilito, Playa Conchal, Santa Cruz, Guanacaste

Tel: +506 2654 4123
Web: www.johansens.com/paradisusplayaconchal

COSTA RICA - OSA PENISULA (PUERTO JIMENEZ)

Lapa Rios Eco Lodge

Puerto Jimenez, Osa Penisula

Tel: +506 2735 5130
Web: www.johansens.com/laparios

COSTA RICA - PUNTARENAS (MANUEL ANTONIO)

Arenas del Mar

KM 3.7 Carretera Quepos, Manuel Antonio, Puntarenas

Tel: +506 2777 2777
Web: www.johansens.com/areanasdelmar

COSTA RICA - PUNTARENAS (MANUEL ANTONIO)

Gaia Hotel & Reserve

Km 2.7 Carretera Quepos, Manuel Antonio, Puntarenas

Tel: +506 2777 9797
Web: www.johansens.com/gaiahr

GUATEMALA - LA ANTIGUA GUATEMALA

El Convento Boutique Hotel Antigua Guatemala

2a Avenue Norte 11, La Antigua Guatemala, Antigua

Tel: +502 7720 7272
Web: www.johansens.com/elconventoantigua

GUATEMALA - LA ANTIGUA GUATEMALA

Hotel Vista Real La Antigua

3a Calle Oriente 16, La Antigua Guatemala

Tel: +502 7832 9715/6
Web: www.johansens.com/vistareal

GUATEMALA - LA ANTIGUA GUATEMALA (SAN FELIPE)

Filadelfia Coffee Resort & Spa

150 meters North of the San Felipe Chapel,
La Antigua Guatemala

Tel: +502 7728 0800
Web: www.johansens.com/filadelfia

HONDURAS - ATLÁNTIDA (LA CEIBA)

The Lodge at Pico Bonito

A. P. 710, La Ceiba, Atlántida, C. P. 31101

Tel: +504 440 0388
Web: www.johansens.com/picobonito

HONDURAS - BAY ISLANDS (ROATAN)

Barefoot Cay

Roatan, Bay Islands

Tel: +504 455 6235
Web: www.johansens.com/barefootcay

HONDURAS - BAY ISLANDS (ROATAN)

Mayoka Lodge

Sandy Bay, Roatan, Bay Islands

Tel: +504 445 3043
Web: www.johansens.com/mayokalodge

Recommendations in South America

ARGENTINA - BUENOS AIRES (CIUDAD DE BUENOS AIRES)

Home Buenos Aires

Honduras 5860, 1414 Ciudad de Buenos Aires,
Buenos Aires

Tel: +54 11 4778 1008
Web: www.johansens.com/homebuenosaires

ARGENTINA - BUENOS AIRES (CIUDAD DE BUENOS AIRES)

Krista Hotel Boutique

Bonpland 1665, CP1414 Ciudad de Buenos Aires,
Buenos Aires

Tel: +54 11 4771 4697
Web: www.johansens.com/kristahotel

ARGENTINA - BUENOS AIRES (CIUDAD DE BUENOS AIRES)

Legado Mitico

Gurruchaga 1848, C1414DIL Ciudad de Buenos Aires,
Buenos Aires

Tel: +54 11 4833 1300
Web: www.johansens.com/legadomitico

ARGENTINA - BUENOS AIRES (CIUDAD DE BUENOS AIRES)

Mine Hotel Boutique

Gorriti 4770, Palermo Soho, C1414BJL Ciudad de
Buenos Aires, Buenos Aires

Tel: +54 11 4832 1100
Web: www.johansens.com/minehotel

Hotels - The Americas

Properties listed below can be found in our Recommended Hotels, Inns, Resorts & Spas - The Americas, Atlantic, Caribbean & Pacific 2009 Guide. More information on our portfolio of guides can be found on page 13

ARGENTINA - BUENOS AIRES (CIUDAD DE BUENOS AIRES)

Moreno Hotel Buenos Aires

Moreno 376, C1091AAH Ciudad de Buenos Aires, San Telmo, Buenos Aires

Tel: +54 11 6091 2000
Web: www.johansens.com/moreno

BRAZIL - BAHIA (CORUMBAU)

Fazenda São Francisco

Ponta do Corumbau s/n, Prado, Bahia

Tel: +55 11 3078 4411
Web: www.johansens.com/fazenda

ARGENTINA - BUENOS AIRES (CIUDAD DE BUENOS AIRES)

Vain Boutique Hotel

Thames 2226/8, C1425FiF Ciudad de Buenos Aires, Buenos Aires

Tel: +54 11 4776 8246
Web: www.johansens.com/vainuniverse

BRAZIL - BAHIA (CORUMBAU)

Vila Naiá - Paralelo 17°

Ponta do Corumbau, Bahia

Tel: +55 11 3061 1872
Web: www.johansens.com/vilanaia

ARGENTINA - CHUBUT (PATAGONIA - PUERTO MADRYN)

Territorio

Boulevard Alte. G. Brown 3251, U9120ACG Puerto Madryn, Patagonia - Chubut

Tel: +54 11 4114 6029
Web: www.johansens.com/hotelterritorio

BRAZIL - BAHIA (ITACARÉ)

Txai Resort

Rod. Ilhéus-Itacaré km 48, Itacaré, Bahia 45530-000

Tel: +55 73 2101 5000
Web: www.johansens.com/txairesort

ARGENTINA - NEUQUÉN (PATAGONIA - VILLA LA ANGOSTURA)

Correntoso Lake & River Hotel

Av. Siete Lagos 4505, Villa La Angostura, Patagonia

Tel: +54 11 4803 0030
Web: www.johansens.com/correntoso

BRAZIL - BAHIA (PENINSULA OF MARAÚ - MARAÚ)

Kiaroa Eco-Luxury Resort

Loteamento da Costa, área SD6, Distrito de barra grande, Municipio de Maraú, Bahia, CEp 45 520-000

Tel: +55 71 3272 1320
Web: www.johansens.com/kiaroa

ARGENTINA - NEUQUÉN (PATAGONIA - VILLA LA ANGOSTURA)

Hotel Las Balsas

Bahía Las Balsas s/n, 8407 Villa La Angostura, Neuquén

Tel: +54 2944 494308
Web: www.johansens.com/lasbalsas

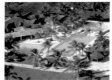

BRAZIL - BAHIA (PRAIA DO FORTE)

Tivoli Ecoresort Praia do Forte

Avenida do Farol, Praia do Forte - Mata de São João, Bahia

Tel: +55 71 36 76 40 00
Web: www.johansens.com/praiadoforte

ARGENTINA - RÍO NEGRO (PATAGONIA - SAN CARLOS BARILOCHE)

Isla Victoria Lodge

Isla Victoria, Parque Nacional Nahuel Huapi, C.C. 26 (R8401AKU)

Tel: +54 43 94 96 05
Web: www.johansens.com/islavictoria

BRAZIL - BAHIA (TRANCOSO)

Etnia Pousada and Boutique

Trancoso, Bahia 45818-000

Tel: +55 73 3668 1137
Web: www.johansens.com/etnia

BRAZIL - ALAGOAS (SÃO MIGUEL DOS MILAGRES)

Pousada do Toque

Rua Felisberto de Ataide, Povoado do Toque, São Miguel dos Milagres, 57940-000 Alagoas

Tel: +55 82 3295 1127
Web: www.johansens.com/pousadadotoque

BRAZIL - MINAS GERAIS (TIRADENTES)

Pousada dos Inconfidentes

Rua João Rodrigues Sobrinho 91, 36325-000, Tiradentes, Minas Gerais

Tel: +55 32 3355 2135
Web: www.johansens.com/inconfidentes

BRAZIL - BAHIA (ARRAIAL D'ÁJUDA)

Maitei Hotel

Estrada do Mucugê 475, Arraial D'Ájuda, Porto Seguro, Bahia 45816-000

Tel: +55 73 3575 3877
Web: www.johansens.com/maitei

BRAZIL - MINAS GERAIS (TIRADENTES)

Solar da Ponte

Praça das Mercês S/N, Tiradentes, Minas Gerais 36325-000

Tel: +55 32 33 55 12 55
Web: www.johansens.com/solardaponte

Properties listed below can be found in our Recommended Hotels, Inns, Resorts & Spas - The Americas, Atlantic, Caribbean & Pacific 2009 Guide.
More information on our portfolio of guides can be found on page 13

BRAZIL - PERNAMBUCO (FERNANDO DE NORONHA)

Pousada Maravilha LIDA

Rodovia BR-363, s/n, Sueste, Ilha de Fernando de
Noronha, Pernambuco 53990-000

Tel: +55 81 3619 0028
Web: www.johansens.com/maravilha

BRAZIL - RIO DE JANEIRO (RIO DE JANEIRO)

Hotel Marina All Suites

Av. Delfim Moreira, 696, Praia do Leblon,
Rio de Janeiro 22441-000

Tel: +55 21 2172 1001
Web: www.johansens.com/marinaallsuites

BRAZIL - PERNAMBUCO (PORTO DE GALINHAS)

Nannai Beach Resort

Rodovia PE-09, acesso à Muro Alto, Km 3, Ipojuca,
Pernambuco 55590-000

Tel: +55 81 3552 0100
Web: www.johansens.com/nannaibeach

BRAZIL - RIO GRANDE DO NORTE (PRAIA DA PIPA)

Toca da Coruja

Av. Baia dos Golfinhos, 464, Praia da Pipa, Tibau do Sul,
Rio Grande do Norte 59178-000

Tel: +55 84 3246 2226
Web: www.johansens.com/rocadacoruja

BRAZIL - RIO DE JANEIRO (ARMAÇÃO DOS BÚZIOS)

Villa Rasa Marina

Av. José Bento Ribeiro Dantas 299,
Armação dos Búzios, Rio de Janeiro 28950-000

Tel: +55 21 2172 1000
Web: www.johansens.com/villarasamarina

BRAZIL - RIO GRANDE DO SUL (GRAMADO)

Estalagem St. Hubertus

Rua Carrieri, 974, Gramado,
Rio Grande do Sul 95670-000

Tel: +55 54 3286 1273
Web: www.johansens.com/sthubertus

BRAZIL - RIO DE JANEIRO (BÚZIOS)

Casas Brancas Boutique-Hotel & Spa

Alto do Humaitá 10, Armação dos Búzios,
Rio de Janeiro 28950-000

Tel: +55 22 2623 1458
Web: www.johansens.com/casasbrancas

BRAZIL - RIO GRANDE DO SUL (GRAMADO)

Kurotel

Rua Nacões Unidas 533, P.O. Box 65, Gramado,
Rio Grande do Sul 95670-000

Tel: +55 54 3295 9393
Web: www.johansens.com/kurotel

BRAZIL - RIO DE JANEIRO (BÚZIOS)

Insólito Boutique Hotel

Rua E1 - Lot 3 e 4 , Condomínio Atlântico, Armação de
Búzios, Rio de Janeiro 28,950-000

Tel: +55 22 2623 2172
Web: www.johansens.com/insolitos

BRAZIL - RIO GRANDE DO SUL (SÃO FRANCISCO DE PAULA)

Pousada do Engenho

Rua Odon Cavalcante, 330, São Francisco de Paula
95400-000, Rio Grande do Sul

Tel: +55 54 3244 1270
Web: www.johansens.com/pousadadoengenho

BRAZIL - RIO DE JANEIRO (PETRÓPOLIS)

Parador Santarém Marina

Estrada Correia da Veiga, 96, Petrópolis,
Rio de Janeiro 25745-260

Tel: +55 24 2222 9933
Web: www.johansens.com/paradorsantarem

BRAZIL - SANTA CATARINA (GOVERNADOR CELSO RAMOS)

Ponta dos Ganchos

Rua Eupídio Alves do Nascimento, 104, Governador
Celso Ramos, Santa Catarina 88190-000

Tel: +55 48 3262 5000
Web: www.johansens.com/pontadosganchos

BRAZIL - RIO DE JANEIRO (PETRÓPOLIS)

Solar do Império

Koeler Avenue, 376 - Centro, Petrópolis, Rio de Janeiro

Tel: +55 24 2103 3000
Web: www.johansens.com/solardoimperio

BRAZIL - SANTA CATARINA (PALHOÇA)

Ilha do Papagaio

Ilha do Papagaio, Palhoça, Santa Catarina 88131-970

Tel: +55 48 3286 1242
Web: www.johansens.com/ilhadopapagaio

BRAZIL - RIO DE JANEIRO (PETRÓPOLIS)

Tankamana EcoResort

Estrada Júlio Cápua, S/N Vale Do Cuiabá, Itaipava -
Petrópolis, Rio De Janeiro 25745-050

Tel: +55 24 2103 3000
Web: www.johansens.com/tankamana

BRAZIL - SANTA CATARINA (PRAIA DO ROSA)

Pousada Solar Mirador

Estrada Geral do Rosa s/n, Praia do Rosa, Imbituba,
Santa Catarina 88780-000

Tel: +55 48 3355 6144
Web: www.johansens.com/solarmirador

Hotels - The Americas

Properties listed below can be found in our Recommended Hotels, Inns, Resorts & Spas - The Americas, Atlantic, Caribbean & Pacific 2009 Guide. More information on our portfolio of guides can be found on page 13

BRAZIL - SÃO PAULO (CAMPOS DO JORDÃO)

Hotel Frontenac

Av. Dr. Paulo Ribas, 295 Capivari,
Campos do Jordão 12460-000

Tel: +55 12 3669 1000
Web: www.johansens.com/frontenac

BRAZIL - SÃO PAULO (ILHABELA)

DPNY Beach Hotel

Av. José Pacheco do Nascimento, 7668, Praia do Curral,
Ilhabela, São Paulo 11630-000

Tel: +55 12 3894 2121
Web: www.johansens.com/dpnybeach

BRAZIL - SÃO PAULO (SÃO PAULO)

Hotel Emiliano

Rua Oscar Freire 384, São Paulo, SP 01426-000

Tel: +55 11 3068 4393
Web: www.johansens.com/emiliano

BRAZIL - SÃO PAULO (SÃO PAULO)

Hotel Unique

Av. Brigadeiro Luis Antonio, 4.700, São Paulo,
São Paulo 01402-002

Tel: +55 11 3055 4710
Web: www.johansens.com/hotelunique

BRAZIL - SÃO PAULO (SERRA DA CANTAREIRA)

Spa Unique Garden

Estrada Laramara, 3500, Serra da Cantareira,
São Paulo 07600-970

Tel: +55 11 4486 8700
Web: www.johansens.com/uniquegarden

CHILE - REGIÓN DE ARAUCANÍA (VILLARRICA)

Villarrica Park Lake Hotel

Camino a Villarrica km.13, Villarrica,
Región de Araucanía

Tel: +56 2 207 7070
Web: www.johansens.com/villarrica

CHILE - REGIÓN DE ATACAMA (SAN PEDRO DE ATACAMA)

Alto Atacama

Camino Pucarà S/N, Sector Suchor, Ayllù de Quitor,
San Pedro de Atacama, Región de Atacama

Tel: +562 436 0265
Web: www.johansens.com/altoatacama

CHILE - REGION DE AYSEN (PATAGONIA - PUERTO GUADAL)

Hacienda Tres Lagos

Carretera Austral Sur Km 274, Localidad Lago Negro,
Puerto Guadal, Region de Aysen, Patagonia

Tel: +56 2 333 4122
Web: www.johansens.com/treslagos

CHILE - REGIÓN DE MAGALLANES
(PATAGONIA - PUERTO NATALES)

Indigo Patagonia Hotel & Spa

Ladrilleros 105, Puerto Natales, Región de Magallanes

Tel: +566 141 3609
Web: www.johansens.com/indigopatagonia

CHILE - REGIÓN DE VALPARAÍSO (VALPARAÍSO)

Hotel Manoir Atkinson

Paseo Atkinson 165, Cerro Concepcion, Valparaíso,
Región de Valparaíso

Tel: +563 2235 1313
Web: www.johansens.com/hotelatkinson

CHILE - REGIÓN DE VALPARAÍSO (VIÑA DEL MAR)

Hotel Del Mar - Enjoy Hotels

Av. Perú Esquina Av. Los Héroes, Viña del Mar,
Región de Valparaíso

Tel: +56 32 284 6100
Web: www.johansens.com/hoteldelmarcl

CHILE - REGIÓN DO LOS LAGOS (PATAGONIA - PUERTO MONTT)

Nomads of the Seas

Puerto Montt, Región do los Lagos

Tel: +562 414 4600
Web: www.johansens.com/nomadsoftheseas

ECUADOR - AZUAY (CUENCA)

Mansión Alcázar Boutique Hotel

Calle Bolívar 12-55 Y Tarqui, Cuenca, Azuay

Tel: +593 72823 918
Web: www.johansens.com/mansionalcazar

ECUADOR - COTOPAXI (LASSO)

Hacienda San Agustin de Callo

77km south of Quito on the Panamerican Highway,
Lasso, Cotopaxi

Tel: +593 3 2719 160
Web: www.johansens.com/haciendasanagustin

ECUADOR - IMBABURA (ANGOCHAGUA)

Hacienda Zuleta

Angochagua, Imbabura

Tel: +593 6 266 2182
Web: www.johansens.com/zuleta

ECUADOR - IMBABURA (COTACACHI)

La Mirage Garden Hotel and Spa

Cotacachi, Imbabura

Tel: +593 6 291 5237
Web: www.johansens.com/mirage

Hotels - Americas, Atlantic & Caribbean

Properties listed below can be found in our Recommended Hotels, Inns, Resorts & Spas - The Americas, Atlantic, Caribbean & Pacific 2009 Guide.
More information on our portfolio of guides can be found on page 13

PERU - LIMA PROVINCIAS (YAUYOS)

Refugios Del Peru - Viñak Reichraming

Santiago de Viñak, Yauyos, Lima

Tel: +511 421 7777
Web: www.johansens.com/refugiosdelperu

Recommendations in the Caribbean

URUGUAY - MALDONADO (PUNTA DEL ESTE)

L'Auberge

Carnoustie y Av. del Agua, Barrio Parque de Golf,
Punta del Este CP20100

Tel: +598 42 48 2601
Web: www.johansens.com/laubergeuruguay

CARIBBEAN - ANGUILLA (RENDEZVOUS BAY)

CuisinArt Resort & Spa

P.O. Box 2000, Rendezvous Bay

Tel: +1 264 498 2000
Web: www.johansens.com/cuisinartresort

CARIBBEAN - ANGUILLA (WEST END)

Sheriva Villa Hotel

Maundays Bay Road, West End AI-2640

Tel: +1 264 498 9898
Web: www.johansens.com/sheriva

Recommendations in the Atlantic

ATLANTIC - BAHAMAS (GRAND BAHAMA ISLAND)

Old Bahama Bay by Ginn Sur Mer

West End, Grand Bahama Island

Tel: +1 242 350 6500
Web: www.johansens.com/oldbahamabay

CARIBBEAN - ANTIGUA (ST. JOHN'S)

Galley Bay Resort & Spa

Five Islands, St. John's

Tel: +1 954 481 8787
Web: www.johansens.com/galleybay

ATLANTIC - BERMUDA (HAMILTON)

Rosedon Hotel

P.O. Box Hm 290, Hamilton Hmax

Tel: +1 441 295 1640
Web: www.johansens.com/rosedonhotel

CARIBBEAN - ANTIGUA (ST. JOHN'S)

Hermitage Bay Hotel

St. John's

Tel: +1 268 562 5500
Web: www.johansens.com/hermitagebay

ATLANTIC - BERMUDA (SOMERSET)

Cambridge Beaches Resort & Spa

Sandys, Somerset

Tel: +1 441 234 0331
Web: www.johansens.com/cambeaches

CARIBBEAN - ANTIGUA (ST. JOHN'S)

The Verandah Resort & Spa

Indian Town Road, St. John's

Tel: +1 954 481 8787
Web: www.johansens.com/verandah

ATLANTIC - BERMUDA (SOUTHAMPTON)

The Reefs

56 South Shore Road, Southampton

Tel: +1 441 238 0222
Web: www.johansens.com/thereefs

CARIBBEAN - ANTIGUA (ST. JOHN'S)

Blue Waters

P.O. Box 257, St. John's

Tel: +44 870 360 1245
Web: www.johansens.com/bluewaters

For further information, hotel search, gift certificates, online bookshop and special offers visit:

www.johansens.com

Annually Inspected for the Independent Traveler

Hotels - Caribbean

Properties listed below can be found in our Recommended Hotels, Inns, Resorts & Spas - The Americas, Atlantic, Caribbean & Pacific 2009 Guide. More information on our portfolio of guides can be found on page 13

CARIBBEAN - ANTIGUA (ST. JOHN'S)

Curtain Bluff

P.O. Box 288, St. John's

Tel: +1 268 462 8400
Web: www.johansens.com/curtainbluff

CARIBBEAN - CURAÇAO (WILLEMSTAD)

Avila Hotel on the Beach

Penstraat 130, Willemstad

Tel: +599 9 461 4377
Web: www.johansens.com/avilabeach

CARIBBEAN - ANTIGUA (ST. MARY'S)

Carlisle Bay

Old Road, St. Mary's

Tel: +1 268 484 0000
Web: www.johansens.com/carlislebay

CARIBBEAN - DOMINICAN REPUBLIC (PUERTA PLATA)

Maxim Bungalows Resort and Spa

1 Paradise Drive, Cofresi Beach, Puerto Plata

Tel: +1 866 970 3364
Web: www.johansens.com/maximbungalows

CARIBBEAN - BARBADOS (CHRIST CHURCH)

Little Arches

Enterprise Beach Road, Christ Church

Tel: +1 246 420 4689
Web: www.johansens.com/littlearches

CARIBBEAN - DOMINICAN REPUBLIC (PUERTO PLATA)

Casa Colonial Beach & Spa

P.O. Box 22, Puerto Plata

Tel: +1 809 320 3232
Web: www.johansens.com/casacolonial

CARIBBEAN - BARBADOS (ST. JAMES)

Coral Reef Club

St. James

Tel: +1 246 422 2372
Web: www.johansens.com/coralreefclub

CARIBBEAN - DOMINICAN REPUBLIC (PUNTA CANA)

Agua Resort & Spa

Uvero Alto, Punta Cana

Tel: +1 809 468 0000
Web: www.johansens.com/aguaresort

CARIBBEAN - BARBADOS (ST. JAMES)

The Sandpiper

Holetown, St. James

Tel: +1 246 422 2251
Web: www.johansens.com/sandpiper

CARIBBEAN - DOMINICAN REPUBLIC (PUNTA CANA)

Sivory Punta Cana

Playa Sivory, Uvero Alto/Punta Cana

Tel: +1 809 333 0500
Web: www.johansens.com/sivory

CARIBBEAN - BRITISH VIRGIN ISLANDS (PETER ISLAND)

Peter Island Resort

Peter Island

Tel: +770 476 9988
Web: www.johansens.com/peterislandresort

CARIBBEAN - DOMINICAN REPUBLIC (PUNTA CANA)

Tortuga Bay, Puntacana Resort & Club

Dominican Republic

Tel: +1 809 959 2262
Web: www.johansens.com/puntacana

CARIBBEAN - BRITISH VIRGIN ISLANDS (PETER ISLAND)

The Villas at Peter Island

Peter Island

Tel: +770 476 9988
Web: www.johansens.com/villaspeterisland

CARIBBEAN - GRENADA (ST. GEORGE'S)

Spice Island Beach Resort

Grand Anse Beach, St. George's

Tel: +1 473 444 4423/4258
Web: www.johansens.com/spiceisland

CARIBBEAN - BRITISH VIRGIN ISLANDS (VIRGIN GORDA)

Biras Creek Resort

North Sound, Virgin Gorda

Tel: +1 248 364 2421
Web: www.johansens.com/birascreek

CARIBBEAN - JAMAICA (MONTEGO BAY)

Half Moon

Rose Hall

Tel: +1 876 953 2211
Web: www.johansens.com/halfmoon

Properties listed below can be found in our Recommended Hotels, Inns, Resorts & Spas - The Americas, Atlantic, Caribbean & Pacific 2009 Guide.
More information on our portfolio of guides can be found on page 13

CARIBBEAN - JAMAICA (MONTEGO BAY)

Tryall Club

P.O. Box 1206, Montego Bay

Tel: +1 876 956 5660

Web: www.johansens.com/tryallclub

CARIBBEAN - ST. LUCIA (SOUFRIÈRE)

Anse Chastanet

Soufrière

Tel: +1 758 459 7000

Web: www.johansens.com/ansechastanet

CARIBBEAN - JAMAICA (OCHO RIOS)

Royal Plantation

Main Street , P.O. Box 2, Ocho Rios

Tel: +1 876 974 5601

Web: www.johansens.com/royalplantation

CARIBBEAN - ST. LUCIA (SOUFRIÈRE)

Jade Mountain at Anse Chastanet

Soufrière

Tel: +1 758 459 4000

Web: www.johansens.com/jademountain

CARIBBEAN - PUERTO RICO (OLD SAN JUAN)

Chateau Cervantes

Recinto Sur 329, Old San Juan

Tel: +787 724 7722

Web: www.johansens.com/cervantes

CARIBBEAN - ST. LUCIA (SOUFRIÈRE)

Ladera Resort

Soufrière

Tel: +1 758 459 7323

Web: www.johansens.com/ladera

CARIBBEAN - PUERTO RICO (RINCÓN)

Horned Dorset Primavera

Apartado 1132, Rincón 00677

Tel: +1 787 823 4030

Web: www.johansens.com/horneddorset

CARIBBEAN - ST. MARTIN (BAIE LONGUE)

La Samanna

P.O. Box 4077, 97064 CEDEX

Tel: +590 590 87 64 00

Web: www.johansens.com/lasamanna

CARIBBEAN - SAINT-BARTHÉLEMY (ANSE DE TOINY)

Hôtel Le Toiny

Anse de Toiny

Tel: +590 590 27 88 88

Web: www.johansens.com/letoiny

CARIBBEAN - THE GRENADINES (MUSTIQUE)

Firefly

Mustique Island

Tel: +1 784 488 8414

Web: www.johansens.com/firefly

CARIBBEAN - SAINT-BARTHÉLEMY (GRAND CUL DE SAC)

Hotel Guanahani & Spa

Grand Cul de Sac

Tel: +590 590 27 66 60

Web: www.johansens.com/guanahani

CARIBBEAN - THE GRENADINES (PALM ISLAND)

Palm Island

Palm Island

Tel: +1 954 481 8787

Web: www.johansens.com/palmisland

CARIBBEAN - ST. KITTS & NEVIS (NEVIS)

Montpelier Plantation

P.O. Box 474, Nevis

Tel: +1 869 469 3462

Web: www.johansens.com/montpelierplantation

CARIBBEAN - TURKS & CAICOS ISLANDS (GRACE BAY BEACH)

The Estate at Grace Bay Club

P.O. Box 128, Providenciales

Tel: +649 946 8323

Web: www.johansens.com/estateatgracebay

CARIBBEAN - ST. LUCIA (CASTRIES)

Windjammer Landing Villa Beach Resort & Spa

P.O. Box 1504, Castries, St. Lucia

Tel: 1 758 456 9000

Web: www.johansens.com/windjammerlanding

CARIBBEAN - TURKS & CAICOS ISLANDS (GRACE BAY BEACH)

Grace Bay Club

P.O. Box 128, Providenciales

Tel: +1 649 946 5050

Web: www.johansens.com/gracebayclub

Hotels - Caribbean & Pacific

Properties listed below can be found in our Recommended Hotels, Inns, Resorts & Spas - The Americas, Atlantic, Caribbean & Pacific 2009 Guide. More information on our portfolio of guides can be found on page 13

CARIBBEAN - TURKS & CAICOS ISLANDS (GRACE BAY BEACH)

The Regent Palms, Turks & Caicos

P.O. Box 681, Grace Bay, Providenciales

Tel: +649 946 8666
Web: www.johansens.com/regentpalms

PACIFIC - FIJI ISLANDS (QAMEA ISLAND)

Qamea Resort & Spa

P.A. Matei, Taveuni

Tel: +649 360 0858
Web: www.johansens.com/qamea

CARIBBEAN - TURKS & CAICOS ISLANDS (GRACE BAY BEACH)

The Somerset on Grace Bay

Princess Drive, Providenciales

Tel: +1 649 946 5900
Web: www.johansens.com/somersetgracebay

PACIFIC - FIJI ISLANDS (SAVUSAVU)

Jean-Michel Cousteau Fiji Islands Resort

Lesiaceva Point, SavuSavu

Tel: +1 415 788 5794
Web: www.johansens.com/jean-michelcousteau

CARIBBEAN - TURKS & CAICOS ISLANDS (PARROT CAY)

Parrot Cay & COMO Shambhala Retreat

P.O. Box 164, Providenciales

Tel: +1 649 946 7788
Web: www.johansens.com/parrotcay

PACIFIC - FIJI ISLANDS (SAVUSAVU)

Namale - Fiji islands Resort & Spa

P.O. Box 244, Savusavu

Tel: +679 8850 435
Web: www.johansens.com/namale

CARIBBEAN - TURKS & CAICOS ISLANDS (POINT GRACE)

Point Grace

P.O. Box 700, Providenciales

Tel: +1 649 946 5096
Web: www.johansens.com/pointgrace

PACIFIC - FIJI ISLANDS (SIGATOKA)

Myola Plantation

P.O. Box 638, Sigatoka

Tel: +679 652 1084
Web: www.johansens.com/myola

CARIBBEAN - TURKS & CAICOS ISLANDS (WEST GRACE BAY BEACH)

Turks & Caicos Club

West Grace Bay Beach, P.O. Box 687, Providenciales

Tel: +1 649 946 5800
Web: www.johansens.com/turksandcaicos

PACIFIC - FIJI ISLANDS (UGAGA ISLAND)

Royal Davui Island Resort - Fiji

P.O. Box 3171, Lami

Tel: +679 336 1624
Web: www.johansens.com/royaldavui

Recommendations in the Pacific

PACIFIC - FIJI ISLANDS (YAQETA ISLAND)

Navutu Stars Resort

P.O. Box 1838, Lautoka

Tel: +679 664 0553 and +679 664 0554
Web: www.johansens.com/navutustars

PACIFIC - FIJI ISLANDS (LABASA)

Nukubati Island, Great Sea Reef, Fiji

P.O. Box 1928, Labasa

Tel: +61 2 93888 196
Web: www.johansens.com/nukubati

PACIFIC - FIJI ISLANDS (YASAWA ISLAND)

Turtle Island

P.O. Box 9317, Nadi, Yasawa Island

Tel: +1 360 256 4347
Web: www.johansens.com/turtleisland

PACIFIC - FIJI ISLANDS (LAUTOKA)

Blue Lagoon Cruises

183 Vitogo Parade, Lautoka

Tel: +679 6661 622
Web: www.johansens.com/bluelagooncruises

PACIFIC - FIJI ISLANDS (YASAWA ISLAND)

Yasawa Island Resort & Spa

P.O. Box 10128, Nadi Airport, Nadi

Tel: +679 672 2266
Web: www.johansens.com/yasawaislan

Index by Property

A

The Anchor Inn at Sutton Gault ....Sutton 39
The Angel Hotel ....Lavenham 138
Ard Na Sidhe ....Killarney 169
Auberge du Lac ....Welwyn 85
The Austwick Traddock ....Austwick 156
Aylestone Court ....Hereford 78

B

Bae Abermaw ....Barmouth 196
Balcary Bay Hotel ....Auchencairn 173
Barnsdale Lodge ....Rutland Water 120
Beaumont House ....Cheltenham 69
Beechfield House ....Bath 145
The Bell At Skenfrith ....Monmouth 198
Bellplot House Hotel ....Chard 127
Beryl ....Wells 132
Bibury Court ....Bibury 67
Bindon Country House ....Taunton 131
Binham Grange ....Minehead 129
Braunston Manor ....Braunston 105
BridgeHouse Beaminster ....Beaminster 64
Broad House ....Norwich 104
Broadoaks Country House......................................Windermere 53
Brooklands Country Retreat & Health Spa ....Garstang 96
Burford House ....Burford 112
Burford Lodge Hotel & Restaurant............................Burford 113

C

Cantley House Hotel ....Wokingham 36
The Castle Inn ....Castle Combe 147
Castle Venlaw ....Peebles 187
Channels Lodge ....Little Waltham 66
The Chase Hotel ....Ross-On-Wye 80
Château La Chaire ....Jersey 19
The Christopher Hotel Bar & Grill ....Eton 32
Clarice House..Bury St. Edmunds 136
Cockliffe Country House Hotel ....Nottingham 110
Compton House..Axbridge 125
The Cormorant Hotel and Restaurant ....Fowey 41
Cornfields Restaurant & Hotel ....Colmworth 31
The Cornwallis Country Hotel & Restaurant ....Eye 137
Corsewall Lighthouse Hotel ....Stranraer 174
Crosby Lodge Country House Hotel ....Carlisle 48
The Crown ....Old Amersham 38
The Crown At Whitebrook.......................................Whitebrook 199
The Crown Hotel ....Stamford 98
The Crown Inn ....Ashbourne 54
The Crown Inn ....Chiddingfold 140
Culzean Castle – The Eisenhower Apartment............Maybole 188

D

Dannah Farm Country House ....Belper 56
Darroch Learg ....Ballater 172
The Devonshire Fell ....Burnsall 158
The Dial House ....Bourton-On-
                                                         The-Water 68
Donington Manor Hotel...Castle Donington 57
Duke Of Marlborough Country Inn ....Woodstock 118
Dunain Park Hotel & Restaurant ....Inverness 178
Dunsley Hall ....Whitby 159
Dunsley Hall Hotel...Kinver 134
The Dusty Miller & Coiners Restaurant......................Hebden Bridge 162

E

East Lodge Country House Hotel ....Bakewell 55
The Edgemoor ....Bovey Tracey 60

Egerton Grey ....Porthkerry 202
Episode Hotel ....Royal Leamington Spa ..143

F

The Farmhouse..Guernsey 18
Farthings Country House Hotel & Restaurant............Near Taunton 130
Fauhope Country House ....Melrose 186
Fayrer Garden House Hotel ....Windermere 52
Felbrigg Lodge ....Cromer 100
Ferrari's Restaurant & Hotel ....Preston 97
Forss House Hotel ....Thurso 184
Fox Country Inn ....High Wycombe 37

G

George and Dragon Inn ....Aysgarth 157
The George Hotel ....Shipston-on-Stour 144
Glewstone Court ....Ross-on-Wye 82
The Goose ....Britwell Salome 117
The Grange at Oborne ....Sherborne 65
Greenwood Lodge ....Nottingham 109
Greshornish House ....Isle of Skye 180

H

The Hambrough ....Ventnor 89
Hey Green Country House Hotel ....Marsden 163
Hipping Hall..Kirkby Lonsdale 51
The Hudson Hotel ....Edinburgh 175

I

The Inn at Grinshill ....Shrewsbury 123
The Inn on the Green, Restaurant with Rooms ....Maidenhead 34

K

Karslake Country House and Cottage......................Winsford 133
Kick & Dicky ....Standon 83
Kilham Hall ....Kilham 155
The Kings Head Hotel ....Great Bircham 101
Kingston House ....Staverton 63
Knockomie Hotel ....Forres 185

Index by Property/Location

L

La Sablonnerie	Guernsey	17
The Lake Isle Hotel & Restaurant	Uppingham	121
The Lamb at Hindon	Hindon	149
The Lamb Inn	Burford	114
Langar Hall	Nottingham	111
Langrish House	Petersfield	76
Little Silver Country Hotel	Tenterden	94
Llwyndu Farmhouse	Barmouth	197
Loch Ness Lodge	Inverness	179
Lower Brook House	Moreton-in-Marsh	73
Lypiatt House	Cheltenham	70

M

The Manor at Hanchurch	Stoke-on-Trent	135
Marmadukes Hotel	York	160
The Mill At Gordleton	Lymington	74
Mill End	Chagford	61
The Mill House Hotel	Ashington	142
Moccas Court	Moccas	79

N

New Inn At Coln	Cirencester	71
Nick's Restaurant	Oakham	119
Number One South Beach	Blackpool	95
The Nurse's Cottage Restaurant with Rooms	Lymington	75
The Nut Tree Inn	Oxford	115

O

The Old Coastguard Hotel	Mousehole	44
The Old House Hotel	Wickham	77
The Old Rectory	Norwich	103
The Old Rectory	Ipsley	153
The Olde Bell Coaching Inn	Hurley	33
The Orchard House	Rothbury	108
The Otterburn Tower	Otterburn	107

P

The Pear Tree Inn	**Melksham**	**150**
Pen-Y-Dyffryn Country Hotel	Oswestry	122
Penally Abbey	Tenby	200
Pentre Mawr Country House	Denbigh	194
The Pheasant	Bassenthwaite Lake	47
The Plough Inn	Hathersage	58
Porth Tocyn Country House Hotel	Abersoch	195
Pride of the Valley	Farnham	141
The Priory Bay Hotel	Seaview	87

R

The Redesdale Arms	Moreton-in-Marsh	72
Riverside Hotel and Restaurant	Evesham	152
Romney Bay House Hotel	New Romney	92
Rose-In-Vale Country House Hotel	**St Agnes**	**46**
The Rosevine	Porthcurnick Beach	45
Royal Forester Country Inn	Callow Hill	151
The Royal Harbour Hotel	Ramsgate	93
Royal Marine Hotel, Restaurant & Spa	Brora	176
Ruddyglow Park	Loch Assynt	183
Rylstone Manor	Shanklin	88

S

Saco House, Bath	Bath	30
The Shibden Mill Inn	Shibden	164
Skeabost Country House	Isle of Skye	181
Soulton Hall	Shrewsbury	124
Stanton Manor Hotel & Gallery Restaurant	Chippenham	148
The Steadings at The Grouse & Trout	Farr	177
Stirrups Country House Hotel	Windsor	35

T

Talland Bay Hotel	Looe	42
Tan-Y-Foel Country House	Betws-y-Coed	193
Three Acres Country House	Dulverton	128
The Tickell Arms, Restaurant	Whittlesford	40
Titchwell Manor Hotel	King's Lynn	102
Toravaig House	Isle of Skye	182
Tree Tops Country House Restaurant & Hotel	Southport	99
Trevalsa Court Country House Hotel	Mevagissey	43
The Turtley Corn Mill	Avonwick	59
Ty Mawr Country Hotel	Brechfa	192

W

Wallett's Court Hotel & Spa	Dover	91
Waren House Hotel	Bamburgh	106
West Vale Country House & Restaurant	Hawkshead	49
The Westleton Crown	Southwold	139
Weston Manor	Oxford	116
The Wheatsheaf @ Brigsteer	Kendal	50
The White Cliffs Hotel	Dover	90
The White House	Guernsey	16
The White House	Chillington	62
The White House and Lion & Lamb Bar & Restaurant	Stansted Airport	84
The White Lion Hotel	Upton-upon-Severn	154
Widbrook Grange	Bath	146
Wilton Court Hotel	Ross-on-Wye	81
Winterbourne Country House	Bonchurch	86
Wolfscastle Country Hotel & Restaurant	Wolf's Castle	201
Woodlands Country House Hotel	Brent Knoll	126
The Worsley Arms Hotel	York	161

Index by Location

England

A

Ashbourne ....The Crown Inn 54
Ashford ....Little Silver Country Hotel 94
Ashington ....The Mill House Hotel 142
Austwick...................................The Austwick Traddock 156
Avonwick..................................The Turtley Corn Mill 59
Axbridge...................................Compton House 125
Aysgarth ....George and Dragon Inn 157

B

Bakewell ....East Lodge Country House Hotel 55
Bamburgh ....Waren House Hotel 106
Bassenthwaite Lake ....The Pheasant 47
Bath ....Beechfield House 145
Bath ....Saco House, Bath 30
Bath ....Widbrook Grange 146
Beaminster ....BridgeHouse Beaminster 64
Beanacre..................................Beechfield House 145
Bedford ....Cornfields Restaurant & Hotel 31
Belper.......................................Dannah Farm Country House.............56
Bewdley....................................Royal Forester Country Inn 151
Bibury.......................................Bibury Court 67
Blackpool ....Number One South Beach 95
Blockley....................................Lower Brook House 73
Bonchurch ....Winterbourne Country House 86
Bourton-On-The-Water ....The Dial House 68
Bovey Tracey............................The Edgemoor......................................60
Bowness....................................Fayrer Garden House Hotel 52
Bradford-On-Avon ....Widbrook Grange 146
Brancaster ....Titchwell Manor Hotel 102
Braunston.................................Braunston Manor.................................105
Brent Knoll ....Woodlands Country House Hotel 126
Brigsteer...................................The Wheatsheaf @ Brigsteer 50
Bristol.......................................Woodlands Country House Hotel 126
Britwell Salome ....The Goose..117
Brome ....The Cornwallis Country Hotel & Restaurant 137
Burford ....Burford House......................................112
Burford ....Burford Lodge Hotel & Restaurant......113
Burford ....The Lamb Inn 114
Burnsall ....The Devonshire Fell 158
Burntstump Hill ....Cockliffe Country House Hotel 110
Bury St. Edmunds ....Clarice House 136

C

Callow Hill ....Royal Forester Country Inn 151
Cambridge.................................The Tickell Arms, Restaurant 40
Carlisle.....................................Crosby Lodge Country House Hotel 48
Castle Combe ....The Castle Inn 147
Castle Donington ....Donington Manor Hotel 57
Chagford ....Mill End 61
Chard ....Bellplot House Hotel 127
Cheddar ....Compton House 125
Chelmsford ....Channels Lodge 66
Cheltenham ....Beaumont House 69
Cheltenham ....Lypiatt House.......................................70
Chiddingfold.............................The Crown Inn 140
Chillington ....The White House 62
Chilterns ....The Crown..38
Chippenham..............................Stanton Manor Hotel & Gallery Restaurant ...148
Cirencester...............................New Inn At Coln 71
Colmworth ....Cornfields Restaurant & Hotel 31
Coln St-Aldwyns ....New Inn At Coln 71

Cookham Dean ....The Inn on the Green, Restaurant with Rooms 34
Cotswolds ....Burford House.......................................112
Cotswolds ....Burford Lodge Hotel & Restaurant....113
Cotswolds ....Duke Of Marlborough Country Inn 118
Cotswolds ....The Lamb Inn 114
Cromer ....Felbrigg Lodge 100

D

Dartmoor ....The Edgemoor......................................60
Dartmouth.................................The White House 62
Derby ....Donington Manor Hotel 57
Dover ....Wallett's Court Hotel & Spa 91
Dover ....The White Cliffs Hotel 90
Driffield ....Kilham Hall 155
Dulverton ....Three Acres Country House 128

E

Ely ....The Anchor Inn at Sutton Gault...........39
Eton ....The Christopher Hotel Bar & Grill 32
Evesham ....Riverside Hotel and Restaurant..........152
Exmoor National Park ....Karslake Country House and Cottage 133
Eye..The Cornwallis Country Hotel & Restaurant 137

F

Far Sawrey ....West Vale Country House & Restaurant 49
Farnham ....Pride of the Valley 141
Formby......................................Tree Tops Country House Restaurant & Hotel.......99
Fowey ....The Cormorant Hotel and Restaurant.................41

G

Garstang ....Brooklands Country Retreat & Health Spa 96
Glewstone ....Glewstone Court 82

Golant ....The Cormorant Hotel and Restaurant..............41
Great Bircham ....The Kings Head Hotel 101
Grinshill....................................The Inn at Grinshill 123

H

Halifax ....The Shibden Mill Inn 164
Hanchurch ....The Manor at Hanchurch 135
Hatch Beauchamp ....Farthings Country House Hotel & Restaurant......130
Hathersage ....The Plough Inn 58

Index by Location

Hawkshead ....West Vale Country House & Restaurant 49
Hay-on-Wye ....Moccas Court 79
Hebden Bridge ....The Dusty Miller & Coiners Restaurant..............162
Henley ....The Olde Bell Coaching Inn 33
Hereford ....Aylestone Court 78
High Crosby ....Crosby Lodge Country House Hotel 48
High Wycombe ....Fox Country Inn 37
Hindon ....The Lamb at Hindon 149
Hordle ....The Mill At Gordleton 74
Hovingham ....The Worsley Arms Hotel 161
Hurley ....The Olde Bell Coaching Inn 33

I

Ipsley ....The Old Rectory 153

K

Kendal ....The Wheatsheaf @ Brigsteer 50
Kilham ....Kilham Hall 155
King's Lynn ....Titchwell Manor Hotel 102
Kinver............................Dunsley Hall Hotel 134
Kirkby Lonsdale.....................Hipping Hall 51

L

Langar ....Langar Hall 111
Langford Budville ....Bindon Country House 131
Langrish ....Langrish House 76
Lavenham ....The Angel Hotel 138
Little Waltham ....Channels Lodge 66
Littlestone ....Romney Bay House Hotel 92
Longridge ....Ferrari's Restaurant & Hotel 97
Looe ....Talland Bay Hotel 42

Lymington ....**The Mill At Gordleton** **74**
Lymington ....The Nurse's Cottage Restaurant with Rooms 75

M

Maidenhead ....The Inn on the Green, Restaurant with Rooms......34
Maidens Green ....Stirrups Country House Hotel.............................35
Malvern ....The White Lion Hotel 154
Marsden ....Hey Green Country House Hotel 163
Marston Montgomery ....The Crown Inn 54

Melksham ....The Pear Tree Inn 150
Mevagissey ....Trevalsa Court Country House Hotel 43
Minehead ....Binham Grange 129
Mithian ....Rose-In-Vale Country House Hotel 46
Moccas ....Moccas Court 79
Moreton-in-Marsh ....Lower Brook House 73
Moreton-in-Marsh ....The Redesdale Arms 72
Mousehole ....The Old Coastguard Hotel 44
Murcott ....The Nut Tree Inn 115
Mytholmroyd ....The Dusty Miller & Coiners Restaurant..............162

N

New Forest ....The Nurse's Cottage Restaurant with Rooms 75
New Romney ....Romney Bay House Hotel...................................92
North Norfolk ....The Kings Head Hotel 101
Norwich ....Broad House 104
Norwich ....The Old Rectory 103
Nottingham ....Cockliffe Country House Hotel 110
Nottingham ....Greenwood Lodge 109
Nottingham ....Langar Hall 111

O

Oakham ....Nick's Restaurant 119
Oborne ....The Grange at Oborne 65
Offenham ....Riverside Hotel and Restaurant........................152
Old Amersham ....The Crown 38
Oswestry.........................Pen-Y-Dyffryn Country Hotel 122
Otterburn ....The Otterburn Tower..107
Oxford ....The Nut Tree Inn 115
Oxford ....Weston Manor 116

P

Penzance ....The Old Coastguard Hotel 44
Petersfield ....Langrish House 76
Porthcurnick Beach ....The Rosevine 45
Portsmouth ....The Old House Hotel 77
Preston ....Ferrari's Restaurant & Hotel 97

R

Ramsgate ....The Royal Harbour Hotel 93
Redditch ....The Old Rectory 153
Roseland Peninsula ....The Rosevine 45
Ross-On-Wye ....The Chase Hotel 80
Ross-on-Wye ....Glewstone Court 82
Ross-on-Wye ....Wilton Court Hotel...81
Rothbury.........................The Orchard House 108
Rowsley ....East Lodge Country House Hotel 55
Royal Leamington Spa ....Episode Hotel 143
Rutland Water ....Barnsdale Lodge 120

S

St Agnes ....Rose-In-Vale Country House Hotel....................46
St Margarets-at-Cliffe ....The White Cliffs Hotel................................90
Seaview...........................The Priory Bay Hotel 87
Shanklin ....Rylstone Manor 88
Sherborne ....The Grange at Oborne 65
Sheringham ....Felbrigg Lodge 100
Shibden...........................The Shibden Mill Inn 164
Shipston-on-Stour ....The George Hotel 144
Shrewsbury ....The Inn at Grinshill 123
Shrewsbury ....Soulton Hall 124
Skipton ....The Devonshire Fell 158
Southport........................Tree Tops Country House Restaurant & Hotel........99
Southwold ....The Westleton Crown 139
Stamford.........................The Crown Hotel 98

Index by Location

Standon ....Kick & Dicky 83
Stansted Airport ....The White House and
                                                 Lion & Lamb Bar & Restaurant 84
Staverton ....Kingston House 63
Stoke-on-Trent......................The Manor at Hanchurch 135
Stratford-upon-Avon ....The George Hotel 144
Sutton ....The Anchor Inn at Sutton Gault 39

T

Takeley ....The White House and
                                            Lion & Lamb Bar & Restaurant 84
Taunton ....Bindon Country House 131
Taunton ....Farthings Country House Hotel & Restaurant......130
Tenterden ....Little Silver Country Hotel 94
Thorpe St Andrew ....The Old Rectory 103
Totnes ....Kingston House 63
Totnes ....The Turtley Corn Mill 59
Troutbeck ....Broadoaks Country House 53

U

Uppingham...........................The Lake Isle Hotel & Restaurant 121
Upton-upon-Severn ....The White Lion Hotel 154

V

Ventnor.................................The Hambrough 89

W

Watlington............................The Goose 117
Wells.....................................Beryl 132
Welwyn.................................Auberge du Lac 85
Wem.....................................Soulton Hall 124
West Cliffe ....Wallett's Court Hotel & Spa 91
Westleton..............................The Westleton Crown 139
Weston-On-The-Green........Weston Manor 116
Whitby..................................Dunsley Hall 159
Whitley ....The Pear Tree Inn 150
Whittlesford ....The Tickell Arms, Restaurant 40
Wickham...............................The Old House Hotel 77
Windermere ....Broadoaks Country House 53
Windermere ....Fayrer Garden House Hotel 52
Windsor.................................The Christopher Hotel Bar & Grill 32
Windsor.................................Stirrups Country House Hotel..........................35
Winsford ....Karslake Country House and Cottage 133
Wokingham ....Cantley House Hotel 36
Woodstock ....Duke Of Marlborough Country Inn 118
Wroxham ....Broad House 104

Y

York......................................Marmadukes Hotel 160
York......................................The Worsley Arms Hotel 161
Yorkshire Dales ....The Austwick Traddock 156

Channel Islands

Guernsey ....The Farmhouse 18
Guernsey ....La Sablonnerie...17
Guernsey ....The White House 16
Jersey ....Château La Chaire 19

Ireland

Caragh Lake ....Ard Na Sidhe 169
Killarney ....Ard Na Sidhe 169

Scotland

Auchencairn ....Balcary Bay Hotel 173
Ballater ....Darroch Learg 172
Brora.....................................Royal Marine Hotel, Restaurant & Spa 176
Castle Douglas ....Balcary Bay Hotel 173
Dunvegan ....Greshornish House 180
Edinburgh ....Castle Venlaw 187
Edinburgh ....The Hudson Hotel 175
Farr ....The Steadings at The Grouse & Trout 177
Forres ....Knockomie Hotel 185
Inverness ....Dunain Park Hotel & Restaurant 178
Inverness ....Loch Ness Lodge 179
Inverness ....The Steadings at The Grouse & Trout 177
Isle of Skye ....Greshornish House 180
Isle of Skye ....Skeabost Country House 181
Isle of Skye ....Toravaig House 182
Kirkcolm ....Corsewall Lighthouse Hotel 174
Loch Assynt..........................Ruddyglow Park..183

Lochinver ....**Ruddyglow Park** **183**
Maybole ....Culzean Castle – The Eisenhower Apartment....188
Melrose ....Fauhope Country House 186
Peebles ....Castle Venlaw 187
Portree..................................Skeabost Country House 181
Royal Deeside......................Darroch Learg 172
Sleat ....Toravaig House 182
Stranraer ....Corsewall Lighthouse Hotel 174
Thurso ....Forss House Hotel 184

Wales

Abersoch ....Porth Tocyn Country House Hotel....................195
Barmouth ....Bae Abermaw 196
Barmouth ....Llwyndu Farmhouse 197
Betws-y-Coed ....Tan-Y-Foel Country House 193
Brechfa ....Ty Mawr Country Hotel.....................................192
Cardiff ....Egerton Grey 202
Carmarthen ....Ty Mawr Country Hotel.....................................192
Denbigh ....Pentre Mawr Country House 194
Haverfordwest ....Wolfscastle Country Hotel & Restaurant 201
Llanaber ....Llwyndu Farmhouse 197
Monmouth ....The Bell At Skenfrith 198
Monmouth ....The Crown At Whitebrook 199
Porthkerry ....Egerton Grey 202
Ruthin ....Pentre Mawr Country House 194
Skenfrith ....The Bell At Skenfrith 198
Tenby ....Penally Abbey 200
Whitebrook ....The Crown At Whitebrook 199
Wolf's Castle ....Wolfscastle Country Hotel & Restaurant 201

Tell us about your stay

Following your stay in a Condé Nast Johansens Recommendation, please spare a moment to complete this Guest Survey Report. This is an important source of information for Condé Nast Johansens, in order to maintain the highest standards for our Recommendations and to support our team of Inspectors. It is also the prime source of nominations for Condé Nast Johansens Awards for Excellence, which are held annually and include properties from all over the world that represent the finest standards and best value for money in luxury, independent travel.

1. Your details

Your name: _____

Your address: _____

Postcode: _____

Country: _____

Please leave your email address if you would like to receive our monthly e-newsletter, with details of special offers and competitions

E-mail: _____

Please tick if you would like to receive information or offers from The Condé Nast Publications Ltd by SMS ☐ or E-mail ☐. Please tick if you would like to receive information or offers from other selected companies by SMS ☐ or E-mail ☐. Please tick this box if you prefer not to receive direct mail from The Condé Nast Publications Ltd ☐ and other reputable companies ☐

2. Hotel details

Name of hotel: _____

Country: _____

Date of visit: _____ Room No: _____

3. How did you book?

○ Telephone ○ E-Mail ○ Hotel Website
○ Internet ○ Travel Agent

Are you: ○ Guide User ○ Web User ○ or both

4. Any other comments

_____

_____

If you wish to make additional comments, please write separately to the Publisher,
Condé Nast Johansens Ltd, 6-8 Old Bond Street, London W1S 4PH, Great Britain

5. Your rating of the hotel

Please tick one box in each category below (as applicable)

	EXCELLENT	GOOD	DISAPPOINTING	POOR
Bedrooms				
Comfort	○	○	○	○
Amenities	○	○	○	○
Bathroom	○	○	○	○
Public Areas				
Inside	○	○	○	○
Outdoor	○	○	○	○
Housekeeping				
Cleanliness	○	○	○	○
Maintenance	○	○	○	○
Service				
Check in/out	○	○	○	○
Professionalism	○	○	○	○
Friendliness	○	○	○	○
Dining	○	○	○	○
Internet Facilities				
Bedrooms	○	○	○	○
Public Areas	○	○	○	○
Ambience	○	○	○	○
Value for Money	○	○	○	○
Food and drink				
Breakfast	○	○	○	○
Lunch	○	○	○	○
Dinner	○	○	○	○
Choice of dishes	○	○	○	○
Wine List	○	○	○	○
Did The Hotel Meet Your Expectations?	○	○	○	○

I most liked: _____

I least liked: _____

My favourite member of staff: _____

Please fax your completed survey to +44 (0)207 152 3566